ASSIGNMENTS IN PRACTICAL CHEMISTRY

ASSIGNMENTS IN PRACTICAL CHEMISTRY
A Teacher's Guide

contains a balanced collection of fifty-three assignments combining practical work with the theoretical background necessary to form the basis of a sixth form/introductory undergraduate course in practical chemistry. Each assignment is amply supported by notes, for the teacher's guidance, including a difficulty grading, an estimate of the average time required and a list of the apparatus and reagents needed. These notes also contain sample data and answers to the questions based on the Assignment Sheets.

The Assignment Sheets are available separately, in sets of fifty three, punched ready for loose-leaf filing together with the pupil's own notes.

ASSIGNMENTS IN PRACTICAL CHEMISTRY

T. E. ROGERS and **B. C. WILLIAMS**

 HUTCHINSON EDUCATIONAL

HUTCHINSON EDUCATIONAL LTD
3 Fitzroy Square, London W1

London Melbourne Sydney Auckland
Wellington Johannesburg Cape Town
and agencies throughout the world

First published 1972

*This book has been cold typeset by Design Practitioners Ltd., Sevenoaks
printed in Great Britain by Anchor Press and
bound by Wm. Brendon, both of Tiptree, Essex*

ISBN 0 09 108240 4 (cased)
      0 09 108241 2 (Set of fifty-three Assignment Sheets)

Index of Assignments

Introduction

This book contains a collection of fifty-three assignments, combining practical work with the theoretical background, which could form the basis of a course in chemistry for schools and colleges. The assignments are not all of a uniform standard, so a grading system is used to help the teacher make an appropriate selection.

The grading system is as follows:

* * fundamental topics with simple treatment
* ** fundamental topics with more advanced treatment
* *** advanced topics and treatment

Teachers in British schools and colleges should find the * and ** assignments suitable for their GCE Advanced level courses, and the *** assignments suitable for post-Advanced level work.

In America the * assignments should be suitable for high school pupils (Grades 10–12), and the ** and *** assignments should be of use in junior colleges and university freshman/sophomore courses.

With one or two small exceptions, the assignments can be performed entirely by the pupils, but in a few cases we have included experiments which are best demonstrated by the teacher, or performed by the pupil *only* under the close supervision of the teacher. Furthermore, if time is short, or if there is insufficient apparatus to allow an experiment to be done by each member of the class, the assignments may be completed by the pupils, with the teacher demonstrating the experimental work. Alternatively, if the data is provided by the teacher, the assignment could be set as an exercise in data analysis for homework, or in an examination.

In this volume, both the pupils' material (**Assignment sheets**) and useful information for teachers (**Notes**) are provided for each assignment, The pupils' material is produced in the form of separate sheets (obtainable in pads of 53) which can be incorporated in a loose-leaf file. Each sheet gives instructions for carrying out the experimental work, and contains questions designed to prompt the pupil to consider the operations he is performing and to interpret the experimental results. The teachers' material bears the grading for each assignment and an estimate of the time needed by an average pupil, together with a list of the apparatus and reagents needed. The quantities listed in round brackets [e.g. $(50cm^3)$]represent the volumes, or weights, of reagents needed per pupil, or group of pupils working together as one unit. We have also included sample data and answers to the questions posed on the Assignment Sheets. We hope this will serve as a valuable time-saver for over-worked teachers, as a guide to the sort of results expected and as data for use in case of minor disasters which pupils often encounter.

The suggested procedure for using these assignments is that the teacher selects those he wishes to be done and issues the appropriate sheets to the pupils, if possible during the lesson prior to the practical session. During the practical session, he will need to give assistance with the experimental work and the questions according to the intelligence and experience of the pupils.

Since the pupil need only be issued with the assignment he is to do, he will not be daunted by seeing the more difficult ones, nor will he be able to embarrass the teacher by suggesting experiments in the collection, which are not suitable at the time.

It is recommended that in answering the questions pupils should include a rewording of the question or place their answers alongside the original question. The method used for correction and assessment of the pupils' work depends largely on the numbers involved. It can be a tedious and unnecessary task to work through each pupil's work individually. A possible solution is a discussion session with the whole class, at which the analysis of results and answers to questions can be discussed, and reasonable answers given, to enable pupils to make their own corrections.

Units

We have adopted the policy outlined in the Royal Institute of Chemistry Monograph for Teachers, Number 15, *Physico-Chemical Quantities and Units—The Grammar and Spelling of Physical Chemistry* by Professor M.L. McGlashan. The use of such units as moles per cubic decimetre ($mol\ dm^{-3}$) for concentration, joules for energy, pascals for pressure ($1\ Pa = 1\ N\ m^{-2}$ and 1 atmosphere = 76cm of Hg = 101.3 kPa) and nanometres (nm) instead of Angstrom units may excite some comment, but, in view of the current drive by GCE Examining Boards and by the Nuffield Advanced Level teams to introduce SI units, we feel that no other policy is tenable.

Nomenclature

Any attempt to adopt a completely systematic nomenclature promotes considerable confusion with regard to the many simple compounds which enjoy universally used trivial names (e.g. acetone and urea). By the same token it would be absurd to make no attempt to introduce systematic names. In general, we have restricted the use of trivial names to compounds which either contain a very small number of carbon atoms (e.g. formaldehyde) or, if more complex, rejoice in universally used names (e.g. aniline). In some instances this policy has necessitated that very arbitary decisions be made as to when trivial names are adopted.

Laboratory Reagents

In certain assignments the term 'common laboratory reagents' appears under the *Reagents required* heading in the **Notes**. We intend this term to include the bench reagent solutions listed below. In no case is their concentration critical, but, as a rough guide, approximate details are given of the strengths of the reagents used in the Marlborough College Laboratories:

ammonia solution (ammonium hydroxide)	2M
ammonium carbonate	1M
ammonium chloride	2M
barium chloride	0.5M
bromine water	(saturated)
copper (II) sulphate	•
Fehling's Solutions A and B	(As supplied by B.D.H.)
hydrochloric acid	2M
iron (III) chloride	•
iron (II) sulphate	•
lead acetate	•
lime water	(saturated)
mercury (II) chloride	(saturated)
nitric acid	2M
potassium bromide	•
potassium dichromate	M/60
potassium hexacyanoferrate (II)	•
potassium hexacyanoferrate (III)	•
potassium iodide	•
potassium nitrate	•
potassium permanganate	M/50

silver nitrate	M/10
sodium carbonate	●
sodium hydroxide	1M
sodium hypochlorite	14% wt/vol.
	(As supplied by B.D.H.)
	(Approx 2M)
sodium thiosulphate	●
sulphuric acid	1M

N.B. ● Indicates that the solution is made by dissolving 10g solute per 100cm^3 of solution

T.E.R.
B.C.W.
Marlborough College
December 1970

Assignment 1
The Relative Strengths of Acids and Bases

INTRODUCTION

Using the idea of an acid as a proton donor and a base as a proton acceptor we can arrange all acids and bases in a 'league' table as shown below. If an acid is weak (i.e. has little tendency to donate protons) it follows that the corresponding base will be strong (i.e. will have a strong affinity for protons) e.g. the NH_4^+ ion is a weak acid while the NH_3 molecule is a strong base. Thus, in the following table the acids become increasingly strong down the page while for bases the reverse is true.

Name of acid	Acid	$\rightleftharpoons$	H^+	+ Base	Name of base
water	H_2O	$\rightleftharpoons$	H^+	+ OH^-	hydroxide ion
ammonium ion	NH_4^+	$\rightleftharpoons$	H^+	+ NH_3	ammonia
carbonic acid	H_2CO_3	$\rightleftharpoons$	$2H^+$	+ CO_3^{2-}	carbonate ion
anilinium ion	$C_6H_5NH_3^+$	$\rightleftharpoons$	H^+	+ $C_6H_5NH_2$	aniline
hydrosulphuric acid	H_2S	$\rightleftharpoons$	$2H^+$	+ S^{2-}	sulphide ion
formic acid	HCO_2H	$\rightleftharpoons$	H^+	+ HCO_2^-	formate ion
sulphurous acid	H_2SO_3	$\rightleftharpoons$	$2H^+$	+ SO_3^{2-}	sulphite ion
hydronium ion	H_3O^+	$\rightleftharpoons$	H^+	+ H_2O	water
sulphuric acid	H_2SO_4	$\rightleftharpoons$	$2H^+$	+ SO_4^{2-}	sulphate ion
hydrochloric acid	HCl	$\rightleftharpoons$	H^+	+ Cl^-	chloride ion
perchloric acid	$HClO_4$	$\rightleftharpoons$	H^+	+ ClO_4^-	perchlorate ion

EXPERIMENT 1: To find the positions of benzoic and acetic acids on the table

(a) Prepare a solution of sodium benzoate in distilled water and place about $2-3cm^3$ in each of three test-tubes. To the first tube add about $1-2cm^3$ of dilute hydrochloric acid, to the second a similar volume of dilute formic acid and to the last tube a like volume of a saturated solution of hydrogen sulphide in water. Note your observations and check the identity of any precipitate by slowly adding an excess of sodium hydroxide solution. How does this help?

(b) Repeat the above experiment using sodium acetate instead of sodium benzoate. Do you see anything? If not, why not? Gently warm the sodium acetate/dilute hydrochloric acid mixture and smell the vapours. What is evolved?

(c) Add a little dilute acetic acid to a portion of the aqueous solution of sodium benzoate.

Interpret your results for all three parts of this experiment and *pencil* in the position of benzoic acid and acetic acid on the table.

EXPERIMENT 2: To find the position of ethanol (alias ethyl alcohol), C_2H_5OH, on the table

Put 2–3cm³ of ethanol in an evaporating basin and add a *small* piece of sodium (freshly cut and no bigger than a grain of rice). Describe your observations. What gas is evolved? How is the ethanol behaving in this reaction?

Repeat the experiment using water instead of the ethanol. Is water more or less acidic than ethanol? Pencil in the position of ethanol on the table. Write ionic equations for the reactions of ethanol and water with sodium. Predict whether the ethoxide ion should be more basic than the hydroxide ion or not.

EXPERIMENT 3: To find the position of phenol (alias carbolic acid). C_6H_5OH, on the table

N.B. Take care throughout as phenol is a very corrosive poison which is readily absorbed through the skin.

(a) Repeat **Experiment 2** using a solution of phenol in a little *ethanol*. Compare the rate of gas evolution with that obtained when sodium was added to pure ethanol.

(b) Add 3 drops of Universal Indicator Solution to similar portions of (i) ammonium chloride solution, (ii) a dilute solution of phenol in distilled water and (iii) water.
Try to estimate the *relative* acidities of the solutions.

(c) Add a few turnings of magnesium to similar portions of the above three solutions. Record the relative ease with which hydrogen is evolved in each case.

(d) Make a more concentrated solution of phenol in water. Add excess solid phenol and examine the effects of adding excess sodium hydroxide solution followed by excess hydrochloric acid. Explain your observations. From your results to experiments 3(a) – (d), place H_2O, NH_4^+ and C_6H_5OH in order of increasing acidity and enter phenol in its correct position on the table.

SUMMARY

The term 'acid-base reaction' implies a competition for protons. Every acid has a corresponding base (conjugate base) and *vice-versa*. Their relative strengths vary. Thus, all acids and bases can be arranged in a table such that *any acid will react with any base above it in the table*. In general, strong acids and bases react to form weak acids and bases.

Notes 1

Standard: *

Time required: 1½ hours of practical work

Reagents required:

ethanol	(5cm^3)	phenol	(2g)
dilute formic acid	(4cm^3)	sodium benzoate	(1g)
dilute acetic acid	(4cm^3)	sodium acetate	(1g)
saturated aqueous solution of H$_2$S	(4cm^3)	sodium	(0·1g)
Universal indicator solution	(0·5cm^3)	magnesium turnings	(0·5g)
common laboratory reagent solutions			

Apparatus required:

test-tubes and an evaporating basin

INTRODUCTION

This experiment (See Footnote) is designed to illustrate the Brønsted-Lowry acid—base concept and allows emphasis to be placed on the idea of competition for protons. It does not seem wise to extend acid—base theory to include Lewis acids and bases at this stage.

EXPERIMENT 1:

Reagent added	Effect on sodium benzoate solution	on sodium acetate soln.
Dilute HCl	Immediate white precipitate	No apparent reaction seen; on warming pungent vinegar smell of acetic acid can be noted.
Dilute HCO$_2$H	Immediate white precipitate	No effect seen.
H$_2$S satd soln	No apparent effect	No apparent effect.
Dilute CH$_3$CO$_2$H	Slow formation of white ppt	No apparent effect.

N.B. (i) All precipitates dissolve readily in sodium hydroxide solution, suggesting that they are acids rather than 'salted-out' salts.

(ii) Acetic acid is very soluble in water whereas benzoic acid is not. However, the former is much more volatile than the latter.

Foot-Note:

*Although the experimental observations do suggest the correct sequence of the acids and bases considered, it cannot be claimed that they *prove* it because the observations are governed by the kinetics of competing reactions. Strictly, such evidence cannot be used to infer a thermodynamic sequence. However, this is meant to be an elementary experiment and many teachers may feel that they do not wish to draw attention to this point, important though it is, at this stage.

CONCLUSION

Both benzoic and acetic acids must be weaker than hydrochloric and formic acids and yet benzoic acid appears to be stronger than H_2S. This *suggests* that benzoic and acetic acids lie between H_2S and HCO_2H in the table. Furthermore, since Experiment 1(c) shows that acetic acid is stronger than benzoic acid we can conclude that the order is:

H_2S
$C_6H_5CO_2H$
CH_3CO_2H
HCO_2H $\downarrow$ Increasing acidity

EXPERIMENT 2

Ethanol reacts gently with sodium to form hydrogen and a colourless solution of sodium ethoxide in excess ethanol:

$$2Na(s) + 2C_2H_5OH(l) = 2C_2H_5O^-(alc) + 2Na^+(alc) + H_2(g)$$

This is entirely analogous to the action of water on sodium:

$$2Na(s) + 2HOH(l) = 2HO^-(aq) + 2Na^+(aq) + H_2(g)$$

except that the latter reaction is more violent, the sodium getting hot enough to melt. This experiment suggests that ethanol can behave as an acid but that it is a weaker acid than water. Thus, ethanol should be written at the top of the table.

If ethanol is a weaker acid than water it is entirely reasonable to expect the ethoxide ion to be a stronger base than the hydroxide ion.

EXPERIMENT 3

(a) Sodium reacts with an ethanolic solution of phenol more rapidly than it does with ethanol itself. Thus, phenol is probably more acidic than ethanol.

(b) Although the observations here will allow pupils to conclude that both ammonium chloride and phenol solutions are more acidic than water, no great significance should be attached to the *relative* colours of the indicator in the ammonium chloride and phenol solutions.

(c) Quite rapid evolution of hydrogen is obtained when magnesium turnings are added to ammonium chloride solution. In the case of the aqueous phenol solution gas evolution is distinct but is usually insufficient to allow identification of the gas. The reaction of magnesium with cold distilled water is so slow that it is several minutes before any hydrogen can be seen. Thus, the order of increasing acidity is:

water
phenol
ammonium chloride. $\downarrow$

(d) If several grams of phenol are shaken (precaution: use a stoppered tube) with a similar mass of water, a milky suspension of phenol saturated with water in water saturated with phenol is obtained. Addition of sodium hydroxide solution gives a clear, homogeneous solution of sodium phenoxide (ionic) in water. However, acidification again results in the two phase system and this time it is usually easier to get the suspension to coalesce into two distinct phases.

$$C_6H_5OH(l) + OH^-(aq) = C_6H_5O^-(aq) + H_2O(l)$$
$$C_6H_5O^-(aq) + H_3O^+(aq) = C_6H_5OH(l) + H_2O(l)$$

FURTHER PROJECT

Look up (or try to investigate) the compositions of the two phases formed by phenol and water at room temperature. Is there a temperature above which the two substances are completely miscible?

At $20°C$ percentages by weight of phenol in the two layers are 72% and 8%. (The consolute temperature for phenol and water is $66°C$.)

4

For more accurate data see *An Introduction to Physical Chemistry* by A. Findlay, Longmans

USEFUL HOMEWORK EXERCISES

The Assignment Sheets for this experiment provide all the information needed.

(i) Acid–base reactions can be considered to be reactions in which there is competition for what?

(ii) When a solution of HX in water is added to an aqueous solution of NaY, the acid HY is precipitated. Which of the following seem probable?

    (a) HY is a stronger acid than HX

    (b) Y^- is a stronger base than X^-

    (c) HY has a relatively high molecular weight

(iii) The following is a list of acids and bases:

$$H_3O^+, HCl, C_6H_5CO_2^-, HCO_2H, C_2H_5OH, OH^-, C_6H_5O^-, H_2O$$

    (a) Write down the bases that appear in the above list in order of increasing power.

    (b) Write down the acids that appear in the above list in order of increasing power.

(iv) Which acids will react with sulphites to produce sulphur dioxide?

(v) In each case below two substances are listed. Say whether reaction ought to occur between them and if you think it should, give the ionic equation:

    (a) the hydronium and sulphide ions

    (b) hydrogen chloride and water

    (c) perchloric acid and ammonia

    (d) hydrogen sulphide and the sulphite ion

    (e) the sulphate ion and perchloric acid

(vi) Suggest why acids are more usually positive ions or neutral molecules rather than negative ions whereas bases are rarely positive ions.

Assignment 2

Determination of Dissociation Constants of Weak Acids by pH Measurements

THEORETICAL INTRODUCTION

For a weak acid, HX, dissociating according to the equation,

$$HX \rightleftharpoons H^+ + X^-$$

the dissociation constant, K_a, is given by,

$$K_a = \frac{[H^+] \, [X^-]}{[HX]} \quad \ldots eqn\ 1$$

where $[H^+]$, $[X^-]$ and $[HX]$ are the molar concentrations at equilibrium.

Now if the acid is a weak acid (i.e. a weak electrolyte), and its salts are strong electrolytes, then for a mixture of the acid with one of its salts, it *may* be possible to assume that

$$[HX] \triangleq total \text{ acid concentration}$$

$$[X^-] \triangleq total \text{ salt concentration}$$

1. Explain why it is reasonable to make these assumptions for a weak acid.
Using these assumptions, and rearranging eqn 1, we have

$$[H^+] = K_a \frac{[HX]}{[X^-]} \text{ and thus } [H^+] \triangleq K_a \frac{[acid]\ total}{[salt]\ total}$$

2. If the concentrations of the acid and salt in the mixture are equal, what is the relationship between the hydrogen ion concentration and the dissociation constant of the weak acid?

3. If the pK_a of the acid is the negative logarithm, to the base 10, of the dissociation constant of the acid, what is the relationship between the pH of a solution of equal concentrations of acid and salt, and the pK_a of the acid?

EXPERIMENTAL PROCEDURE

(a) Calibrate the pH meter, using a buffer solution of accurately known pH
(b) Pipette 20·0cm³ of 0·10M acetic acid into a conical flask.
(c) Titrate with 0·10M sodium hydroxide solution, using phenolphthalein as indicator, until the solution is just pink
(d) Add a further 20·0cm³ of the same acetic acid solution to the flask and mix thoroughly
(e) Determine the pH of the resulting solution
(f) Repeat the above procedure but substituting for the acetic acid (i) monochloracetic acid (ii) dichloracetic acid
(g) Calculate K_a and/or pK_a of the three acids used

4. Is it important that the titre should be exactly 20·0cm³?

5. If the titre were, say $22 \cdot 0 \text{cm}^3$, should one add a further $20 \cdot 0 \text{cm}^3$ of acid, or a further $22 \cdot 0 \text{cm}^3$ of acid? Explain.

6. How do the values you obtained for K_a compare with the literature values? Which values show the greatest divergence from the accepted values?

7. What explanation can you offer for the divergence of these results from the accepted values?

8. What suggestions can you make to explain the relative values of K_a for the three acids?

9. Could this method be used to determine the dissociation constant of weak bases? If you think so, suggest how you would determine K_b for ammonia.

Notes 2

Standard: *

Time required: 1½ hours

Reagents required:

0·10M sodium hydroxide solution	(100cm³)
0·10M acetic acid solution	(50cm³)
0·10M monochloracetic acid solution	(50cm³)
0·10M dichloracetic acid solution	(50cm³)
phenolphthalein solution	(1cm³)

Apparatus required:

20·0cm³ pipette

100 or 250cm³ conical flask

burette

4 x 150cm³ beakers

pH meter

Notes on questions and specimen results

1. For a weak acid, the degree of dissociation will be small and thus only a small proportion of the HX molecules will be ionized, unless the dilution is very large. The salt, being a strong electrolyte will be in the form of ions, and, provided the ratio of the concentration of acid to salt is not exceptionally high, few X^- ions will be produced by ionization of the acid, relative to the number of X^- ions provided by the salt.

2. $[H^+] \simeq K_a \frac{[\text{acid}]_{total}}{[\text{salt}]_{total}}$ and if $[\text{acid}]_{total} = [\text{salt}]_{total}$, $[H^+] = K_a$

3. $pK_a = -\log_{10} K_a$ and pH $= -\log_{10} [H^+]$ so under the same conditions as in question 2 above, pH = pK_a

Results

Acetic acid

20·0cm³ of the acetic acid solution required 20·2cm³ of the NaOH

On addition of a further 20·0cm³ of the acetic acid solution and mixing,

pH = 4·7 thus pK_a = 4·7 (Literature value = 4·76)

Monochloracetic acid

20·0cm³ of the acid solution required 20·6cm³ of the NaOH

On addition of a further 20·0cm³ of the acid solution and mixing,

pH = 3·0 thus pK_a = 3·0 (Literature value = 2·85)

Dichloracetic acid

20·0cm³ of the acid solution required 19·9cm³ of the NaOH

On·addition of a further 20·0cm³ of the acid solution and mixing,

pH = 2·2 thus pK_a = 2·2 (Literature value = 1·30)

4. It is not essential for the titre to be 20·0cm³ (i.e. for the acid and alkali to be

equimolar). If the titration is performed accurately, the number of moles of acid taken initially determines the number of moles of salt formed, and if the same number of moles of acid as before are then added the salt concentration will be equal to the acid concentration.

5. The same quantity of acid should be added as was used in the titration i.e. $20.0 cm^3$ in order to make the salt concentration and acid concentration equal.

6. The lower the value of the pK_a of the acid, (i.e. the stronger the acid), the greater the divergence from the literature values.

7. The assumptions made in these experiments are only valid for weak acids ($pK_a > 3$). For acids stronger than this, the ionization of the acid will not be negligible, so that [HX] will be lower than assumed, and [X$^-$] greater than assumed. This will give low values for K_a and high values for pK_a – the situation indicated by the experimental results shown above.

8. The difference in structure of the three acids may be used to explain the relative values of pK_a. Chlorine is more electronegative than hydrogen, so by replacing a hydrogen atom of the methyl group, by a chlorine atom, electrons are withdrawn from the carboxyl group, so that its hydrogen atom will be more readily ionized. The replacement of a second hydrogen atom by chlorine, as in dichloracetic acid, increases the electron withdrawal even more and this acid is thus the strongest of the three.

Thus the order of increasing electron withdrawal from the carboxyl group, and hence increasing acid strength is

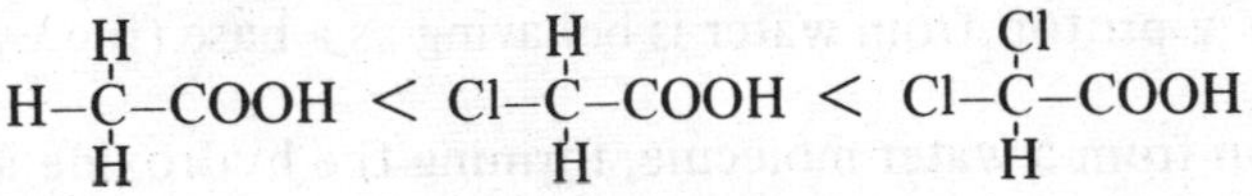

$$\underset{\overset{|}{H}}{\overset{\overset{H}{|}}{H-C-COOH}} < \underset{\overset{|}{H}}{\overset{\overset{H}{|}}{Cl-C-COOH}} < \underset{\overset{|}{H}}{\overset{\overset{Cl}{|}}{Cl-C-COOH}}$$

9. This method could be used to determine the dissociation constant of bases. For ammonia, one could pipette $20.0 cm^3$ of 0.1M ammonia solution into a flask and neutralize it by titration with hydrochloric acid, then add a further $20.0 cm^3$ of the ammonia solution and after mixing determine the pH of the solution.

In this case, for a weak base: e.g. ammonia

$$NH_3 + H_2O \rightleftharpoons NH_4^+ + OH^-$$

The equilibrium constant, $K = \dfrac{[NH_4^+] [OH^-]}{[NH_3] [H_2O]}$

[H$_2$O] is relatively very large and thus virtually constant, so if [H$_2$O] is multiplied by K, a new constant, K_b, is obtained

$$K_b = \dfrac{[NH_4^+] [OH^-]}{[NH_3]}$$

and when the concentrations of salt and base are equal:

$$[OH^-] = K_b . \dfrac{[NH_3]}{[NH_4^+]}$$

The [OH$^-$] can be calculated from the [H$^+$] and the ionic product for water

$$K_w = [H^+] [OH^-] = 10^{-14} \text{ mol}^2 \text{ dm}^{-6}$$

Further Project

Use this method to investigate other series of acids e.g. acetic, propionic and butyric acids.

Assignment 3

Ionic Equilibria in Aqueous Solution-Acid /Base Reactions

INTRODUCTION

In aqueous solution, a substance which donates a proton to a water molecule is behaving as an acid:

e.g. hydrogen chloride added to water, gives a proton to a water molecule, forming the hydronium ion.

$$HCl + H_2O \rightleftharpoons H_3O^+ + Cl^-$$

acid 1 base 2   acid 2   base 1

A substance which accepts a proton from water is behaving as a base (the water behaving as an acid).

e.g. ammonia takes a proton from a water molecule, forming the hydroxide ion

$$NH_3 + H_2O \rightleftharpoons NH_4^+ + OH^-$$

base 1   acid 2   acid 1   base 2

It is worth noting that any base, taking a proton from water, produces the hydroxide ion, and that the addition to water, of any substance which produces more hydroxide ions than were present in the pure water, results in a basic solution. Thus the addition of sodium hydroxide to water forms a basic solution.

Aqueous solutions of hydrogen chloride and ammonia will be readily recognised as examples of an acidic and a basic solution, respectively, but substances regarded as salts may act as acids or bases.

For example, the hydrated aluminium ion, of aluminium chloride, may donate a proton to a water molecule, thereby acting as an acid.

$$[Al(H_2O)_6]^{3+} + H_2O \rightleftharpoons [Al(H_2O)_5(OH)]^{2+} + H_3O^+$$

The carbonate ion of sodium carbonate may accept a proton from a water molecule, thereby acting as a base.

$$CO_3^{2-} + H_2O \rightleftharpoons HCO_3^- + OH^-$$

Water itself can act both as an acid and a base,

$$H_2O + H_2O \rightleftharpoons H_3O^+ + OH^-$$

and in pure water, there is a small, but measurable concentration of hydronium and hydroxide ions. Consideration of the above equation shows that, in pure water, the concentration of the hydronium ions is exactly equal to that of the hydroxide ions.

1. Write the equilibrium constant for this ionization of pure water.

Since the ionization of water is very slight, the concentration of water is very much greater than that of the hydronium and hydroxide ions, and is therefore virtually constant. Thus the equilibrium constant can be simplified to give a new constant, K_w, known as the ionic product for water

$$K_w = [H_3O^+] [OH^-]$$

2. What is the relationship between the equilibrium constant for the ionization of water and the ionic product for water? Calculate an approximate value for the 'concentration' of pure water in $mol\ dm^{-3}$

A solution which has a higher concentration of hydronium ions than pure water is said to be acidic; a solution with a higher concentration of hydroxide ions than pure water is said to be basic. Since the product of the concentration of hydronium and of hydroxide ions is a constant, at a given temperature, the concentration of only one of these ions need be stated to indicate the concentration of both. It is usually the concentration of hydronium ions which is used to specify the acidity or basicity of a solution, and because the values may be very low, and subject to great variation, the pH scale is used.

3. What is the pH of a solution?

4. How could a basic solution be defined in terms of its pH?

Determination of pH of Salt Solutions

Determine the pH of a 1·00M aqueous sodium acetate solution, using a pH meter. Wash the probe of the pH meter in distilled water immediately after use.

5. Explain the behaviour of the sodium acetate in water.

6. Would the pH of the solution be different if you used (a) potassium acetate, (b) ammonium acetate?

Determine the pH of 0·10M aqueous solutions of the following substances, recording your results in the form of a table and make out an order of decreasing acidity:

hydrated aluminium chloride	hydrated magnesium sulphate
hydrated iron (III) chloride	hydrated sodium sulphate
hydrated iron (II) chloride	hydrated tin (IV) chloride

7. Will the chloride or sulphate ion have much influence on the pH of the solution?

8. Relate the acidity of the solution to the charge on the metal ion.

9. What other factors might determine the pH of the solution?

BUFFER SOLUTIONS

Prepare a buffer solution as follows:
Pipette 20·0cm³ of 0·10M sodium hydroxide solution into a 100cm³ beaker and add 40·0cm³ of 0·10M acetic acid. Mix thoroughly and determine the pH of the solution.

Prepare a solution of the same pH, which does not act as a buffer, as follows:
Place about 25cm³ of 0·10M sodium hydroxide solution in a 100cm³ beaker and run in 0·10M hydrochloric acid from a burette until the pH of this solution is approximately the same as that of the buffer solution, prepared in the previous experiment.

Compare the behaviour of these two solutions in the following three experiments:
(a) Take 5cm³ of each solution and dilute to about 50cm³ by adding distilled water. Determine the pH of the two diluted solutions.
(b) Take 20cm³ of each solution and determine the pH of each, after the addition of 0·5cm³ of 0·10M hydrochloric acid. Add a further 0·5cm³ of the acid to each solution and determine the pH, and finally add a further 4·0cm³ of acid and again determine the pH in each case.
(c) Repeat experiment (b) but add 0·10M sodium hydroxide instead of the hydrochloric acid.

10. Define the term 'buffer solution', incorporating the characteristics of the buffer solution you have prepared and studied.

11

11. Attempt to explain how this buffer solution works.

TITRATION CURVES

Titration of sodium hydroxide with hydrochloric acid
Pipette 20·0cm³ of 0·10M sodium hydroxide solution into a 100cm³ beaker, insert the probe of the pH meter and determine the pH of this solution. Run in from a burette, 5·0cm³ of 0·10M hydrochloric acid, mix the solution and determine the pH. Continue adding 5·0cm³ portions of acid, determining the pH after each addition, until a total of 15cm³ has been added. Then add the acid in 1·0cm³ portions until a total of 25cm³ has been added, then revert to 5·0cm³ portions until a total of 40cm³ of acid has been added, determining the pH throughout.

Plot the graph of pH of the solution (vertical axis) against the volume of 0·10M hydrochloric acid added.

Repeat the experiment using the following pairs of reagents, with the acid in the burette throughout:

    ammonia solution and hydrochloric acid
    sodium hydroxide and acetic acid
    ammonia solution and acetic acid.

In each case, plot a graph of pH of the solution against the volume of acid added.

12. How is the end-point of the titration indicated on your graphs? Is it clearly defined in each case?

13. For each titration, name the substance which will be present in aqueous solution at the end-point.

14. Sometimes the pH of the solution at the end-point is 7; sometimes it is not. Explain this statement with reference to the titrations you have performed.

15. Phenolphthalein changes colour at a pH of approximately 10; methyl orange changes colour at a pH of approximately 4. Which of these indicators could be used to indicate the end-point of the titrations you have performed?

16. On your graphs are several regions in which the pH changes very slightly as acid is added. Which mixtures, represented by these regions on the graphs, could be used as buffer solutions?

Repeat the experiment using sodium carbonate solution and hydrochloric acid, determining the pH of the solution after each addition.
Plot a graph of pH of the solution against volume of acid added.

17. Explain the shape of the graph.

18. At what pH should an indicator change colour if it is to be used to indicate when
(a) all the carbonate ions have been converted to bicarbonate ions?
(b) all the carbonate ions have been converted to carbonic acid (or carbon dioxide and water)?

19. What would you suggest for the value of the dissociation constant of the indicator you would use to show when all the carbonate ions had been converted to bicarbonate ions?

Notes 3

Standard: *
Time required: 3 hours (not necessarily in the same session).
Reagents required:
   0·10M aqueous solutions of the following substances:

hydrated aluminium chloride	(25cm³)
hydrated iron (III) chloride	(25cm³)
hydrated iron (II) chloride	(25cm³)
hydrated magnesium sulphate	(25cm³)
hydrated sodium sulphate	(25cm³)
hydrated tin (IV) chloride	(25cm³)
sodium hydroxide	(150cm³)
acetic acid	(150cm³)
hydrochloric acid	(200cm³)
ammonia solution	(75cm³)
sodium carbonate	(40cm³)
1·0M sodium acetate	(25cm³)
distilled water	(200cm³)
phenolphthalein	(1cm³)
methyl orange	(1cm³)

Apparatus required:
   pH meter
   4 x 150cm³ beakers
   1 x 250cm³ beaker
   burette
   20·0cm³ pipette
   stirring rod

Notes on questions and typical results:

1. The equilibrium constant for the ionization of water, as written

$$H_2O + H_2O \rightleftharpoons H_3O^+ + OH^-$$

is given by

$$K = \frac{[H_3O^+]\,[OH^-]}{[H_2O]^2}$$

2. The relationship between this equilibrium constant and the ionic product for water is

$$K_w = K[H_2O]^2 = [H_3O^+]\,[OH^-] \qquad [H_2O] \simeq \frac{1000}{18} \simeq 56 \text{ mol dm}^{-3}$$

3. The pH of a solution can be defined as the logarithm, to the base 10, of the reciprocal of the hydronium ion concentration (i.e. minus the logarithm to the base of 10 of the hydronium ion concentration).

13

$$pH = \frac{1}{\lg[H_3O^+]} = -\lg[H_3O^+] \quad , \text{ where } [H_3O^+] = \text{molar concentration of } H_3O^+.$$

4. A basic solution could be defined as a solution which has a pH greater than 7, since when the hydroxide ion concentration is greater than that in pure water, the hydronium ion concentration must be less than that in pure water i.e. less than 10^{-7} mol dm^{-3}.

The pH of a 1·0M solution of sodium acetate was found to be 8·0.

5. This indicates that the solution is basic, meaning that there is a higher concentration of hydroxide ions and a lower concentration of hydronium ions than in pure water. This is because the acetate ion, being the conjugate base of a moderately weak acid, is a moderately strong base and accepts a proton from a water molecule to produce an extra hydroxide ion.

$$H_2O + H_2O \rightleftharpoons H_3O^+ + OH^-$$

$$OAc^- + H_2O \rightleftharpoons HOAc + OH^-$$

The sodium ion acts neither as an acid nor a base and thus does not affect the pH of the solution.

6. (a) The potassium ion, like the sodium ion, neither accepts nor donates protons, so the pH of potassium acetate would be the same as the pH of sodium acetate solution.
(b) The ammonium ion can act as an acid, donating a proton to a water molecule, so the pH of ammonium acetate solution would be lower than that of sodium acetate — probably about pH = 7.

$$OAc^- + H_2O \rightleftharpoons HOAc + OH^-$$

$$NH_4^+ + H_2O \rightleftharpoons NH_3 + H_3O^+$$

The pH of these solutions was found to be:

Solution	pH	Order of decreasing acidity
aluminium chloride	3·2	tin (IV) chloride
iron (III) chloride	1·8	iron (III) chloride
iron (II) chloride	3·4	aluminium chloride
magnesium sulphate	5·5	iron (II) chloride
sodium sulphate	6·0	magnesium sulphate
tin (IV) chloride	1·4	sodium sulphate

7. Both chloride and sulphate ions being the conjugate bases of very strong acids, are very weak bases. Thus the tendency to accept protons from water molecules is negligible and will not influence the pH of the solution to a significant extent. It is thus valid to make a comparison of the pH of solutions of metal ions with either chloride or sulphate ions present.

8. The order of decreasing acidity is the same as the order of decreasing charge on the metal ion. This would thus seem likely to be a significant factor determining the release of protons from hydrated ions.

9. If one assumes that the acidity of the solution is caused by the metal ion attracting electrons from the coordinated water molecules thus releasing protons, one would expect that the size of the metal ion and the screening effect of the electrons around the nucleus would, with the charge on the ion, determine the extent to which electrons are attracted by the metal ion, and this in turn would determine the pH of the solution. Another factor might be the solubility of the metal hydroxide, since this would affect the equilibrium between the hydrated metal ion and the hydroxide.

e.g. $[Fe(H_2O)_6]^{3+} \rightleftharpoons [Fe(H_2O)_5(OH)]^{2+} \rightleftharpoons [Fe(H_2O)_4(OH)_2]^+ \rightleftharpoons Fe(H_2O)_3(OH)_3$

$\qquad\qquad +H^+aq \qquad\qquad\qquad +H^+aq \qquad\qquad\qquad +H^+aq$

BUFFER SOLUTIONS

The results are as follows:

	pH of buffer solution	pH of non-buffer solution
As prepared	5·4	5·4
After 50cm³ of water added	5·4	6·0
After addition of 0·5cm³ of 0·M HCl	5·4	3·6
After addition of 1·0cm³ of 0·10M HCl	5·3	3·3
After addition of 5·0cm³ of 0·10M HCl	4·8	2·8
After addition of 0·5cm³ of 0·10M NaOH	5·5	11·5
After addition of 1·0cm³ of 0·10M NaOH	5·6	11·9
After addition of 5·0cm³ of 0·10M NaOH	6·3	12·6

10. A buffer solution is a solution which resists a change of pH on dilution, or on addition of acid or alkali. It usually contains a high concentration of a weak acid and a high concentration of its conjugate base.

11. This buffer solution consists of equimolar concentrations of acetic acid and the acetate ion. Equilibrium will be achieved for the reaction as represented in the equation

$$H_2O + CH_3COOH \rightleftharpoons CH_3COO^- + H_3O^+$$

The equilibrium constant for the reaction is given by

$$K' = \frac{[CH_3COO^-][H_3O^+]}{[CH_3COOH][H_2O]}$$

Since $[H_2O]$ is virtually constant in aqueous solution (unless the concentration of solutes is exceptionally high) a different equilibrium constant can be defined incorporating $[H_2O]$

$$K = \frac{[CH_3COO^-][H_3O^+]}{[CH_3COOH]}$$

The hydronium ion concentration in the buffer solution is given by

$$[H_3O^+] = K\frac{[CH_3COOH]}{[CH_3COO^-]}$$

Hence, since dilution will not alter the ratio of the concentration of acetic acid to the concentration of the acetate ion (unless exceptionally large quantities of water are added), it will not alter the pH of a buffer solution.

On addition of hydronium ions, the acetate ions will accept protons from the hydronium ions forming acetic acid, and the concentration of hydronium ions in the solution will not alter appreciably unless large quantities are added.

$$CH_3COO^- + H_3O^+ \rightarrow CH_3COOH + H_2O$$

On addition of hydroxide ions, the acetic acid will donate protons to the hydroxide ions and the concentration of hydroxide ions, and hence hydronium ions, in the solution will not alter appreciably.

$$CH_3COOH + OH^- \rightarrow CH_3COO^- + H_2O$$

15

TITRATION CURVES

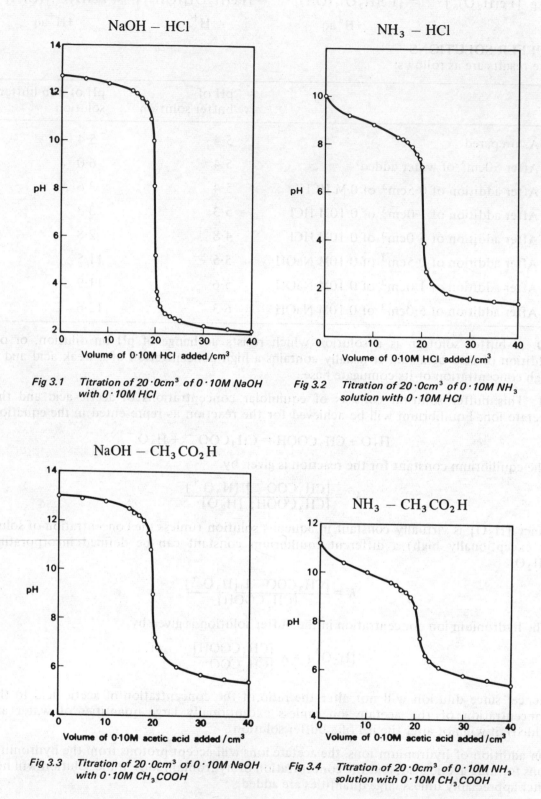

NaOH – HCl

Fig 3.1   Titration of 20·0cm³ of 0·10M NaOH with 0·10M HCl

NH₃ – HCl

Fig 3.2   Titration of 20·0cm³ of 0·10M NH₃ solution with 0·10M HCl

NaOH – CH₃CO₂H

Fig 3.3   Titration of 20·0cm³ of 0·10M NaOH with 0·10M CH₃COOH

NH₃ – CH₃CO₂H

Fig 3.4   Titration of 20·0cm³ of 0·10M NH₃ solution with 0·10M CH₃COOH

12. The end-point of each titration is indicated on the graph by a sudden change of pH as small quantities of acid are added. This is clearly defined in all the examples except for the titration between ammonia solution and acetic acid.

16

13. In the aqueous solution at the end-point will be:

Titration between	Substance present in solution
sodium hydroxide/hydrochloric acid	sodium chloride
ammonia solution/hydrochloric acid	ammonium chloride
sodium hydroxide/acetic acid	sodium acetate
ammonia solution/acetic acid	ammonium acetate

14. The pH at the end-point is approximately 7 for the titration between sodium hydroxide and hydrochloric acid (strong base and strong acid) since the solution contains only sodium ions and chloride ions neither of which donate or accept protons to an appreciable extent.

The pH at the end-point when ammonia solution and hydrochloric acid are titrated is less than 7, since the solution contains ammonium ions, which donate protons to water molecules increasing the hydronium ion concentration; the chloride ion neither accepts nor donates protons appreciably. (This pH of less than 7 is typical for the end-point of titrations between weak base and strong acid).

The pH at the end-point when sodium hydroxide and acetic acid are titrated is greater than 7, since although the sodium ion does not donate or accept protons appreciably, the acetate ion accepts protons thus decreasing the hydronium ion concentration. (A pH greater than 7 is typical for titrations between strong base and weak acid.)

In a titration between weak acid and weak base, the pH at the end-point depends on the relative values of the dissociation constants of the weak acid–base. In the example considered — ammonia solution and acetic acid — the dissociation constants are similar, so the ammonium ion donates protons to a similar extent as the acetate ion accepts them and the pH at the end-point is thus approximately 7.

15. Phenolphthalein and methyl orange can both be used for sodium hydroxide/hydrochloric acid.
Methyl orange can be used for ammonia solution/hydrochloric acid.
Phenolphthalein can be used for sodium hydroxide/acetic acid.
Neither methyl orange nor phenolphthalein gives a satisfactory end-point for ammonia solution/acetic acid.

16. A buffer solution must contain a high concentration of a weak acid and its conjugate base. Thus mixtures of ammonium ions and ammonia solution, and acetic acid and acetate ions could be used as buffer solutions.
Some of the other mixtures will resist the change of pH on addition of acid, but would not effectively resist the change of pH on addition of alkali or dilution.

Teachers may wish to leave pupils to discover for themselves the practical details of how to obtain maximum information from the sodium carbonate/hydrochloric acid titration, or they may wish to provide it or, in some cases, to save time, they may wish to give the pupils the results and get them to answer the questions using this information.

Results for addition of 0·10M HCl to 20·0cm³ of 0·05M Na_2CO_3 solution 0°C as follows:

Volume of 0·10M HCl added/cm³		Volume of 0·10M HCl added/cm³	pH
0·0	11·7	17·0	6·7
5·0	10·5	19·0	6·2
7·0	10·2	20·0	4·6
9·0	9·7	21·0	3·5
10·0	9·3	25·0	3·0
11·0	8·1	30·0	2·8
13·0	7·5	35·0	2·7
15·0	7·1	40·0	2·6

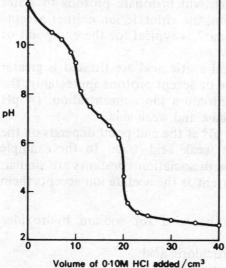

Fig 3.5   Titration of 20·0cm³ of 0·050M Na_2CO_3 with 0·10M HCl

17. The graph shows two regions in which there is a rapid change of pH, as acid is added. These correspond to the conversion of all carbonate ions to bicarbonate ions, and the conversion of all bicarbonate ions to carbonic acid.

18. (a) The indicator should change at pH ≃ 9
(b) The indicator should change at pH ≃ 5

19. Acid—base indicators are usually weak, or moderately weak, acids having a different colour from that of their conjugate base. The colour changes at the hydronium ion concentration at which the two forms of the indicator are in equal concentration.

If the acid form of the indicator is represented by HX, then it can donate a proton to a water molecule according to the equation:

$$H_2O + HX \rightleftharpoons H_3O^+ + X^-$$

The dissociation constant for the acid is usually represented as

$$K = \frac{[H_3O^+]\,[X^-]}{[HX]}$$

Hence $\qquad [H_3O^+] = K\,\dfrac{[HX]}{[X^-]}$

If we assume the colour changes when $[HX] = [X^-]$, then the colour change occurs when the hydronium concentration is equal to the numerical value of the dissociation constant of the indicator.

Since in this case the indicator must change when the pH $\simeq$ 9, i.e. when the hydronium ion concentration in the solution is approximately 10^{-9} mol dm^{-3} the indicator should have an acid dissociation constant of approximately 10^{-9} mol dm^{-3}.

REFERENCE

Mahan College Chemistry, Addison Wesley (1966)

Assignment 4
Conductometric Titrations

INTRODUCTION

The conductance of a cell, containing an aqueous solution of an electrolyte, depends on:
(a) the number of free ions in the cell
(b) the number of charges on each ion
(c) the speed at which the ions move

1. What factors determine the speed at which the ions move?

In the course of a titration, the number of free ions in the cell and/or their identity will change. As a result, the conductance of the cell containing the solution will change as the titration is performed. In many cases, the rate of change of conductance as one solution is added, is different when reaction occurs on addition, from the rate of change of conductance when excess of the solution is being added.

2. If the conductance of the cell is plotted against the volume of the solution added to a given volume of the other solution, how will the end-point be obtained from the graph?

EXPERIMENTAL WORK

(I) Titration of sodium hydroxide solution against hydrochloric acid
Pipette $10.0cm^3$ of $0.10M$ hydrochloric acid into a $250cm^3$ beaker and add approximately $100cm^3$ of distilled water.
Determine the conductance of the cell, containing this solution.
Fill a burette with $0.10M$ sodium hydroxide solution and run $2.0cm^3$ of this solution into the acid. Mix thoroughly and determine the conductance of the cell containing this solution. Continue adding $2.0cm^3$ portions of alkali and determining the conductance of the cell containing the solution until a total of $20cm^3$ of alkali has been added.

Plot a graph of conductance of the cell containing the solution against the volume of sodium hydroxide solution added.

3. Why is $100cm^3$ of distilled water added to the hydrochloric acid in the beaker? (Apart from the need to have sufficient solution to immerse the electrodes)

4. What is the end-point of the titration?

5. Explain the shape of the graph in terms of the molar conductivity of the ions. (See below)

(II) Titration of sodium hydroxide solution against acetic acid
Pipette $10.0cm^3$ of $0.10M$ acetic acid into a $250cm^3$ beaker and add approximately $100cm^3$ of distilled water. Determine the conductance of the cell, containing this solution, and then add $2.0cm^3$ portions of $0.10M$ sodium hydroxide solution, proceeding as in experiment (1).
Plot a graph of conductance of the cell, containing the solution, against the volume of sodium hydroxide solution added.

6. Explain the shape of the graph, making use of the molar conductivity of the ions and the relative extent of dissociation of the compounds involved.

(III) Titration of silver nitrate solution against potassium chloride solution

Pipette $10.0cm^3$ of $0.10M$ potassium chloride solution into a $250cm^3$ beaker and add approximately $100cm^3$ of distilled water. Determine the conductance of the cell containing this solution, and then add $2.0cm^3$ portions of $0.10M$ silver nitrate solution, proceeding as before.

Plot a graph of conductance of the cell, containing the solution, against the volume of silver nitrate solution added.

7. Explain the shape of the graph in terms of the molar conductivity of the ions and any other relevant factor.

(IV) Titration of an aqueous solution of iron (III) ions against an aqueous solution of the disodium salt of ethylenediamine tetra-acetic acid (EDTA)

Pipette $10.0cm^3$ of the $0.05M$ solution of iron (III) ions into a $250cm^3$ beaker and add approximately $100cm^3$ of distilled water. Determine the conductance of the cell, containing this solution, and then add $2.0cm^3$ portions of $0.05M$ EDTA solution proceeding as in previous experiments.

Plot graph of the conductance of the cell containing the solution against the volume of EDTA solution added.

8. Explain the shape of the graph in terms of the molar conductivity of the ions and any other relevant factors. Predict the relative values of the molar conductivity of $EDTA^{2-}$ and Fe^{3+}.

9. What does this suggest for the formula of the iron (III)/EDTA complex?

10. What are the most useful applications of conductance measurements for the determination of the end-point of titrations?

Molar conductivity of some ions at 25°C

Ion	Molar Conductivity $/\Omega^{-1}\ cm^2\ mol^{-1}$	Ion	Molar Conductivity $/\Omega^{-1}\ cm^2\ mol^{-1}$
Na^+	50·1	CH_3COO^-	40·9
H^+	349·8	Ag^+	61·9
OH^-	198·3	NO_3^-	71·5
Cl^-	76·4	K^+	73·5

Notes 4

Standard: **

Time required: 1½ hours practical work

Reagents required:

    0·10M sodium hydroxide solution   (75cm³)

    0·10M hydrochloric acid   (30cm³)

    0·10M acetic acid   (30cm³)

    0·10M silver nitrate   (30cm³)

    0·10M potassium chloride   (50cm³)

    0·05M solution of iron(III) ions, which may be made using 24·1g of ammonium iron
        (III) sulphate-$NH_4Fe(SO_4)_2.12H_2O$ per dm³ (50cm³)

    0·05M disodium ethylenediamine tetracetic acid (50cm³)

    distilled water (600cm³)

Apparatus required:

    conductance bridge and conductance cell

    burette

    1 x 250cm³ beaker

    3 x 150cm³ beakers

    1 x 100cm³ measuring cylinder

    1 x 10·0cm³ pipette

Notes on questions and typical results:

1. The speed at which ions move in an aqueous solution depends on (i) temperature (ii) viscosity of solution — itself dependent on temperature (iii) potential gradient (iv) charge on the ion (v) size of the aqueous ion i.e. the size of the ion and the attached water molecules.

In the case of the aqueous hydrogen and hydroxide ions, it seems likely that a different mechanism is involved — namely a proton transfer from one water molecule to a neighbouring one, so that it may not in fact be the same proton which passes from one point in the solution to another, but rather that one proton displaces another.

2. The end-point of a titration will appear on a graph as a point at which there is a sudden change of gradient, marked by a discontinuity. In some cases the conductance may fall on approach to the end-point and then rise — i.e. a change from negative gradient to positive gradient at the end-point, but this is not necessarily so; it may rise on approach to the end-point and then drop, or there may be a discontinuity in the graph without a change of the sign of the gradient.

(I) Titration of sodium hydroxide against hydrochloric acid

3. A large quantity of water is added so that the diluting effect of the sodium hydroxide solution is minimised.

4. The end-point of this titration is shown on the graph as the point of minimum conductance i.e. when 10·0cm³ of sodium hydroxide solution has been added.

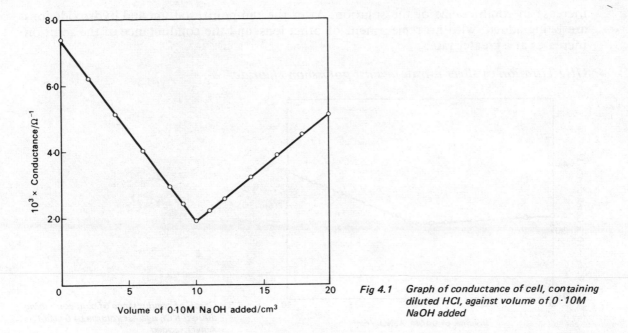

Fig 4.1 *Graph of conductance of cell, containing diluted HCl, against volume of 0·10M NaOH added*

5. The reaction may be summarised as follows:

$$H^+ + Cl^- + Na^+ + OH^- \rightarrow Na^+ + Cl^- + H_2O$$

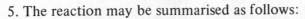

In flask initially   added

Before the end-point has been reached, each hydrogen ion is effectively replaced by one sodium ion, which has a smaller molar conductivity, so the conductance of the solution decreases. After the end-point, no ions are being replaced and consequently the sodium and hydroxide ions added increase the conductivity of the solution.

(II) Titration of sodium hydroxide against acetic acid

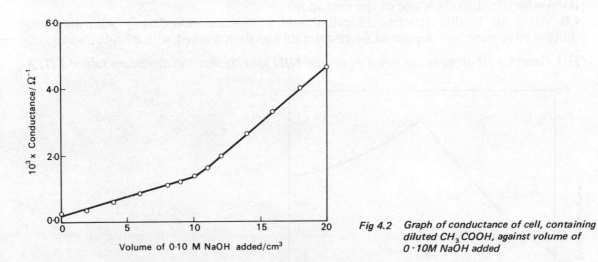

Fig 4.2 *Graph of conductance of cell, containing diluted CH_3COOH, against volume of 0·10M NaOH added*

6. The reaction may be summarised as follows:

$$CH_3COOH \rightleftharpoons CH_3COO^- + H^+$$
In flask initially

$$Na^+ + OH^-$$
added

$$\rightarrow H_2O + Na^+ + CH_3COO^-$$

Before the end-point, each sodium ion replaces one hydrogen ion, but more acetic acid molecules dissociate producing more hydrogen and acetate ions — the result being a slight

23

increase in conductance of the solution. After the end-point, sodium and hydroxide ions are being added, with no replacement of other ions, and the conductance of the solution increases at a greater rate.

(III) Titration of silver nitrate against potassium chloride:

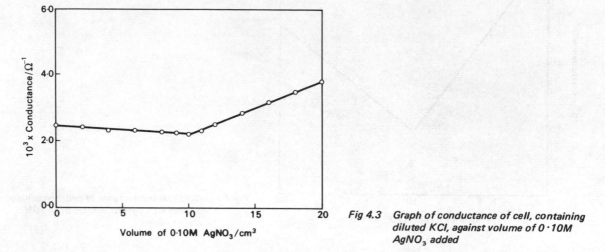

Fig 4.3 *Graph of conductance of cell, containing diluted KCl, against volume of 0·10M AgNO₃ added*

7. The reaction may be summarised as follows:

$$K^+ + Cl^- + Ag^+ + NO_3^- \rightarrow AgCl(s) + K^+ + NO_3^-$$

In flask initially   added

Before the end-point, chloride ions are effectively replaced in the solution by nitrate ions which have a very slightly lower molar conductivity, so the conductance of the solution falls very slightly. After the end-point, no ions are being replaced and the silver and nitrate ions added increase the conductance of the solution. It is interesting to compare the much slower increase in conductance of this solution with that in titrations (I) and (II) in which hydroxide is one of the ions added.

N.B. After use in this titration the cell should be washed immediately with ammonia solution to remove any deposit of silver chloride and then washed with distilled water.

(IV) Titration of an aqueous solution of iron (III) ions against the disodium salt of EDTA

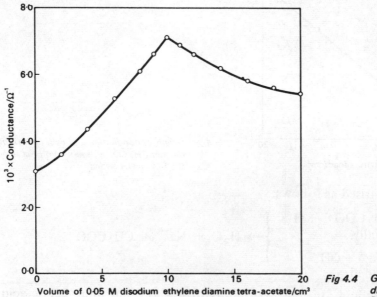

Fig 4.4 *Graph of conductance of cell, containing diluted iron (III) ions, against volume of 0·050M EDTA added.*

8. The very large $EDTA^{2-}$ ion is likely to have a much lower molar conductivity than the Fe^{3+} ion.

If ethylenediaminetetra-acetic acid,

$$\begin{array}{c} HOOCCH_2 \\ HOOCCH_2 \end{array}\!\!\!\!>\!NCH_2CH_2N<\!\!\!\!\begin{array}{c} CH_2COOH \\ CH_2COOH \end{array}$$

is represented by H_4Y, the reaction may be interpreted at:

$$Fe^{3+} + H_2Y^{2-} + 2\,Na^{+} \rightarrow FeY^{-} + 2\,H^{+} + 2\,Na^{+}$$

        In flask   Added
        initially

Hence, before the end-point, each Fe^{3+} ion is effectively replaced by one FeY^{-}, two H^{+} and two Na^{+} ions so the conductance of the solution rises. After the end-point, the H_2Y^{2-} ions added presumably accept protons forming H_3Y^{-} ions and the removal of the highly conducting hydrogen ions more than balances the addition of sodium ions, so the conductance of the solution falls.

9. Since the end-point is indicated when equal volumes of 0·05M Fe^{3+} and 0·05M disodium salt of EDTA solutions have been mixed, the formula of the complex must be that of a 1 : 1 complex i.e. FeY^{-}.

10. Conductometric titrations are useful for titrations of coloured acids or bases when a normal acid—base indicator would not be suitable.
A second important application is for weak acid — weak base titrations, which cannot be performed using acid—base indicators.
A third application is for titration in which precipitation occurs. These may not involve acids or bases and hence cannot then be performed with the usual indicators.
Fourthly, conductometric titrations may be used to investigate complex formation and this is particularly useful for complexes which are not strongly coloured.

SUGGESTIONS FOR FURTHER PROJECTS

1. A conductometric titration could be performed for the weak acid—weak base reaction. Ammonia solution and acetic acid are suitable reagents.
2. The interpretation of the reaction between iron (III) ions and the disodium salt of EDTA would suggest that hydrogen ions are being displaced from the EDTA by the iron (III) ions before the end-point, and then hydrogen ions present in the solution are being accepted by EDTA ion after the end-point. This would indicate a variation in pH of the solution as the titration is performed and it would be possible to investigate this using a pH meter.

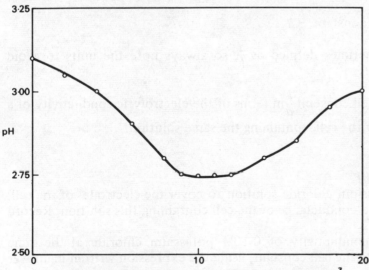

Fig 4.5
Graph of variation of pH as 0·050M EDTA is added to 10·0cm³ of 0·050M solution of iron (III) ions

Volume of 0·05M disodium ethylene diamine tetra-acetate/cm³

25

Assignment 5

Electrolytic Conductance-Basic Ideas

INTRODUCTION

If R is the resistance of an electrolyte solution, measured in a cell of cross-sectional area, a, with electrodes separated by a distance l then

$$R = \rho \cdot \frac{l}{a}$$

1. What does ρ represent in this equation?

Since the conductance of the cell, C, is the reciprocal of the resistance of the cell containing the same solution,

$$C = \frac{1}{\rho} \cdot \frac{a}{l}$$

The electrolytic conductivity of the solution in the cell is the reciprocal of its resistivity, hence

$$K = \frac{1}{\rho} = C\frac{l}{a}$$

2. If the cross-sectional area of the cell was exactly $1 \mathrm{cm}^2$, and the electrodes were exactly 1cm apart, what would the electrolytic conductivity equal?

If the electrodes are *not* exactly 1cm apart and/or the cross-sectional area of the cell is

not exactly $1 \mathrm{cm}^2$, then the proportionality constant, $\frac{l}{a}$, known as the cell constant has some value other than one, and its value must be known if the electrolytic conductivity of a solution is to be calculated from the conductance of the cell, containing the same solution.

3. What are the units of the cell constant, $\frac{l}{a}$?

N.B. The cell constant is sometimes defined as $\frac{a}{l}$, so always note the units to avoid confusion.

4. Write an expression for the cell constant $\frac{l}{a}$ in terms of the electrolytic conductivity of a solution and the conductance of the cell, containing the same solution.

EXPERIMENTAL WORK

(1) Determination of cell constant
(a) Pour sufficient 0·10M potassium chloride solution to cover the electrodes of the cell, into a beaker and determine the conductance of the cell containing this solution. Record the temperature of the solution.
(b) Look up the electrolytic conductivity of 0·10M potassium chloride at the same temperature, and hence calculate the cell constant, using the expression written in answer to question 4.

(II) Electrolytic conductivity
(a) Pipette 25·0cm³ of 0·10M potassium chloride solution into a 150cm³ beaker and add 25·0cm³ of distilled water. Mix thoroughly and determine the conductance of the cell containing this solution.
(b) Repeat the determination of conductance after the successive addition of three more 25cm³ portions of distilled water.
(c) Calculate the electrolytic conductivity of the potassium chloride at each of the concentrations used.

5. Explain, in terms of the number of ions present in a unit cube of solution, why the electrolytic conductivity of potassium chloride solution varies as it is diluted.

If dilution is defined as the volume of solution which contains one mole of electrolyte (i.e. the reciprocal of the concentration of the solution), calculate the dilution of each solution studied and plot a graph of the electrolytic conductivity of potassium chloride solutions against the dilution.

(III) Molar conductivity
The conductance of the same amount of electrolyte, at different dilutions, can be compared by making use of the concept of molar conductivity. The molar conductivity can be thought of as the conductance of the solution if that volume of solution which contains one mole of the electrolyte (its dilution) were placed between extensive electrodes one centimetre apart. The value of the molar conductivity of a solution can be calculated as the product of the electrolytic conductivity of the solution and its dilution, (or by dividing the electrolytic conductivity of the solution by its concentration). Thus,

Molar conductivity = electrolytic conductivity x dilution. $\Lambda = KV$

or Molar conductivity = $\dfrac{\text{electrolytic conductivity}}{\text{concentration}}$ $\Lambda = K/Concentration$

If the dilution is expressed in cm³, then it will be appreciated that the molar conductivity is equal to the conductance of a 1cm cube of the solution multiplied by the number of centimetre cubes of the solution which together contain a mole of electrolyte.
Calculate the molar conductivity of potassium chloride at the dilutions used and plot a graph of molar conductivity against dilution.

6. What explanation can you give for the shape of the graph?

(IV) Strong and weak electrolytes
Substances which, in dilute solution, have molar conductivities which do not vary with dilution are called strong electrolytes.

7. How would you classify potassium chloride as a result of your experiments?

8. Suggest factors which might cause molar conductivity to vary with dilution.

Determine the electrolytic conductivity of acetic acid at different dilutions, as described above for potassium chloride, and plot a graph of the molar conductivity of acetic acid against dilution, using the same axes as the graph for potassium chloride.

9. Comment on the shape of the graph, and on the values of the molar conductivity of acetic acid relative to those for potassium chloride.

Substances which, in dilute solution, have molar conductivities which increase with dilution, and do not reach a limiting value at finite values of dilution, are called weak electrolytes.

10. How would you classify acetic acid as a result of your experiments?

Notes 5

Standard: *

Time required: 1½ hours practical work

Apparatus required:
   Conductance cell (The electrodes must be fixed so that the distance between them does not vary during the experiment)
   Conductance bridge (The model produced by Grayshaw Instruments is very suitable)
   2 x 150cm³ beakers
   3 beakers as receptacles for solutions — 250, 150 or 100cm³ will do
   2 x 25cm³ pipettes

Reagents required:
   0·10M potassium chloride solution (50cm³)
   0·10M acetic acid   (50cm³)
   distilled water   (250cm³)

Notes on questions and typical results

1. ρ represents the resistivity of the solution, and could be considered as the resistance of a unit cube of solution (i.e. a cm cube or a metre cube).

2. If the cross-sectional area of the cell were 1cm³ and the electrodes were 1cm apart, the electrolytic conductivity would equal the conductance of the cell containing the solution. In other words the electrolytic conductivity could be considered as the conductance of a unit cube of solution — in this case a 1cm cube.

3. The units of the cell constant $\frac{l}{a}$ are cm^{-1} (or m^{-1}). The former being the more useful.

4. The cell constant $\frac{l}{a} = \frac{K}{C}$ i.e. the electrolytic conductivity of a solution divided by the conductance of the cell containing an identical solution.

Results of experiment to determine the cell constant

Conductance of the cell containing 0·10M KCl = 0·0205Ω^{-1}

Electrolytic conductivity of 0·10M KCl = 0·0112Ω^{-1} cm^{-1}

whence, cell constant = 0·55cm^{-1}

Results of determination of electrolytic conductivity of potassium chloride

Molarity of KCl solution	Dilution of KCl solution/dm³ mol^{-1}	Conductance of cell/Ω^{-1}	Electrolytic conductivity/Ω^{-1} cm^{-1}
0·050	20	1·15 x 10^{-2}	6·3 x 10^{-3}
0·033	30	7·6 x 10^{-3}	4·2 x 10^{-3}
0·025	40	5·7 x 10^{-3}	3·1 x 10^{-3}
0·020	50	4·6 x 10^{-3}	2·5 x 10^{-3}

5. If the degree of dissociation of potassium chloride does not change as it is diluted, the number of ions per unit cube will be decreased in direct proportion to the concentration of the solution, and would thus be inversely proportional to the dilution. Thus one would expect the electrolytic conductivity of the potassium chloride solution to decrease as it is diluted, because there will be fewer ions in the unit cube to conduct.

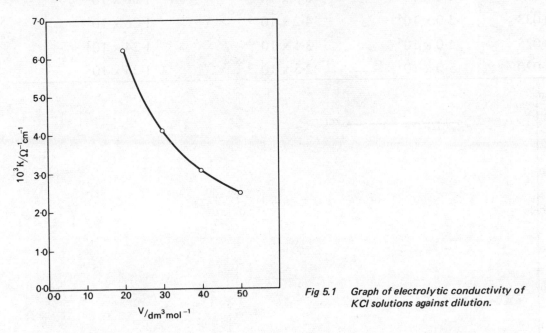

Fig 5.1   *Graph of electrolytic conductivity of KCl solutions against dilution.*

It is instructive to plot electrolytic conductivity against concentration (not against dilution, as is more frequently done) and teachers may wish to recommend this. For strong electrolytes in dilute solution the plot is linear; for weak electrolytes it is a curve.

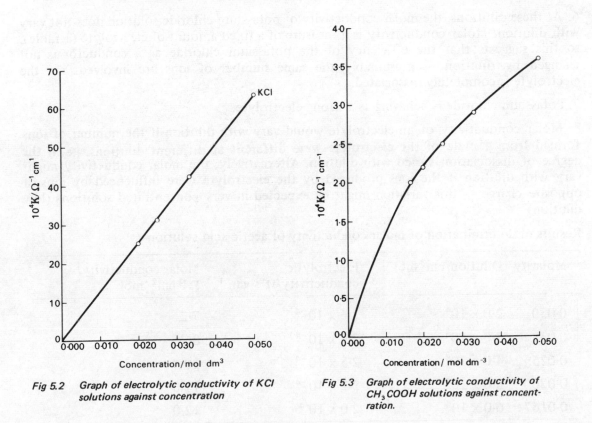

Fig 5.2   *Graph of electrolytic conductivity of KCl solutions against concentration*

Fig 5.3   *Graph of electrolytic conductivity of CH_3COOH solutions against concentration.*

29

Results of determination of molar conductivity of potassium chloride solutions

Molarity of KCl	Dilution/ cm³ mol⁻¹	Electrolytic conductivity/Ω^{-1} cm⁻¹	Molar conductivity/ Ω^{-1} cm² mol⁻¹
0·050	$2·0 \times 10^4$	$6·3 \times 10^{-3}$	$1·26 \times 10^2$
0·033	$3·0 \times 10^4$	$4·2 \times 10^{-3}$	$1·26 \times 10^2$
0·025	$4·0 \times 10^4$	$3·1 \times 10^{-3}$	$1·24 \times 10^2$
0·020	$5·0 \times 10^4$	$2·5 \times 10^{-3}$	$1·25 \times 10^2$

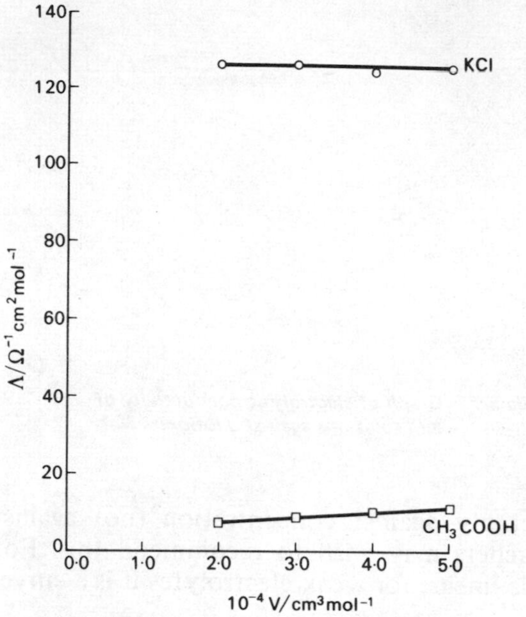

Fig 5.4   *Graph of molar conductivity of KCl and CH₃COOH solutions against dilution*

6. At these dilutions, the molar conductivity of potassium chloride solution does not vary with dilution. Molar conductivity is a measure of a fixed amount of electrolyte (1 mole), so this suggests that the efficiency of the potassium chloride as a conductor is not changed by dilution — presumably the same number of ions are involved, i.e. the electrolyte is completely dissociated.

7. Potassium chloride is behaving as a strong electrolyte.

8. Molar conductivity of an electrolyte would vary with dilution if the number of ions formed from a mole of the electrolyte were different at different dilutions. i.e. if the degree of dissociation varied with dilution. Alternatively, the molar conductivity might vary with dilution if the ions produced by the electrolyte were influenced by ions of opposite charge — this variation might be expected in very concentrated solutions (low dilution).

Results of determination of molar conductivity of acetic acid solutions

Molarity	Dilution/cm³ mol⁻¹	Electrolytic conductivity/Ω^{-1} cm⁻¹	Molar conductivity/ Ω^{-1} cm² mol⁻¹
0·050	$2·0 \times 10^4$	$3·6 \times 10^{-4}$	7·2
0·033	$3·0 \times 10^4$	$2·9 \times 10^{-4}$	8·7
0·025	$4·0 \times 10^4$	$2·5 \times 10^{-4}$	10·0
0·020	$5·0 \times 10^4$	$2·2 \times 10^{-4}$	11·0
0·0167	$6·0 \times 10^4$	$2·0 \times 10^{-4}$	12·0

9. The graph is linear but increases with increasing dilution; the values of molar conductivity of acetic acid are much lower than the values for potassium chloride at the same dilution. This would suggest that the acetic acid forms very few ions at these dilutions, and that the degree of dissociation increases as the dilution increases.

10. Acetic acid is behaving as a weak electrolyte.

The rinse is linear but the rinse with dilution. In adding the acid, however, solubility of acid at the surface is greater than the value by percentage of it with the one dilution. This would appear that the acetic acid forms regularly formal. In other dilution and that the degree of dissociation increases the dilution increases.

Assignment 6

Determination of the Dissociation Constant of Acetic Acid by a Conductance Method

INTRODUCTION

An electrolyte is assumed to be completely dissociated when further dilution does not produce an increase in its molar conductivity. The dilution at which the value of the molar conductivity reaches a maximum is referred to as infinite dilution.

Whilst the value of the molar conductivity of a strong electrolyte, at infinite dilution, can be determined directly, this is not so for weak electrolytes.

1. Why cannot the molar conductivity, at infinite dilution, of a weak electrolyte be determined directly?

However, it has been shown that the molar conductivity, at infinite dilution, of an electrolyte is the sum of the molar conductivity of its constituent ions, i.e. the individual ionic conductivities are additive. For example, the molar conductivity, at infinite dilution of sodium nitrate,

$$\Lambda\infty_{NaNO_3} = \Lambda_{Na^+} + \Lambda_{NO_3^-} = 50 \cdot 1 + 71 \cdot 5 = 121 \cdot 6\Omega^{-1} \text{ cm}^2 \text{mol}^{-1} \text{ at } 25°C.$$

Thus the molar conductivity, at infinite dilution, of a weak electrolyte can be calculated from the values obtained for strong electrolytes.

2. Write an expression for the molar conductivity at infinite dilution of, (a) acetic acid (b) potassium chloride (c) potassium acetate (d) hydrochloric acid, in terms of the ionic conductivities of the relevant ions.

3. Write an expression for the molar conductivity of acetic acid, at infinite dilution, in terms of the molar conductivity, at infinite dilution, of potassium chloride, potassium acetate and hydrochloric acid.

Determination of Molar Conductivity of Acetic Acid at Infinite Dilution

Determine the molar conductivity, at infinite dilution, of potassium chloride, potassium acetate and hydrochloric acid as follows:

Pipette 25·0cm³ of a 0·10M solution of the electrolyte into a 150cm³ beaker and determine the conductance of the cell containing the solution. Repeat the determination of the conductance after successive additions of 25·0cm³ of distilled water, until infinite dilution is reached.

4. What quick calculation can you make to ascertain whether infinite dilution has been reached?

5. How is the value of the molar conductivity of an electrolyte calculated from the conductance of the cell containing the solution?

6. What is the dilution of a 0·10M solution?

7. If an aqueous solution of a substance has a dilution of 10dm³ mol⁻¹, what does its dilution become if the volume of the solution is (a) doubled (b) trebled (c) quadrupled by the addition of water?

Set the results out in the form of a table, with headings as follows:

Electrolyte   Volume of solution   Dilution   Conductance of cell   Molar conductivity

Plot a graph of molar conductivity against dilution, for each of the three electrolytes on the same axes.

8. Should the graphs go through the origin? Explain.

9. Can you suggest a reason why the molar conductivity of a strong electrolyte should be much lower than its maximum value at low values of dilution?

10. What is the value of the molar conductivity, at infinite dilution, of (a) potassium chloride (b) potassium acetate (c) hydrochloric acid?

11. What is the value of the molar conductivity, at infinite dilution of acetic acid?

Determination of Molar Conductivity of Acetic Acid at a Given Dilution

Acetic acid dissociates as follows:

$$CH_3COOH \rightleftharpoons CH_3COO^- + H^+$$

If the degree of dissociation at dilution V is α

	Number of moles at dilution, V	$1 - \alpha$	α	α
	Concentration at dilution, V	$\dfrac{1 - \alpha}{V}$	$\dfrac{\alpha}{V}$	$\dfrac{\alpha}{V}$

12. What is the expression for the dissociation constant of acetic acid in terms of α and V?

Since the molar conductivity of the acetic acid solution at dilution, V, is proportional to the number of ions in a given volume,

$\Lambda_v = k\alpha$ where k is a constant,

and since at infinite dilution the acetic acid is completely dissociated i.e. $\alpha = 1$.

$\Lambda_\infty = k$

Hence,

$$\alpha = \frac{\Lambda_v}{\Lambda_\infty}$$

Place sufficient 0·10M acetic acid in a beaker to cover the electrodes of the cell and determine the conductance.
Calculate the molar conductance of acetic acid at this dilution.

13. What is the degree of dissociation of acetic acid at this dilution?

14. Substitute the values of degree of dissociation, and the dilution at which it was determined, in the expression for the dissociation constant and calculate the value at the temperature at which the experiments were performed.

15. Is this dissociation constant of constant value independent of
(a) temperature?
(b) dilution?
(c) the nature of the solvent for the acetic acid?

16. Which is a better indication of the strength of an acid, the degree of dissociation or the dissociation constant?

Notes 6

Standard: **

Time required: 1½ hours of practical time

Reagents required:

0·10M potassium chloride	(50cm³) (unless results from Assignment 5 be used)
0·10M potassium acetate	(50cm³)
0·10M hydrochloric acid	(50cm³)
0·10M acetic acid	(50cm³)
distilled water or conductivity water (400cm³)	

Apparatus required:

Conductance bridge and conductance cell (of known cell constant)

2 x 25cm³ pipettes

4 x 150cm³ beakers

Notes on questions and typical results

1. Using a conductance cell, there would be little, if any, ions present in the cell when an acetic acid solution was of infinite dilution. It is thus not possible to obtain a result of any accuracy by direct measurement — one would obtain a value for the conductance of distilled water long before infinite dilution was reached.

2. $\Lambda\infty_{CH_3COOH} = \Lambda\infty_{H^+} + \Lambda_{CH_3COO^-}$ $\Lambda\infty_{KCl} = \Lambda\infty_{K^+} + \Lambda\infty_{Cl^-}$

$\Lambda\infty_{HCl} = \Lambda\infty_{H^+} + \Lambda\infty_{Cl^-}$ $\Lambda\infty_{CH_3COOK} = \Lambda\infty_{K^+} \Lambda\infty_{CH_3COO^-}$

3. Acetic acid, $\Lambda\infty = \Lambda\infty_{HCl} + \Lambda\infty_{CH_3COOK} - \Lambda\infty_{KCl}$

Typical results   Cell constant = 0·54cms⁻¹

Electrolyte	Volume of solution/cm³	Dilution/ dm³ mol⁻¹	Conductance of cell/Ω^{-1}	Molar conductivity /Ω^{-1} cm² mol⁻¹
potassium chloride	25	10	2·10x10⁻²	114
potassium chloride	50	20	1·15x10⁻²	124
potassium chloride	75	30	7·6x10⁻³	123
potassium chloride	100	40	5·7x10⁻³	123
potassium chloride	125	50	4·6x10⁻³	124
potassium acetate	25	10	1·20x10⁻²	65
potassium acetate	50	20	7·5x10⁻³	81

34

potassium acetate	75	30	5.1×10^{-3}	83
potassium acetate	100	40	3.8×10^{-3}	82
potassium acetate	125	50	3.1×10^{-3}	84
hydrochloric acid	25	10	6.2×10^{-2}	334
hydrochloric acid	50	20	3.3×10^{-2}	356
hydrochloric acid	75	30	2.25×10^{-2}	364
hydrochloric acid	100	40	1.70×10^{-2}	367
hydrochloric acid	125	50	1.35×10^{-2}	365

4. It is unnecessary to calculate the value of the molar conductivity to check whether 'infinite' dilution has been reached; when the product of the conductance of the cell and the dilution (or even the number of $25 cm^3$ portions of liquid in the beaker) has reached a maximum value the solution is at 'infinite' dilution.

5. The molar conductivity of the electrolyte solution is calculated by multiplying the conductance of the cell, containing the solution, by the cell constant and the dilution. It is convenient to express the dilution in $cm^3 \ mol^{-1}$ since the molar conductivity is then the electrolytic conductivity (i.e. the conductivity of a $1 cm$ cube of solution) multiplied by the number of cm^3 containing one mole of electrolyte.

6. The dilution of a solution is the reciprocal of the concentration, so the dilution of a $0.10M$ solution is $10 dm^3 \ mol^{-1}$ or $10^4 cm^3 \ mol^{-1}$.

7. If an aqueous solution has a dilution of $10 dm^3 \ mol^{-1}$ and the volume of solution is doubled, the dilution becomes $20 dm^3 \ mol^{-1}$; if its volume is trebled its dilution becomes $30 dm^3 \ mol^{-1}$ and if its volume is quadrupled, its dilution becomes $40 dm^3 \ mol^{-1}$. Thus in the experiment the dilution of the solution may easily be calculated, bearing this in mind.

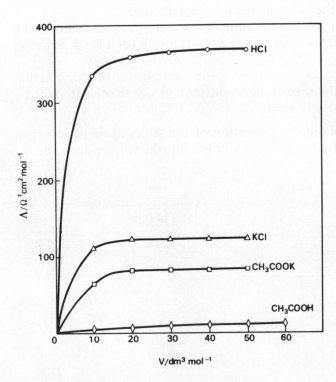

Fig 6.1   Graph of molar conductivity of various electrolyte solutions against dilution

8. Pure hydrogen chloride has a molar conductivity of zero, being a gas at 25°C, so the curve would originate at the zero point on the axes.

The other two electrolytes being solids will have zero molar conductivity in the absence of water, but of course, the concept of molar conductivity has little significance at these dilutions. It is fair to say that in solutions of very low dilution the molar conductivity increases with dilution and the graph would appear to have its origin at the zero points of the axes.

9. At low dilutions it is reasonable to expect considerable interaction between the ions, and whilst the electrolyte may be fully ionized, the ions may not be fully dissociated from each other. The 'atmosphere' of ions of opposite charge, around a central ion, will be attracted in a different direction from the central ion, and the distortion of this 'ion-atmosphere' will retard the movement of the central ion reducing the conductivity of the solution.

10. (a) molar conductivity at infinite dilution of potassium chloride = $124 \Omega^{-1} cm^2 mol^{-1}$
(b) molar conductivity at infinite dilution of potassium acetate = $84 \Omega^{-1} cm^2 mol^{-1}$
(c) molar conductivity at infinite dilution of hydrochloric acid = $365 \Omega^{-1} cm^2 mol^{-1}$

11. The molar conductivity at infinite dilution of acetic acid = $365 + 84 - 124 \Omega^{-1} cm^2 mol^{-1}$

$$= 325 \Omega^{-1} cm^2 mol^{-1}$$

12. The dissociation constant of acetic acid, $K = \dfrac{\alpha/V \times \alpha/V}{(1-\alpha)V} = \dfrac{\alpha}{(1-\alpha)V}$

Molar conductance of acetic acid, at dilution $10 dm^3 mol^{-1} = 9\cdot1 \times 10^{-4} \times 0\cdot54 \times 10^4 \Omega^{-1} cm^2 mol^{-1}$.

$$= 4\cdot9 \Omega^{-1} cm^2 mol^{-1}$$

13. The degree of dissociation is given by the conductance ratio, $\alpha = \dfrac{\Lambda\infty}{\Lambda\infty}$.

Hence $\alpha = \dfrac{4\cdot9}{325}$ at dilution $10 dm^3 mol^{-1} = 1\cdot5 \times 10^{-2}$

14. Hence $K = \dfrac{(1\cdot5 \times 10^{-2})^2}{0\cdot084 \times 10}$ mol dm^{-3} = $2\cdot3 \times 10^{-5}$ mol dm^{-3} at room temperature.

15. (a) The dissociation constant varies with temperature; the value determined above is the value at the temperature at which the experiments were conducted.
(b) The dissociation constant is independent of dilution; the expression includes the dilution and although the degree of dissociation varies with dilution for a weak acid, the dissociation constant does not.
(c) The dissociation constant of acetic acid determined is the constant for the dissociation of the acid in water; the value for the dissociation constant in other solvents will be different.

16. The dissociation constant is a more useful indication of the strength of an acid than the degree of dissociation, since the latter varies with dilution but the former does not.

FURTHER PROJECT

Test of the constancy of the expression for the dissociation constant.

Determine the conductance of the cell containing acetic acid of dilution 20, 30, 40 and 50dm^3 mol^{-1}. Hence calculate the molar conductivity of acetic acid at these dilutions and from these results calculate the value of the dissociation constant for acetic acid at these dilutions.

Typical results

Dilution /dm^3 mol^{-1}	Conductance of cell/Ω^{-1}	Molar conductivity/ Ω^{-1}cm^{2}mol^{-1}	Degree of dissociation	Dissociation constant/mol dm^{-3}
10	9·1x10^{-4}	4·9	1·6x10^{-2}	2·6x10^{-5}
20	6·6x10^{-4}	7·1	2·3x10^{-2}	2·7x10^{-5}
30	5·3x10^{-4}	8·6	2·7x10^{-2}	2·5x10^{-5}
40	4·6x10^{-4}	9·9	3·1x10^{-2}	2·5x10^{-5}
50	4·0x10^{-4}	10·8	3·4x10^{-2}	2·4x10^{-5}

Assignment 7
pH Changes During the Precipitation

(a) Titration of magnesium chloride solution with sodium hydroxide solution
Pipette $10cm^3$ of the approximately 1M solution of magnesium chloride provided into a clean $250cm^3$ beaker and add about $50cm^3$ of distilled water using a measuring cylinder. Stir the mixture thoroughly and immerse the electrodes of a pH-meter in it.

Record the pH and then add a few drops of $1.0M$ sodium hydroxide solution from a burette. Once again the mixture must be well stirred before the pH is recorded. Look closely for any signs of precipitation. Note the volume of alkali added.

Continue in this manner until some $25-30cm^3$ of the alkali solution has been added and construct a table showing the variation of the pH of the solution and the corresponding volumes of the alkali solution added.

N.B. For much of the titration it will be possible to add the alkali in $3-4cm^3$ portions, but at stages where the pH is changing rapidly it will be necessary to restrict the portions to $0.2cm^3$.

Plot a graph of the pH of the solution against the volume of $1.0M$ alkali added.

1. Give the ionic equation for the reaction that has occurred during the titration.

2. What explanation can you offer for the shape of this graph?

3. What volume of $1.0M$ NaOH was needed to react with the $10cm^3$ of the $MgCl_2$ solution? (Estimate this from the graph)

4. Assuming that the NaOH solution was exactly $1.0M$, what was the accurate molarity of the original $MgCl_2$ solution?

5. What was the total volume (approximate) of the solution whose pH you measured at the half-way stage of the reaction?

6. What must the concentration of Mg^{2+} ions have been in the solution at the half-way stage of the titration?

7. What was the pH at the half-way stage of the titration?

8. What was the hydrogen ion concentration at the half-way stage?

9. What must the hydroxide ion concentration have been at this stage?

10. What is meant by the term 'solubility product'?

11. Which of the following factors affect the value of the solubility product for a given salt: (a) total reactant concentrations? (b) temperature? (c) amount of precipitate? (d) size of particles of the precipitate?

12. Using your answers to questions 6 and 9, calculate a value for the solubility product of magnesium hydroxide.

13. Why were the values of pH and Mg^{2+} ion concentration used those at the half-way stage of the titration rather than those at the end-point of the titration?

(b) Titration of aluminium chloride solution with sodium hydroxide solution.
Using 10cm³ of an approximately 1M solution of aluminium chloride, together with the same solution of 1·0M NaOH, carry out a similar pH titration. On this occasion continue the titration until 45-50cm³ of the sodium hydroxide solution has been added.

Record the values of the pH for various volumes of alkali added and, once again, plot these data against each other. Carefully record the appearance of the precipitate at various stages in the titration.

14. Your graph should show two 'steps'. What chemical reactions are responsible for this? Give your reasons.

15. Why is aluminium hydroxide amphoteric while magnesium hydroxide is not?

Use the procedure set out in questions 3—10 to calculate a value for the solubility product of aluminium hydroxide.

Notes 7

Standard: **

Time required: 1½ hours

Reagents required:

(approx) 1M MgCl₂ solution	(15cm³)
(approx) 1M AlCl₃ solution	(15cm³)
1·0M NaOH solution	(100cm³)
Distilled water	(100cm³)

Apparatus required:

Burette
10cm³ pipette
250cm³ beaker
100cm³ measuring cylinder
pH meter and electrodes

Typical results

10cm³ of 1M MgCl₂ plus 50cm³ H₂O Volume of 1·0M NaOH added/cm³	pH	10cm³ of 1 M AlCl₃ plus 50cm³ H₂O Volume of 1·0M NaOH added/cm³	pH
0	6·05	0	3·00
0·15	9·50	0·5	3·06
0·25	9·70	1·0	3·09
0·50	9·78	2·0	3·19
1·00	9·81	4·0	3·25
5·00	9·88	10·0	3·45
10·0	10·0	15·0	3·58
15·0	10·1	20·0	3·72
18·0	10·3	22·0	3·82
19·0	10·6	23·5	3·96
19·5	11·1	25·0	4·25
19·8	11·3	25·5	4·52
20·0	11·4	26·0	4·90
21·0	11·6	26·5	5·52
22·0	11·7	27·0	6·39
25·0	11·8	27·5	7·08
		28·0	7·87
		28·5	8·73
		29·0	9·22
		29·5	9·48
		30·0	9·68
		31·0	9·90
		32·0	10·05
		34·0	10·3
		35·0	10·3

36·0	10·4
37·0	10·4
38·0	10·5
39·0	10·8
40·0	11·0
41·0	11·1
42·0	11·2

Notes on Experimental Work and Questions

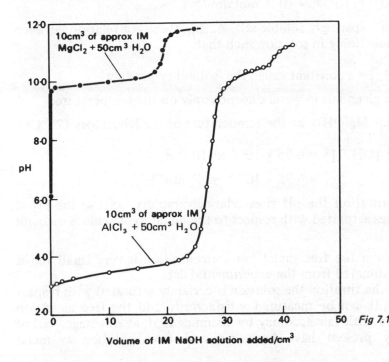

Fig 7.1   Graph of variation of pH as NaOH solution is added to solutions of $MgCl_2$ and $AlCl_3$

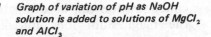

(a) magnesium chloride − sodium hydroxide

The $50cm^3$ of distilled water is added in order that the volume of the solution is sufficient to allow the pH-meter electrodes to be fully immersed in the mixture.

Since $Mg(OH)_2$ is not an extremely insoluble hydroxide, the pH rises rapidly as the first frew drops of alkali are added to the $MgCl_2$ solution. However, two or three drops of the alkali ($0·15cm^3$) should be sufficient to cause a permanent precipitate (colourless and gelatinous) to form.

1. Mg^{2+} (aq) + 2 $OH^-_{(aq)}$ ⇌ $Mg(OH)_2$ (s)

2. The pH rises rapidly until the OH^- concentration is sufficient to exceed the solubility product of $Mg(OH)_2$ and thus cause its precipitation. During precipitation the pH rise is very small as most of the extra OH^- added is removed as insoluble $Mg(OH)_2$. When two moles of OH^- have been added for every mole of Mg^{2+} there is effectively no Mg^{2+} left and addition of further hydroxide ion leads only to a marked increase in the hydroxide ion concentration. In turn this causes a drop in hydrogen ion concentration and a sharp rise in pH.

3. $19·5cm^3$ of 1·0M NaOH was needed to react with $10·0cm^3$ of the $MgCl_2$ solution.

4. Accurate molarity of original $MgCl_2$ solution =

$$\frac{19·5}{1000} \times \frac{1}{2} \times \frac{1000}{10} = 0·975M \text{ (Assuming that the NaOH is 1·0M)}$$

5. Total volume of solution at half-way stage: $10cm^3 + 50cm^3 + 10cm^3 = 70cm^3$

41

6. $[Mg^{2+}]$ at half-way stage = $\frac{10}{70}$ x 0·975 x $\frac{1}{2}$ = 6·95 x 10 $^{-2}$ mol dm $^{-3}$

7. pH at half-way stage was 10·0 (from graph).

8. Since pH is defined as $-\lg[H^+]$, then $[H^+]$ at the half-way stage was $1·0 \times 10^{10}$ mol dm^{-3}

9. $[H^+]\,[OH^-]$ = 1 x 10^{-14} mol^2 dm^{-6} in water. Thus, $[OH^-]$ at the half-way stage was:

$$10^{-14}/10^{-10} = 10^{-4} \text{ mol dm}^{-3}$$

10. For a *saturated* solution of a sparingly soluble salt, A_mB_n, there is a relation between the concentration of the ions remaining in solution such that:

$$[A^{x+}]^m\,[B^{y-}]^n = \text{a constant called the 'solubility product'}.$$

11. The solubility product of a given salt in water depends only on the temperature.

12. Thus, solubility product for $Mg(OH)_2$ at the temperature of the laboratory (21°C) =

$$[Mg^{2+}]\,[OH^-]^2 = 6·95 \times 10^{-2} \times (10^{-4})^2$$
$$= 6·95 \times 10^{-10} \text{ mol}^3 \text{ dm}^{-9}$$

13. At the beginning of the titration the pH rises relatively rapidly, and so the pH at which the solution first becomes saturated with respect to the metal hydroxide is difficult to determine with certainty.

At the end-point of the titration the free metal ion concentration is very small and it cannot be calculated or even estimated from the experimental data.

However, at the mid-point of the titration the solution is certainly saturated with respect to the metal hydroxide, the pH can be measured satisfactorily and the free metal ion concentration can be estimated with fair accuracy by assuming that, at this stage, half of the magnesium ions initially present have been removed from solution as metal hydroxide.

N.B. The stock solutions of $AlCl_3$ and $MgCl_2$ will not be exactly 1·0M. The best procedure is to standardize them against 1·0M NaOH solution, determining the volume of the latter solution needed to react with 10·0cm^3 of the salt solution from the experimental results

(b) aluminium chloride — sodium hydroxide
The experimental procedure here is the same as that of the previous experiment, but it is worth taking particular care to ensure that the mixture is well stirred in the final phase of the experiment (i.e. from 25cm^3 of 1·0M NaOH onwards).

14. The colourless, gelatinous precipitate, which appears from A to B, is hydrated aluminium hydroxide:

$$[Al(H_2O)_6]^{3+} + 3\,OH^- \rightleftharpoons Al(OH)_3\,(H_2O)_3 \downarrow + 3\,H_2O$$

However, as the next 10cm^3 or so of the 1·0M NaOH are added the precipitate redissolves slowly to give a colourless solution. This process is finally complete at C. The ratio of the volume of alkali needed to redissolve the precipitate to that needed to form it, strongly suggests that the precipitate dissolves to form $Al(OH)_4^-$:

$$Al(OH)_3(H_2O)_3 + OH^- \rightleftharpoons [Al(OH)_4(H_2O)_2]^- + H_2O$$

15. The charge to radius ratio of Al^{3+} is about twice that of the Mg^{2+} ion. This results in water molecules of hydrated Al(III) cations being more acidic than those of hydrated Mg(II) ions:

$$H_2O + \left[\begin{matrix} H \\ H \end{matrix} \!\!>\!\! O{:}Al^{3+}(OH^-)_3\,(H_2O)_2 \right] \rightleftharpoons H_3O^+ + [Al^{3+}(OH^-)_4\,(H_2O)_2]$$

27.5cm^3 of 1.0M NaOH react with 10.0cm^3 AlCl$_3$ solution. Hence, the concentration of the aluminium chloride stock solution was 0.92M.

Taking the pH at the half-way stage as 3.5 it follows that:

$$\text{Solubility Product of Al(OH)}_3 = \frac{0.46}{7} \times (10^{-10.5})^3 = 2 \times 10^{-33} \text{ mol}^4\,\text{dm}^{-12}$$

(The values of the solubility products of Mg(OH)$_2$ and Al(OH)$_3$ quoted in the literature are: 9×10^{-12} mol^3 dm^{-9} and 2.5×10^{-32} mol^4 dm^{-12} respectively)

FURTHER WORK

Investigate to see whether it is possible, by this general method, to establish the relative sequence of solubility products for the hydroxides of the metals in the alkaline earth group.

REFERENCE:

R.T. Yingling and H.A. Neidlig, *Chemistry*, 40, No.1, 34 (1967).

Assignment 8

The Dependence of the Silver Electrode Potential on the Silver Ion Concentration

INTRODUCTION

When a metal which does not react with water is dipped into an aqueous solution of its ions two processes will occur.

1. Metal atoms on the surface of the metal will go into solution as hydrated ions, leaving electrons behind on the metal:

$$M_{(s)} \rightarrow M^{n+}_{(aq)} + ne^-$$

2. Hydrated metal ions will combine with electrons on the surface of the metal and become deposited there:

$$M^{n+}_{(aq)} + ne^- \rightarrow M_{(s)}$$

If the tendency of the first reaction to occur outweighs that of the latter then, at equilibrium, the metal will be negatively charged with respect to the solution, and *vice-versa*. In either case a potential will exist between the metal and the solution and this 'electrode potential' will be a measure of the tendency of the metal to form hydrated ions in aqueous solution under the given conditions. It is to be expected that the tendency of reaction 2 (above) to occur, and hence the electrode potential, must depend on the concentration of metal ions in the aqueous solution.

N.B. Single electrode potentials cannot be measured because, although a potential exists between a metal and the solution with which it is in contact, its measurement requires the insertion of another electrical conductor (with its own electrode potential) in the solution. Thus, it is only possible to measure the difference between two electrode potentials.

In these experiments the following apparatus should be used:

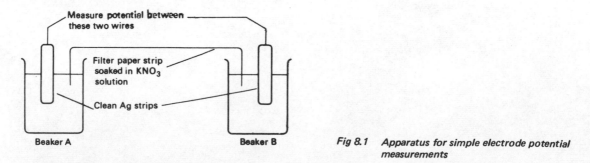

Fig 8.1 Apparatus for simple electrode potential measurements

The concentration of silver ions in the solution in Beaker B will be varied while that in Beaker A will not be changed. The variation of the measured voltage will thus give an indication of the manner in which the electrode potential of the silver in Beaker B varies with the concentration of silver ions in the solution in Beaker B.

Before beginning the practical work try to answer the following questions:

1. The voltage between the two electrodes should be measured in such a way that no current flows between the two electrodes (use a potentiometer). In practice, it may be possible to make reasonable measurements providing that the current flowing is extremely small (use a high impedance voltmeter). Why cannot accurate measurements be made while a current flows between the electrodes?

2. Why is the filter paper strip (a 'salt bridge') dipped in KNO_3 solution necessary?

3. Explain why you would expect to record zero voltage if the solutions in both beakers were identical.

EXPERIMENT (i)

Using the given aqueous solutions of silver nitrate and sodium chloride, together with the burettes and pipettes provided, prepare the following mixtures in clean beakers. Complete the final column of the table. (Where sodium chloride is involved assume that each chloride ion removes one silver ion from solution)

Table 1

Beaker	Amount of $AgNO_3$ solution used	Volume of water added	Volume of 2×10^{-2} M NaCl solution added	Expected $[Ag^+]$
1	$50cm^3$ of 1×10^{-1} M $AgNO_3$	–	–	
2	$25cm^3$ of 2×10^{-2} M	$25 \cdot 0 cm^3$	–	
3	$2 \cdot 5 cm^3$ of 2×10^{-2} M	$47 \cdot 5 cm^3$	–	
4	$25cm^3$ of 2×10^{-2} M	$2 \cdot 5 cm^3$	$22 \cdot 5 cm^3$	
5	$0 \cdot 25 cm^3$ of 2×10^{-2} M	$49 \cdot 75 cm^3$	–	
6	$25 \cdot 0 cm^3$ of 2×10^{-2} M	$0 \cdot 25 cm^3$	$24 \cdot 75 cm^3$	
7	$50 \cdot 0 cm^3$ of 1×10^{-5} M	–	–	

Set up the apparatus as shown in the diagram with Beaker A containing $50cm^3$ of $0 \cdot 1M$ silver nitrate solution and with Beaker 7 used as Beaker B. Measure the voltage between the two strips of silver. Remove Beaker 7, together with the filter paper strip, clean the piece of silver and then place it in Beaker 6. Fit a fresh salt-bridge and once again measure the voltage between the silver strips. Continue in this way using beakers 5, 4, 3, 2 and 1, in turn, as Beaker B, recording your measured potentials in Table 2.

Table 2

$[Ag^+]$ in Beaker A	Beaker used as Beaker B	$[Ag^+]$ in Beaker B	Measured Potential
1×10^{-1} M	7	....	....
1×10^{-1} M	6	....	....
1×10^{-1} M	5	....	....
1×10^{-1} M	4	....	....
1×10^{-1} M	3	....	....
1×10^{-1} M	2	....	....
1×10^{-1} M	1	....	....

4. By inspecting the experimentally measured potentials, $E_{meas.}$, decide which of the following statements best describes the manner in which the potentials depend on the silver ion concentration in Beaker B:

$E_{meas.}$ is directly proportional to (i) $[Ag^+]$; (ii) $[Ag^+]^2$; (iii) $[Ag^+]^{-1}$; (iv) $\lg [Ag^+]$

Draw a graph (Graph I) to confirm the conclusion reached in answering question 4. Graph I should show that there is a simple relation between the measured potential and the silver ion concentration for measurements made at a fixed temperature and with a given silver ion concentration in Beaker A. It should thus be apparent that electrode potential measurements can be of use in estimating the concentration of silver ions in aqueous solution. In fact, this is a very valuable method for determining low concentrations of many ions. This is illustrated by Experiment (ii).

EXPERIMENT (ii)

Using scrupulously cleaned apparatus, prepare the mixtures indicated in Table 3. Make measurements as before, using $0 \cdot 1M$ $AgNO_3$ solution throughout in Beaker A. Record the measured potentials in Table 4.

Table 3.

Beaker	Volume of $2 \times 10^{-2} M$ $AgNO_3$	Volume of distilled water	Amount of NaCl solution	Expected $[Cl^-]$
8	$24 \cdot 75 cm^3$	$0 \cdot 25 cm^3$	$25 \cdot 0 cm^3$ of $2 \times 10^{-2} M$	
9	$2 \cdot 5 cm^3$	$20 \cdot 0 cm^3$	$27 \cdot 5 cm^3$ of $2 \times 10^{-2} M$	
10	$0 \cdot 25 cm^3$	$24 \cdot 5 cm^3$	$25 \cdot 25 cm^3$ of $2 \times 10^{-2} M$	
11	$0 \cdot 1 cm^3$	–	$50 \cdot 0 cm^3$ of $1 \times 10^{-1} M$	

Table 4

$[Ag^+]$ in Beaker A	Beaker used as Beaker B	E_{meas}/volts	Concentrations in Beaker B		
			$[Ag^+]$	$\lg [Ag^+]$	$\lg [Cl^-]$
$1 \times 10^{-1} M$	8	...	...		
$1 \times 10^{-1} M$	9	...	...		
$1 \times 10^{-1} M$	10	...	...		
$1 \times 10^{-1} M$	11	...	...		

Use Graph I to determine the silver ion concentrations in Beakers 8–11 from the measured potentials and complete Table 4.

For sparingly soluble salts of formula MX the relation between the equilibrium concentrations of cations and anions in saturated aqueous solutions of MX is of the form:

$$[M^{n+}] \, [X^-] = K_S$$

where K_S the solubility product of Mx, is a constant at a fixed temperature. If this relation for all saturated solutions of silver chloride at the given temperature then:

$$[Ag^+] \, [Cl^-] = K_S \text{ or } [Ag^+] = K_S [Cl^-]^{-1}$$

Therefore: $\lg [Ag^+] = \lg K_S - \lg [Cl^-]$. Thus, a graph of $\lg [Ag^+]$ against $\lg [Cl^-]$ should be linear with intercepts of $\lg K_S$ when $\lg [Ag^+]$ is zero and when $\lg [Cl^-]$ is zero. Using the data of Table 4, plot such a graph and draw the best straight line which gives the same intercept on both axes. (Graph II)

5. What value of K_s does your graph suggest for silver chloride?

6. How does this compare with literature values for the solubility product of silver chloride at laboratory temperatures?

7. Why is the electrode which dips into Beaker B negative with respect to that in Beaker A throughout most of these experiments?

Notes 8

Standard: ***

Time: 2 hours (This can be conveniently split into two sessions)

Reagents required:

1×10^{-1}M AgNO$_3$ solution   (100cm^3)

2×10^{-2}M AgNO$_3$ solution   (150cm^3)

1×10^{-5}M AgNO$_3$ solution   (50cm^3)

2×10^{-2}M NaCl solution   (150cm^3)

1×10^{-1}M NaCl solution   (50cm^3)

aqueous KNO$_3$ solution; no specified concentration (20cm^3)

distilled water (200cm^3)

Apparatus required:

8 beakers (100 or 150cm^3)

2 strips of clean silver

filter paper strips (about a dozen, each about 6 inches long)

pipettes: One of each of the following

25, 20, 10 and 5cm^3

N.B. The pipettes can be supplemented or substituted by burettes.

microburettes: volumes of less than 5cm^3 can be dispensed from communal microburettes. A minimum of three will be needed (i.e. one each for the 2×10^{-2}M AgNO$_3$, distilled water and the 2×10^{-2}M NaCl)

potential measurements: Teachers will probably wish to demonstrate the use of a potentiometer, but for general class measurements a high impedance voltmeter has many advantages. The results described here were obtained using a Philip Harris pH Meter B5160.

Comments and Notes on Questions:

Introduction

This experiment assumes no previous experience of electrode potentials. The practical work involved is simple, but it is necessary for great care to be taken with regard to cleanliness and accuracy in making up the mixtures involved.

1. If a current flows while potential measurements are made the concentrations of the ions in the solutions will alter. This will, in turn, lead to a change in the potential being measured. In addition, the electrodes may become polarized. When a high impedance voltmeter is used a current flows but it is so small that it exerts no detectable effect on the measured potential.

2. The salt bridge completes the circuit; without it a back e.m.f. will be set up.

3. The two electrodes will generate the same electrode potentials, but, since the two will oppose each other there will be no measurable potential. The tendency for electrons to pass from one electrode towards the other will be exactly balanced by that for electrons to flow in the reverse direction.

EXPERIMENT (i) Sample data for Table 2

[Ag$^+$] in Beaker A	Beaker used as Beaker B	[Ag$^+$] in Beaker B /mol dm^3	Measured Potential/V
1 x 10^{-1} M	7	1 x 10^{-5}	−0·21
1 x 10^{-1} M	6	1 x 10^{-4}	−0·15
1 x 10^{-1} M	5	1 x 10^{-4}	−0·16
1 x 10^{-1} M	4	1 x 10^{-3}	−0·105
1 x 10^{-1} M	3	1 x 10^{-3}	−0·100
1 x 10^{-1} M	2	1 x 10^{-2}	−0·050
1 x 10^{-1} M	1	1 x 10^{-1}	0·000

4. Alternative (iv) is correct; a graph of E_{meas} against $\lg[Ag^+]_B$ should be linear.

The Nernst Equation predicts for the individual silver electrodes:

$$E_{electrode A} = E_O + \frac{RT}{F} \ln [Ag^+]_A$$

$$= E_O + \frac{2 \cdot 3RT}{F} \lg [Ag^+]_A$$

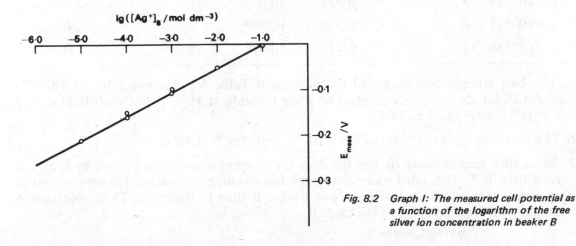

Fig. 8.2   Graph I: The measured cell potential as a function of the logarithm of the free silver ion concentration in beaker B

Similarly,

$$E_{electrode B} = E_O + \frac{2 \cdot 3RT}{F} \lg[Ag^+]_B$$

where E_O is the standard electrode potential for silver.

Thus: $E_{electrode B} - E_{electrode A} = E_{meas} = \frac{2 \cdot 3RT}{F} \lg [Ag^+]_B - \frac{2 \cdot 3RT}{F} \lg [Ag^+]_A$

and if $[Ag^+]_A = 10^{-1}$ M, then $E_{meas} = \frac{2 \cdot 3RT}{F} \lg [Ag^+]_B + \frac{2 \cdot 3RT}{F}$

In all the above expressions: R is the gas constant, T is the temperature in degrees Kelvin and F is the Faraday.

At 18°C this reduces to: E_{meas} (in volts) = 0·058 + 0·058 $\lg [Ag^+]_B$

Graph I, which should be described by the above equation, should show that it is possible to determine unknown silver ion concentrations by means of electrode potential measurements. This is all that is necessary in order to proceed with Experiment (ii).

However, it is important to appreciate that it is the *ratio*: $[Ag^+]_A : [Ag^+]_B$ which determines the measured potential. Thus, the measured potentials for each of the following cells should be the same:

$$Ag / 0 \cdot 1M \; Ag^+ \; // \; KNO_3 \; // \; 1 \times 10^{-3}M \; Ag^+ / Ag$$

$$Ag / 1 \times 10^{-2}M \; Ag^+ \; // \; KNO_3 \; // \; 1 \times 10^{-4}M \; Ag^+ / Ag$$

$$Ag / 1 \times 10^{-3}M \; Ag^+ \; // \; KNO_3 \; // \; 1 \times 10^{-5}M \; Ag^+ / Ag$$

In order to save time, it has not been suggested on the Assignment Sheets that this should be investigated. However, teachers may well feel that it is desirable to get students to establish the validity of the relationship:

$$E_{meas} = 0 \cdot 058 \times \lg \frac{[Ag^+]_B}{[Ag^+]_A}$$

This can be checked readily by making a few measurements with $1 \times 10^{-2}M$ and/or with $1 \times 10^{-3}M$ silver nitrate solution in Beaker A.

EXPERIMENT (ii): Sample data for Table 4:

$[Ag^+]_A$	Beaker used as Beaker B	E_{meas}/V	$[Ag^+]_B/$ mol dm^{-3}	$\lg[Ag^+]_B$ /mol dm^{-3}	$\lg[Cl^-]_B$ mol dm^{-3}
$1 \times 10^{-1}M$	8	$-0 \cdot 26$	10^{-6}	$-6 \cdot 0$	$-4 \cdot 0$
$1 \times 10^{-1}M$	9	$-0 \cdot 375$	$10^{-8 \cdot 3}$	$-8 \cdot 3$	$-2 \cdot 0$
$1 \times 10^{-1}M$	10	$-0 \cdot 375$	$10^{-8 \cdot 3}$	$-8 \cdot 3$	$-2 \cdot 0$
$1 \times 10^{-1}M$	11	$-0 \cdot 43$	$10^{-9 \cdot 3}$	$-9 \cdot 3$	$-1 \cdot 0$

5. The best straight line suggested by the data of Table 4 indicates a value of $10^{-10 \cdot 2}$ mol^2 dm^{-6} for the solubility product of silver chloride at 18°C (See Graph II). i.e. $K_s = 6 \cdot 3 \times 10^{-11}$ mol^2 dm^{-6} at 18°C.

6. The literature quotes a value of $8 \cdot 8 \times 10^{-11}$ mol^2 dm^{-6} at 18°C.

7. In neither Experiments (i) nor (ii) does the concentration of silver ions in Beaker B exceed that in A. This must mean that there is a greater net tendency for silver atoms to dissociate to form hydrated silver ions in Beaker B than in Beaker A. Thus, electrode A will be negative with respect to electrode B.

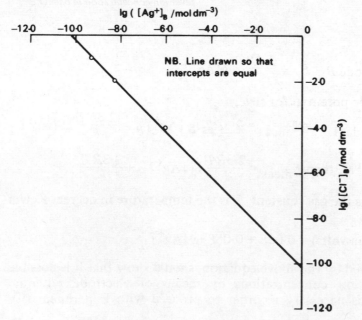

Fig. 8.3
Graph II: The variation of the logarithm of the free silver ion concentration in beaker B with the logarithm of the free chloride ion concentration

USEFUL STUDENT REFERENCES:

Bruce H. Mahan, *College Chemistry, Addison Wesley (1967).*
D.R. Stranks *et al., Chemistry — A Structural View*, Cambridge University Press (1965)

Assignment 9

A Potentiometric Study of a Mixture of Halide Ions

With luck, the previous assignment should have supported the conclusion that the silver electrode potential depends on the silver ion concentration in the solution with which the electrode is in contact. Accurate measurements show that the manner of this dependence, at a temperature of 291K i.e. 18°C, can be expressed by the equation:

$$E = E_O + 0.058 \lg[Ag^+] \ldots \text{Eq. (i)}$$

where E_O, the standard electrode potential, is the potential of the standard silver electrode relative to a standard hydrogen electrode at 298K, i.e. E_O is the e.m.f. of the cell:

$$\text{Pt, H}_2(1 \text{ atm.})/\text{ H}^+ (1 \cdot 0M) // \text{Ag}^+ (1 \cdot 0M) / \text{Ag and } E_O = +0 \cdot 70 \text{ V}$$

INTRODUCTORY PROBLEM

Saturated aqueous solutions of silver chloride and silver bromide were prepared by shaking excess of the silver halide with distilled water. With the saturated silver chloride solution in beaker M of Fig. 9.1 and with 1·0M silver nitrate solution in beaker N, no current was detected by the sensitive ammeter, A, when the jockey made contact with the potentiometer wire, PQ, at B.

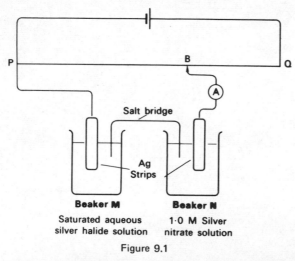

Figure 9.1

When the experiment was repeated with saturated silver bromide solution in beaker M instead of the silver chloride solution, the jockey had to be moved nearer to Q before current was prevented from passing through the ammeter.

1. If E_M and E_N represent the separate potentials of the electrodes in beakers M and N, respectively, which of the following expressions is directly proportional to the distance PB:

$$\text{(i) } (E_M + E_N)? \quad \text{(ii)} \frac{E_N}{E_M}? \quad \text{(iii) } (E_N - E_M)?$$

52

2. Which of the two halide solutions gave rise to the biggest value for E_M?

3. Is silver chloride less soluble in water than silver bromide? (Relate your answer to question 2 to Eqn (i))

4. If the experiment was done with saturated aqueous silver iodide solution in beaker M, how would you expect the distance PB (when no current passes through A) for the silver iodide solution to compare with that for silver bromide?

5. If a drop of silver nitrate solution was added to a solution containing considerable amounts of chloride, bromide and iodide ions, which silver halide should precipitate?

EXPERIMENTAL PROCEDURE

Set up the apparatus shown in Fig. 9.2 and add the reagent solutions shown to beakers K and L. Measuring cylinder accuracy suffices for all except Solution X. The latter is an aqueous solution of a mixture of the chloride, bromide and iodide of potassium.

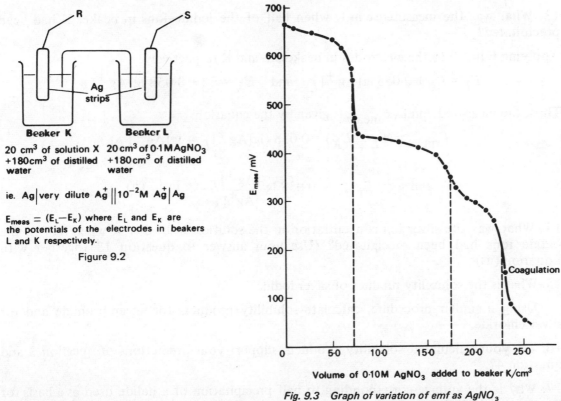

Beaker K
20 cm³ of solution X +180 cm³ of distilled water

Beaker L
20 cm³ of 0·1 M AgNO₃ +180 cm³ of distilled water

ie. Ag | very dilute Ag⁺ ‖ 10⁻² M Ag⁺ | Ag

$E_{meas} = (E_L - E_K)$ where E_L and E_K are the potentials of the electrodes in beakers L and K respectively.

Figure 9.2

Fig. 9.3 *Graph of variation of emf as AgNO₃ solution is added to beaker K*

Clamp a burette filled with 0·10M silver nitrate solution so that it is conveniently placed for titration into beaker K. Using either the potentiometer circuit of Fig. 9.1 or a high impedance voltmeter, measure the potential between the two wires R and S. Then add 1·0 cm³ of 0·10M AgNO₃ solution to beaker K. Stir up the contents of beaker K very thoroughly with a glass rod and measure the potential difference, $(E_L - E_K)$, once more.

Continue in this way, adding the silver nitrate solution in small volumes and stirring each time before measuring the e.m.f. between R and S, until the measured potential difference has dropped to about 50mV.

Record all readings (volume of silver nitrate solution added to beaker K and the corresponding potential differences) in tabular form, being careful to observe and record the appearance of the precipitate throughout the titration. Plot a graph showing how the measured e.m.f. varies with the volume of silver nitrate solution added to beaker K.

6. What explanation can you offer for the shape of this graph? (Your answer to question 5 may help you)

7. What total volume of 0·10M $AgNO_3$ was needed to remove effectively all the halide ions from the solution in beaker K?

8. At what point (if any) in the titration did you observe coagulation in beaker K. How does this support your answer to question 7?

9. What volume of 0·10M $AgNO_3$ was needed to remove effectively all the iodide ions from 20·0cm³ of Solution X?

10. What was the concentration of the iodide ions in Solution X?

    Similarly, calculate the bromide and chloride ion concentrations in Solution X.

11. Why does the measured e.m.f. not remain constant during the precipitation of any one silver halide?

12. What was the iodide ion concentration in beaker K when half of the iodide ions had been precipitated as AgI?

13. What was the measured e.m.f. when half of the iodide ions in beaker K had been precipitated?

Applying Eqn. (i) to the electrodes in beakers L and K respectively:

$$E_L = E_o + 0\cdot058\ \lg[Ag^+]_L \quad \text{and} \quad E_K = E_o + 0\cdot058\ \lg[Ag^+]_K$$

Thus, the measured e.m.f., E_{meas}, is given by the equation:

$$E_{meas} = (E_L - E_K) = 0\cdot058\ (\lg[Ag^+]_L - \lg[Ag^+]_K)$$

and so: $\quad E_{meas} = 0\cdot058\ \lg\dfrac{[Ag^+]_L}{[Ag^+]_K}\ \ldots \text{Eqn. (ii)}$

14. What was the silver ion concentration in the solution in beaker K when half of the iodide ions had been precipitated? (Use your answer to question 13 together with Equation (ii))

15. What is the solubility product of silver iodide?

    Using a similar procedure, calculate solubility products for silver bromide and for silver chloride.

16. Do your calculated solubility products support your predictions of question 3 and question 4?

17. Why is the voltage corresponding to half precipitation of a halide used as a basis for the above calculations?

Notes 9

Standard: ***

Time: Experiment − 1 hour; 30 minutes homework before the experiment and another 30 minutes afterwards

Reagents required:

0·10M $AgNO_3$ solution. (35cm³)

Distilled water (400cm³)

Potassium nitrate and gelatine (for Salt-Bridge)

Solution *X*: Contains the chloride, bromide and iodide of potassium.
The exact composition of this solution is unimportant, but the results described were obtained with a solution made by dissolving 0·56g of KCl, 0·99g of KBr and 1·22g of KI in water and making the solution up to a total volume of 200cm³. (30cm³)

Note (1) Standard electrodes strictly involve unit activities of solutes rather than unit molarities. In cases concerning gases, the term '1 atmosphere' should now read 101·3kPa, or 101·3kN m^{-2}.

(2) The standard electrode potential of silver, 0·70 V, refers to the reaction:

$$\tfrac{1}{2} H_{2\,(g)} + Ag^+_{(aq)} \rightleftharpoons H^+_{(aq)} + Ag_{(s)}$$

Apparatus required:

2 strips of clean silver (4cm x 1cm is ideal)

2 beakers (250cm³)

a 20cm³ pipette

a 100cm³ measuring cylinder

a glass stirring rod

a gelatine-KNO_3 salt bridge (paper strips may be used but are less desirable because of the stirring)

potential measurements: see previous experiment

INTRODUCTORY PROBLEM

1. The distance BP must be zero when the silver ion concentration in Beaker M equals that in Beaker N, i.e. when $E_M = E_N$. Thus, the third expression, $(E_N - E_M)$, is the only one of the three which can be directly proportional to PB.

2. Since $BP_{AgCl} < BP_{AgBr}$ then $(E_N - E_{M_{AgCl}}) < (E_N - E_{M_{AgBr}})$

Therefore, it follows that: $E_{M_{AgCl}} > E_{M_{AgBr}}$

3. Applying eqn (i) of the students' sheets to the answer to question 2:

$$(E_o + 0.058 \lg[Ag^+]_{AgCl}) > (E_o + 0.058 \lg[Ag^+]_{AgBr})$$

$$\text{Therefore: } [Ag^+]_{AgCl} > [Ag^+]_{AgBr}$$

4. In view of the relative positions of the elements chlorine, bromine and iodine in the halogen group, and, knowing that AgBr is less soluble in water than AgCl, it seems reasonable to expect silver iodide to be even less soluble in water than silver bromide.

$$\text{Thus, we can expect: } PB_{AgI} > PB_{AgBr}$$

5. If silver iodide is the least soluble of the three silver halides, it is to be expected that it will be the first of the three to be precipitated.

Experimental data

Volume of 0·10M AgNO$_3$ solution added to K (/cm^3)	Measured Potential Difference (/mV)	Volume of 0·10M AgNO$_3$ solution added to K (/cm^3)	Measured Potl. Difference (/mV)
0·0	665	16·0	395
1·0	655	17·0	370
5·0	630	18·0	325
6·0	615	19·0	305
7·0	575	20·0	295
7·2	550	21·0	280
7·4	470	22·0	260
7·6	440	23·0	150 (coagulates)
8·0	435	23·5	85
10·0	430	24·0	70
12·0	420	25·0	50
14·0	410		

6. Silver iodide, being the least soluble of the three silver halides, will precipitate first. As long as there is a significant concentration of iodide ions in Beaker K, the silver ion concentration cannot rise markedly, and, hence, the measured potential cannot fall sharply. However, when effectively all the iodide ions have been precipitated, the silver ion concentration can rise until:

$$[Ag^+] [Br^-] = K_S$$

at which time silver bromide will begin precipitating. Thus, there will be a very rapid rise in silver ion concentration (with an attendant rapid fall in the measured potential difference) between the precipitation of virtually all the silver iodide and the onset of silver bromide precipitation. A similar sequence of events occurs at the onset of silver chloride precipitation, and the overall effect is to give the graph the appearance of three steps.

7. The end of the third step should correspond to the removal of effectively all the halide ions from solution. For the sample data, this took place when 23·0cm^3 of 0·10M AgNO$_3$ had been added. According to the weights of KCl, KBr and KI used, 20·0cm^3 of Solution X contained:

$$7 \cdot 55 \times 10^{-4} \text{ moles of Cl}^-$$
$$8 \cdot 32 \times 10^{-4} \text{ moles of Br}^- \text{ giving a total of}$$
$$7 \cdot 35 \times 10^{-4} \text{ moles of I}^-$$

2·32m mol of halide ions. This is in good agreement with the volume of 0·10M AgNO$_3$ needed.

8. At the steepest part (or slightly before) of the third step the precipitated silver halide suspension coagulates. As long as silver halides are precipitated in the presence of excess halide ions, the colloidal particles of precipitate will be negatively charged due to the adsorption of halide ions. Since all of the colloidal particles are negatively charged, the colloidal solution is stabilized by electrostatic repulsion. At the end-point of the titration, the stabilizing charge will be removed as the halide ions are desorbed.

9. The steepest part of the first step corresponds to removal of effectively all the iodide ions from solution. For the sample data this occurred when 7·3cm³ of 0·10M AgNO₃ solution had been added.

10. $Ag^+_{(aq)} + I^-_{(aq)} = AgI_{(s)}$

The number of moles of Ag^+ used to precipitate all of the iodide ions from 20·0cm³ of Solution X

$$= \frac{7·3}{1000} \times 0·1$$

Thus, number of moles of I^- ion per litre of Solution $X = \frac{1000}{20} \times \frac{0·73}{1000} = 0·0365$

Similarly, it can be shown that $[Br^-]_{\text{soln } X} = 0·051 \text{ mol dm}^{-3}$

and $[Cl^-]_{\text{soln } X} = 0·0275 \text{ mol dm}^{-3}$

(The reason for the low value of the chloride ion concentration and the high value for the bromide ion concentration may be partial co-precipitation of AgCl with AgBr)

11. During precipitation of any silver halide, AgY, the product of the silver ion and the Y^- ion concentrations will be equal to the solubility product of AgY. As $[Y^-]$ falls during the titration, $[Ag^+]$ must show a corresponding increase.

12. The iodide ion concentration in Beaker K when half of the iodide ions have been precipitated $\approx ½ \times 10^{-1} \times 0·0365 = 1·82 \times 10^{-3} \text{ mol dm}^{-3}$

13. At the mid-point of the first step, the measured potential difference was 617 mV.

14. Thus: Applying eqn (ii) of the Assignment Sheets:

$$\lg \frac{10^{-2}}{[Ag^+]_K} = \frac{0·617}{0·058} = 10·6$$

Hence $\frac{10^{-2}}{[Ag^+]_K} = 10^{10·6}$ and so $[Ag^+]_K = 10^{-12·6} = 2·5 \times 10^{-13} \text{ mol dm}^{-3}$

15. The solubility product of silver iodide $= [Ag^+] [I^-]$
$= 2·5 \times 10^{-13} \times 1·82 \times 10^{-3} \text{ mol}^2 \text{ dm}^{-6}$
$= 4·6 \times 10^{-16} \text{ mol}^2 \text{ dm}^{-6}$

Similarly, it can be shown that

$[Ag^+] [Br^-] = 6·3 \times 10^{-10} \times 2·55 \times 10^{-3} = 1·6 \times 10^{-12} \text{ mol}^2 \text{ dm}^{-6}$

$[Ag^+] [Cl^-] = 1·0 \times 10^{-7} \times 1·38 \times 10^{-3} = 1·4 \times 10^{-10} \text{ mol}^2 \text{ dm}^{-6}$

16. The relative values of the solubility products should support the prediction made in discussing the introductory problem. The above experimental values agree well with those given in the literature:

Solubility Products (at 25°C):   silver chloride: $2 \times 10^{-10} \text{ mol}^2 \text{ dm}^{-6}$
silver bromide: $5 \times 10^{-13} \text{ mol}^2 \text{ dm}^{-6}$
silver iodide: $8 \times 10^{-17} \text{ mol}^2 \text{ dm}^{-6}$

17. When half of any halide ion has been precipitated, it is easy to estimate the remaining free halide ion concentration. Furthermore, at this stage, the measured potential difference is not varying rapidly, so that a reasonable value for the free silver ion concentration in the solution can be calculated.

FURTHER PROJECT

Using the same technique, investigate the addition of iodide ions to a mixture of cations in aqueous solution. (e.g. Pb^{2+} and Ag^+ or even Pb^{2+}, Cu^{2+} and Ag^+.

REFERENCE

G. Birrell, *Chemistry* 41, p.32, (1968).

Assignment 10

Determination of the Solubility Product of Silver Bromate by Titration

INTRODUCTION

This is a group experiment. Each of you will be told to carry out the experiment using a particular pair of volumes of the $0.1M$ $AgNO_3$ and $0.1M$ $KBrO_3$ solutions provided. These pairs of volumes, which will be different for each person, are listed in the table below. At the end of the practical, all results must be collated.

Pair	Volume of $0.1M$ $AgNO_3$/cm^3	Volume of $0.1M$ $KBrO_3$/cm^3
(a)	40·0	10·0
(b)	30·0	20·0
(c)	25·0	25·0
(d)	20·0	30·0
(e)	10·0	40·0
(f)	0·0	50·0

EXPERIMENTAL WORK

Pipette $150cm^3$ of distilled water into a clean, dry $200cm^3$ standard flask. Add exactly the required volume of the silver nitrate solution and swirl the flask for a moment or two to ensure that the silver nitrate solution completely mixes with the water. Finally, add the necessary volume of the potassium bromate solution and shake the flask thoroughly for several minutes. Label the flask and set it aside until the next laboratory period.

By next day the bottom of each flask (except that containing mixture (f)) should be covered by a small amount of a white, crystalline deposit. **Do not shake the flasks.** If the precipitate has completely settled then the rest of the experiment can be conducted using solution pipetted from the top of the standard flask. However, if the flask is at all cloudy, then its contents must be filtered and the filtrate used.

1. What is the precipitated solid likely to be?

2. Suggest an ionic equation for the reaction between potassium bromate and silver nitrate.

Pipette $20cm^3$ of the filtrate or clear solution into a conical flask. Add $20cm^3$ of $0.5M$ potassium iodide solution and $10cm^3$ of $1M$ sulphuric acid. Titrate the resultant mixture to a starch end-point with $0.1M$ sodium thiosulphate solution and record your titration readings. Repeat this operation until you have two concordant results.

3. What did you see when the potassium iodide and the sulphuric acid had been added?

4. What do you think the coloured substance was which was in the conical flask at this stage?

5. What is the ionic equation for the reaction which occurs during the titration?

6. What must have happened before the titration: (a) to the iodide ions? (b) to the bromate ions?

7. What are the oxidation numbers of bromine in the bromate and bromide ions and of iodine in the iodide ion and the iodine molecule?

8. With the answers to question 7 in mind, suggest an equation for the reaction between bromate ions and iodide ions in acid solution.

9. Why was sulphuric acid needed?

10. Why was such a large amount of potassium iodide needed?

11. Why was it not necessary to add exactly the specified volumes of sulphuric acid and potassium iodide solution?

12. Why was water added to the standard flask *before* the potassium bromate and silver nitrate solutions?

13. Why is one experiment, (f), suggested which does not involve silver nitrate?

14. What were the numbers of moles of silver ions and bromate ions initially added to the standard flask?

15. What was the number of moles of thiosulphate ion used per titration?

16. What was the number of moles of iodine formed from $20cm^3$ of the test solution?

17. What were the numbers of moles of the bromate ion: (i) in $20cm^3$ of the test solution? (ii) in the whole $200cm^3$ of solution in the standard flask?

18. How many moles of bromate ions must have been precipitated in the standard flask?

19. How many moles of silver ions must have been precipitated in the standard flask?

20. How many moles of silver ions must have remained *in solution* in the standard flask?

21. What is the concentration of silver ions in solution in the standard flask?

22. What is the concentration of bromate ions in solution in the standard flask?

Tabulate the class results as follows:

Initial volume of $0.1M$ $KBrO_3$/cm^3	Initial volume of $0.1M$ $AgNO_3$/cm^3	$[BrO_3{}^-]$/mol dm^{-3} in resulting solution	$[Ag^+]$/mol dm^{-3} in resulting solution
. . . .	. . . .	. . . .	. . . .
. . . .	. . . .	. . . .	. . . .
. . . .	. . . .	. . . .	. . . .
. . . .	. . . .	. . . .	. . . .
. . . .	. . . .	. . . .	. . . .
. . . .	. . . .	. . . .	. . . .

Plot the silver ion concentration against the reciprocal of the bromate ion concentration and show how the solubility product of silver bromate can be evaluated from the graph.

Notes 10

Standard: *

Time required:
Not more than 30 minutes to prepare the mixture in the standard flask. On the second day the rest of the practical takes about another 30 minutes, assuming that filtration is unnecessary.

Reagents required:
0·10M $AgNO_3$ solution [250cm³ needs 4·25g of solid $AgNO_3$] (150cm³)
0·10M $KBrO_3$ solution [500cm³ needs 8·35g of solid $KBrO_3$] (200cm³)
approx 0·5M KI solution [500cm³ needs about 40g of solid KI]
0·10M $Na_2S_2O_3$ solution [500cm³ needs 12·4g of $Na_2S_2O_3.5H_2O$] (400cm³)
approx 1·0M sulphuric acid (200cm³)
starch solution (30cm³)
N.B. The volumes specified are sufficient to obtain one complete set of results.

Apparatus required:
pipettes: 50cm³ and 20cm³ for each pair. Several 10cm³ and 25cm³ pipettes for communal use.
200cm³ standard flask
conical flask
burette
filtration apparatus
measuring cylinders or 'automatic pipettes' are convenient (but unnecessary) for dispensing the sulphuric acid and the potassium iodide solution

Notes on experimental work and questions

It is a useful teaching point to suggest that the flasks should be stored out of sunlight. However, even if they are exposed and the silver bromate is turned pink by partial reduction to silver, this does not appear to have a significant effect on the experimental results.

1. Silver bromate is a reasonable guess in view of the title of this experiment (!) and the fact that potassium nitrate should be known to be soluble in water.

2. $Ag^+_{(aq)} + BrO_3^-{}_{(aq)} \rightarrow AgBrO_3{}_{(s)}$

3. and 4. A brown solution of iodine, or rather triiodide ions, I_3^-, is formed. In the presence of excess iodide ions, the equilibrium:

$$I_2{}_{(aq)} + I^-{}_{(aq)} \rightleftharpoons I_3^-{}_{(aq)}$$

lies far to the right. However, for simplicity, the iodine will be considered as I_2. This is not unfair as the I_2/I_3^- equilibrium is very mobile. Thus, I_3^- reacts as if it were I_2.

5. $2S_2O_3^{2-}{}_{(aq)} + I_2{}_{(aq)} \rightarrow S_4O_6^{2-}{}_{(aq)} + 2I^-{}_{(aq)}$

6. Since iodine was formed: (a) the iodide ions must have been oxidized and so presumably, (b) the bromate ions have been reduced.

60

7. The Oxidation Number of iodine in I_2 is 0 (all free elements have Oxidation Numbers of 0)

The Oxidation Number of iodine in I^- is $-I$ (all simple ions have Oxidation Numbers equal to their ionic charges).

The Oxidation Number of bromine in Br^- is $-I$

The Oxidation Number of bromine in BrO_3^- is $+V$ ($-II$ for each O, plus V equals the ionic charge, i.e. $-I$)

8. Reduction of one BrO_3^- ion to Br^- ($+V$ to $-I$) would thus result in the oxidation of six I^- ions to I_2 molecules (each $-I$ to 0). Therefore:

$$BrO_3^-{}_{(aq)} + 6I^-{}_{(aq)} + 6H^+{}_{(aq)} \rightarrow Br^-{}_{(aq)} + 3I_2{}_{(aq)} + 3H_2O_{(1)}$$

9. The above equation shows that hydrogen ions are needed for reaction to occur. In neutral solution some iodide would be oxidized, but the reaction would probably be slow and incomplete because of the low hydrogen ion concentration.

10. Six iodide ions are needed to reduce each bromate ion.

11. Excess acid and iodide ions will not interfere with the experiment. However, it is vital to ensure that there is enough of each of these reagents.

12. If the $KBrO_3$ and the $AgNO_3$ were mixed before the water was added a lot of $AgBrO_3$ would be precipitated. When the water was added it would then take a fearful lot of shaking to ensure that the whole solution was saturated with respect to $AgBrO_3$.

13. This is in order to check both the bromate ion concentration in the stock solution and this method of determining bromate ion concentrations.

Throughout the following notes:
x cm^3 is the volume of $0 \cdot 1M$ $AgNO_3$ added to the standard flask,
and t cm^3 is the volume of $0 \cdot 1M$ $Na_2S_2O_3$ needed per titration.

14. (i) Moles of Ag^+ ion originally added $= \dfrac{x}{1000}$ x $0 \cdot 1$

(ii) Moles of BrO_3^- ion originally added $= \dfrac{(50-x)}{1000}$ x $0 \cdot 1$

15. Moles of $S_2O_3^{2-}$ ion used per titration $= \dfrac{t}{1000}$ x $0 \cdot 1$

16. Moles of I_2 formed by 20cm^2 of test solution $= \dfrac{0 \cdot 1\,t}{2000}$ (see question 5)

17. (i) Moles of BrO_3^- ion in 20cm^3 of test solution $= \dfrac{0 \cdot 1\,t}{6000}$ (See question 8)

(ii) Moles of BrO_3^- ion standard flask (i.e. 200cm^3) $= \dfrac{t}{6000}$ moles/200cm^3

18. Moles of BrO_3^- precipitated in standard flask $= \dfrac{0 \cdot 1(50-x)}{1000} - \dfrac{t}{6000} = P$ moles (say)

19. Moles of Ag^+ ion precipitated in the standard flask $= P$ (see question 2)

20. Moles of Ag^+ ion remaining in solution in the standard flask $=$ $\dfrac{0 \cdot 1x}{1000} - P$ moles/200cm^3

21. Ag^+ ion concentration in solution $= 5\left(\dfrac{0 \cdot 1x}{1000} - P\right)$ mol dm^{-3}

22. BrO_3^- ion concentration in solution $= \dfrac{5t}{6000}$ mol dm^{-3}

Typical Class Results

Initial volume of 0·1M KBrO$_3$/cm^3	Initial volume of 0·1M AgNO$_3$/cm^3	[BrO$_3^-$]/mol dm^{-3} in the resultant solution	[Ag$^+$]/mol dm^{-3} in the resultant solution
10	40	0·00475	0·0197
20	30	0·0086	0·0137
25	25	0·0121	0·0121
30	20	0·0134	0·0084
40	10	0·0196	0·0046

A plot of [Ag$^+$] against the reciprocal of [BrO$_3^-$] should be found to be nearly linear.

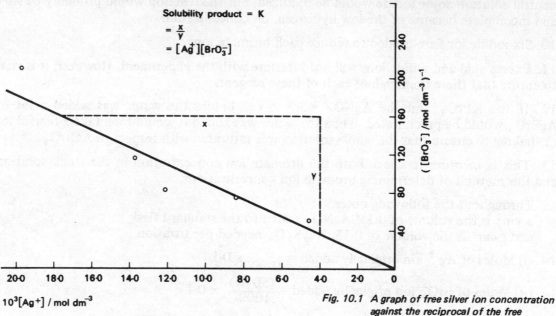

Fig. 10.1 A graph of free silver ion concentration against the reciprocal of the free bromate ion concentration

Thus $[Ag^+] = K \dfrac{1}{[BrO_3^-]}$ where K is a constant, the solubility product.

Hence $\dfrac{[Ag^+]}{1/[BrO_3^=]} = K = [Ag^+][BrO_3^-]$

Typical Class Result: 11×10^{-5} mol^2 dm^{-6} at 18°C

Literature Value: $K = 5\cdot8 \times 10^{-5}$ mol^2 dm^{-6} at 25°C

The fact that class results are usually higher than the accepted value is probably explained by incomplete removal of solid AgBrO$_3$.

N.B. If the class has only got two or three reliable results, the graph may not appear convincingly linear. In this case it may well be desirable to compute the solubility product for each separate experiment.

FURTHER PROJECTS

(1) Determine the solubility product of silver iodate by a similar method.
(2) Study the variation of the solubility product for silver bromate with temperature. Investigate whether a value for the heat of precipitation of silver bromate can be obtained from a plot of log K against $1/T$.

REFERENCE

W.R. Carmody, Variation of the Solubility Product Constant with Ionic Strength, *J. Chem. Ed.*, **36** 3 (1959).

Assignment 11

Determination of the Heat of Hydration of Copper (II) Sulphate (Approximate Method)

INTRODUCTION

This experiment enables an approximate determination of the heat of hydration of copper (II) sulphate to be made, by application of Hess's Law of Constant Heat Summation. The heat change when one mole of anhydrous copper (II) sulphate is dissolved in water is first determined. Secondly, the heat of solution of copper (II) sulphate pentahydrate in water is determined.

1. State Hess's Law of Constant Heat Summation.

2. Write the equations for the reactions taking place, in such a way that they may be linked together as an energy cycle.

3. Label the energy diagram as follows:
ΔH_1 = Heat of solution of anhydrous copper (II) sulphate
ΔH_2 = Heat of solution of copper (II) sulphate pentahydrate
ΔH_3 = Heat of hydration of copper (II) sulphate

4. Write an expression for the heat of hydration of copper (II) sulphate in terms of the other two quantities.

EXPERIMENTAL WORK

(I) Determination of heat of solution of anhydrous copper (II) sulphate

Using a measuring cylinder, place 100cm³ of distilled water in a plastic beaker and record the initial temperature of the water. Weigh a dry watch-glass, and add to it 8·0 of anhydrous copper (II) sulphate. Add the anhydrous copper (II) sulphate to the water in the beaker and stir to dissolve it as quickly as possible.
Record the highest temperature of the solution:
Set out results as shown:

	(I) anhydrous	(II) hydrated
Weight of watch-glass/g	=	=
Weight of watch-glass plus copper sulphate/g		=
Weight of copper sulphate added/g	=	=
Initial temperature of water/°C	=	=
Highest/Lowest temperature of solution/°C		=
Change in temperature/°C	=	=

5. What is the molar heat of solution of anhydrous copper (II) sulphate, ΔH_1?

(II) Determination of heat of solution of copper (II) sulphate pentahydrate

Proceed as in part (I), but use 12·5g of copper (II) sulphate pentahydrate instead of the anhydrous salt. Set out the results as above.

6. What is the molar heat of solution of copper (II) sulphate pentahydrate, ΔH_2?

7. What value does this give for the heat of hydration of copper (II) sulphate, ΔH_3?

8. What assumptions have you made in calculating ΔH_1 and ΔH_2?

9. What errors are there in this experiment?

10. How could these errors be minimised?

11. What is the significance of the heat of hydration of copper (II) sulphate?

Notes 11

Standard: *
Time required: 1½ hours

Reagents required:
   Distilled water (200cm³)
   anhydrous copper(II) sulphate (10g)—this must be a good sample and may be prepared
   by heating the hydrate in an oven at about 200°C overnight; it should be kept in a
   desiccator
   Copper(II) sulphate pentahydrate (14g)—this must be small crystals or dissolving will
   be a slow process and inaccuracies will result

Apparatus required:
   plastic beaker (preferably expanded polystyrene)
   100cm³ measuring cylinder
   0–50°C thermometer – calibrated in 0·1°C units
   2 clean, dry watch-glasses
   Use of a chemical balance

Notes on questions and typical results

1. Hess's Law of Constant Heat Summation states that, provided heat is the only form of
energy to enter or leave the system, the change in heat content accompanying a chemical
reaction is independent of the pathway between the initial and final states.

2. and 3.

$$CuSO_{4\,(s)} + \text{a large quantity of water} \xrightarrow{\Delta H_1} Cu^{2+}(aq) + SO_4{}^{2-}(aq)$$

$$5\,H_2O_{(1)} \downarrow \quad \Delta H_3 \qquad\qquad\qquad\qquad\qquad \Delta H_2 \uparrow$$

$$CuSO_4.5H_2O_{(s)} + \text{a large quantity of water}$$

4. $\Delta H_1 = \Delta H_3 + \Delta H_2$; Hence, $\Delta H_3 = \Delta H_1 - \Delta H_2$

Experimental procedure

The solution should be stirred continuously, after the addition of the solid, so that it
dissolves as quickly as possible. The highest temperature of the *stirred* solution should be
recorded in part (I), and the lowest temperature in part (II). Care must be taken that the
temperature recorded is not just the local temperature in the vicinity of the dissolving
solid.

Specimen results

Weight of anhydrous copper(II) sulphate = 8·1g

Rise in temperature of the solution = 8·0°C

Thus, $\dfrac{8\cdot1}{159\cdot5}$ mol of $CuSO_4$ on dissolving liberate $100 \times 4\cdot2 \times 8\cdot0$J

1 mol of $CuSO_4$ on dissolving liberates $\dfrac{800 \times 4\cdot2 \times 159\cdot5\text{J}}{8\cdot1}$

Hence the heat of solution of $CuSO_4$, $\Delta H_1 = -66 kJ\ mol^{-1}$

Weight of copper(II) sulphate pentahydrate = 13·06g

Fall in temperature of solution = 1·0°C

6. $\dfrac{13·06}{249·5}$ mol of $CuSO_4.5H_2O$ on dissolving absorb 100 x 4·2 x 1·0J

Thus 1 mol of $CuSO_4.5H_2O$ on dissolving absorbs $100 \times 4·2 \times 1·0 \times \dfrac{249·5J}{13·06}$

Hence the heat solution of $CuSO_4.5H_2O.\Delta H_2 = 8·0 kJ\ mol^{-1}$

7. $\Delta H_3 = \Delta H_1 - \Delta H_2$. Thus, heat of hydration of $CuSO_4.\Delta H_3 = -66 -(+8) = -74 kJ\ mol^{-1}$.

Bearing in mind the approximations made, this compares well with the literature values: Heat of hydration of $CuSO_4 = -78·5 kJ\ mol^{-1}$.

8. In calculating these values, the following assumptions have been made:
   (a) that the thermal capacity of the beaker is negligible.
   (b) that the specific heat capacity of copper(II) sulphate solution is similar to that of water.
   (c) that the solids have dissolved quickly so that heat losses are negligible.
   (d) that further dilution of the resulting solutions would cause no heat change.

9. The possible sources of error in this experiment are as follows:
   (a) that heat may be lost to, or gained from, the surroundings.
   (b) that the 'anhydrous' copper(II) sulphate may not be completely anhydrous.
   (c) that the resulting solutions may not be sufficiently dilute to eliminate further heat change on addition of more water.
   (d) that the specific heat capacity of the copper(II) sulphate solutions is not similar to the specific heat of water. (However, the heat capacity of 100g of water is probably close to that of about 110g of copper(II) sulphate solution since the specific heat capacity of approximately 0·05M $CuSO_4$ is $3·8J\ g^{-1}\ °C^{-1}$)

10. (a) Heat losses, or gains, could be minimised by setting the beaker into a block of expanded polystyrene, or by using a vacuum flask.
(b) Heat the sample for several hours at 200°C and keep in a desiccator.
(c) Use smaller quantities of solid, but this would make the temperature reading less accurate.
(d) The specific heat capacity of the copper(II) sulphate solutions could be determined.

11. The significance of the heat of hydration of copper(II) sulphate is that it demonstrates that quite strong bonds are formed between water molecules and copper(II) ions, and sulphate ions.

Assignment 12

Determination of the Heat of Formation of Calcium Carbonate

INTRODUCTION

1. What does the term 'heat of formation' mean?

2. What is the equation for the formation of calcium carbonate from its elements under standard conditions? (Equation 1)

3. What are 'standard conditions' of thermochemistry?

EXPERIMENTAL WORK

Reaction of calcium with dilute hydrochloric acid

Weigh out approximately 1g of calcium metal, recording your weighings in the table below (two decimal places is sufficient accuracy). Using a measuring cylinder, measure out 100cm³ of approximately 1M hydrochloric acid and place it in a plastic beaker. Determine the temperature of the acid and record this also. Then add the weighed portion of calcium and stir thoroughly with the thermometer until all the metal has reacted. Record the maximum temperature attained by the solution. If there is time, repeat the experiment and determine the average temperature rise per gram of calcium used.

Initial mass/g....................	
Final mass/g	
Mass of Ca used/g............	
Final temperature/°C	
Initial temperature/°C	
Temperature rise/deg C	

4. Write an ionic equation for the reaction which has taken place (Equation 2)

5. Assuming that the solution in the plastic beaker has the same specific heat as water, what heat was evolved in the reaction between the calcium and the acid?

6. How much heat would have been evolved by one mole of calcium atoms?

7. Why is the exact concentration of the hydrochloric acid unimportant?

Reaction of calcium carbonate with dilute hydrochloric acid

Weigh out 2–3g of dry, powdered calcium carbonate directly into a clean plastic beaker (same accuracy as before). Place 100cm³ of approximately 1M hydrochloric acid in a measuring cylinder. Record its temperature and then pour the acid on the carbonate in the beaker. Stir briskly with the thermometer and record the maximum temperature reached by the solution. If there is time, repeat the experiment and determine the average temperature rise per gram of calcium carbonate used.

67

Final mass/g ....
Initial mass/g ....

Mass of $CaCO_3$ used/g .....

Final temperature/°C
Initial temperature/°C

Temperature rise/deg C

8. Write an ionic equation for the reaction that has taken place (Equation 3)

9. What heat was evolved in the reaction between the hydrochloric acid and the amount of calcium carbonate used? (Make the same assumption as in question 5.)
10. How much heat would have been evolved by one mole of calcium carbonate?

11. What major sources of inaccuracy are likely in these experiments?

12. How accurate are your answers to questions 6 and 10 likely to be?

13. Can you draw a diagram linking Equations 1, 2 and 3 together in the form of a cycle?

14. Besides your experimental results (see Questions 6 and 10), what other information do you need to enable you to calculate the heat of formation of calcium carbonate? Look up these necessary data.

15. What is the heat of formation of calcium carbonate?

16. State the law which you have used in order to answer question 15.

17. On which thermodynamic principle does this law depend?

18. Why is this law useful?

Notes 12

Standard: **
Time required: 45 minutes for the practical work.
Reagents required:
    calcium metal (granules) (3g)
    calcium carbonate (powdered) (10g)
    1M (approx.) hydrochloric acid (600cm^3)
Apparatus required:
    plastic beaker of about 400–500cm^3 capacity
    thermometer (−10 to 110°C)
    measuring cylinder (100cm^3)

Notes on experimental work and questions

1. The Heat of Formation of a compound is the heat evolved or absorbed when one mole of a compound is formed from its elements in the standard state.

2. $Ca_{(s)} + C_{(s)} + 1\frac{1}{2}O_{2\,(g)} = CaCO_{3\,(s)}$ (Equation 1)

3. The standard conditions are 25°C and one atmosphere pressure

4. $Ca_{(s)} + 2\,H^+_{(aq)} = Ca^{2+}_{(aq)} + H_{2\,(g)}$ (Equation 2)

5. Heat evolved   = mass of 100cm^3 of water x specific heat of water x temperature rise
                    = 100 x 4·18 x 29 (N.B 29 deg C rise per gram of Ca is typical student result)
                    = 12·1 kJ per gram of Ca

6. Thus, heat evolved per mole of Ca atoms is 40 x 12·1 kJ = 484 kJ

                i.e. For Equation 1, $\Delta H = -484$ kJ mol^{-1}

7. It is only necessary that there should be an excess of acid so as to ensure that the reaction takes place according to Equation 2 and that no calcium hydroxide is precipitated.

8. $CaCO_{3\,(s)} + 2\,H^+_{(aq)} = Ca^{2+}_{(aq)} + H_2O_{(1)} + CO_{2\,(g)}$ (Equation 3)

9. As in question 5, heat evolved   = 100 x 4·18 x 1·5 J per 2·5g of CaCO$_3$ (N.B. a temperature rise of 1·5 deg C is typical)

                                    = 627 J per 2·5g of CaCO$_3$

10. Heat evolved per mole of CaCO$_3$ = (M.Wt. of CaCO$_3$/2·5) x 627 J

                                    = (100/2·5) x 627 = 25·1 kJ

                i.e. for Equation 2, $\Delta H = -25·1$ kJ mol^{-1}

11. The heat capacity of the calorimeter is ignored; the heat losses due to evaporation, convection and conduction etc. are ignored; the specific heats of the solutions cannot be exactly $4 \cdot 18 \text{ J g}^{-1} \text{ deg C}^{-1}$

12. Errors are likely to be about 5–10% on the low side.

13.

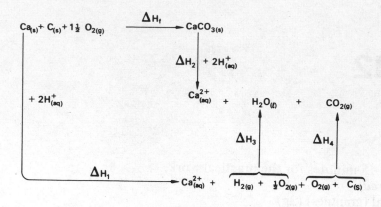

14. The Heats of Formation of $H_2O_{(1)}$ (i.e. -285 kJ) and of $CO_{2\,(g)}$ (i.e. -393 kJ) must be known.

15, 16 and 17. Hess's Law, which depends on the principle that energy cannot be created or destroyed (the First Law of Thermodynamics), states that:
'The change in heat content accompanying a chemical reaction is independent of the pathway between the initial and final states'

Thus, $\Delta H_1 + \Delta H_3 + \Delta H_4 = \Delta H_f + \Delta H_2$

whence: $\Delta H_f = \Delta H_1 + \Delta H_3 + \Delta H_4 - \Delta H_2$

$$= -484 + (-285) + (-393) - (-25)$$

$$= -1162 + 25 = -1137 \text{ kJ mol}^{-1}$$

This result compares quite reasonably with the literature value of -1207 kJ mol^{-1} for calcium carbonate.

18. This law is useful because it enables values to be calculated for the changes in heat content accompanying chemical reactions which cannot be directly studied. It is not possible to measure the heat of formation of calcium carbonate directly.

FURTHER PROJECT
Discuss and/or investigate whether it is possible to determine a sensible value for the Heat of Formation of magnesium carbonate by this method.

REFERENCE
An Introduction to Chemical Energetics, J.J. Thompson (Longmans 1967) gives a useful review of methods of measuring heat changes.

Assignment 13
Determination of the Formulæ of Complex Ions by a Colorimetric Method

INTRODUCTION

Copper(II) ions form complex ions with ammonia molecules, or molecules of 1 : 2–diaminoethane (ethylenediamine), as the ligands. The complex ions are, in these cases, highly coloured and assuming that maximum colour intensity coincides with maximum number of complex ions formed, one can determine the number of ligand molecules surrounding the central copper(II) ion. The method of continuous variation is used, in which solutions, containing different proportions of copper(II) ion to ligand molecule, are mixed and their colour intensity compared, using a colorimeter.

EXPERIMENTAL WORK

(I) Determination of the formula of the $Cu(NH_3)x^{2+}$ complex ion

Take six test-tubes, which will contain at least $15 cm^3$ of solution and fit into the colorimeter, and label them 1 to 6. Using a graduated pipette, or burette, make up the six mixtures as indicated below, shaking the contents of the tube to make sure they are homogeneous. The $5.0 cm^3$ of approximately 1·5M ammonium sulphate should be added to each tube first, since it is present to prevent precipitation. After the mixtures have been made, set the pointer on the colorimeter to the zero mark (minimum absorption of light) with tube 1 in place and no filter. Record the results as shown below:

Test-tube number	1	2	3	4	5	6
Volume of approx. 1·5M $(NH_4)_2SO_4$ solution/cm^3	5·0	5·0	5·0	5·0	5·0	5·0
Volume of 0·10M $CuSO_4$ solution/cm^3	7·5	5·0	2·5	2·0	1·5	1·0
Volume of 0·10M NH_3 solution/cm^3	2·5	5·0	7·5	8·0	8·5	9·0

Colorimeter reading

1. How does the ammonium sulphate solution prevent precipitation?

2. Plot a graph of light absorption (the reading on the colorimeter) against the volume of 0·10M $CuSO_4$ solution, reading from left to right and, on the same scale, the volume of 0·10M NH_3 solution, reading from right to left. What are the volumes of these two solutions which, on mixing would give maximum colour intensity?

3. What is the value of x in the formula $[Cu(NH_3)x]^{2+}$?

(II) Determination of the formula of the $Cu(H_2NCH_2CH_2NH_2)y^{2+}$ complex ion

Take six test-tubes and label them as before. Make up mixtures of the copper sulphate and 1 : 2 diamino-ethane solutions of the compositions shown below, and shake until the mixtures are homogeneous. Place tube 1 in the colorimeter and set the pointer on the zero mark, without using a filter. Record the colorimeter readings for the other tubes relative to this zero reading.

71

Test-tube number	1	2	3	4	5	6
Volume of 0·10M $CuSO_4$ solution/cm³	7·5	5·0	4·0	3·3	3·0	2·0
Volume of 0·10M 1 : 2 diamino-ethane solution/cm³	2·5	5·0	6·0	6·7	7·0	8·0
Colorimeter reading...........						

4. Plot a graph of colorimeter reading against the volume of 0·10M $CuSO_4$ solution, reading from left to right and, on the same scale, the volume of 0·10M 1 : 2 diamino-ethane solution, reading from right to left. What are the volumes of these two solutions which, on mixing would give the maximum colour intensity?

5. What is the value of y in the formula $[Cu(H_2NCH_2CH_2NH_2)_y]^{2+}$?

6. What are the features of a ligand?

7. What explanation can you give for the relative values of x and y in the above formulae?

Notes 13

Standard: *
Time required: 1½ hours for the whole
Reagents required:

approximately $1.5M$ $(NH_4)_2SO_4$ solution ($50cm^3$)

$0.10M$ $CuSO_4$ solution ($60cm^3$)

$0.10M$ NH_3 solution ($50cm^3$)

$0.10M$ $1:2$ diaminoethane ($H_2NCH_2CH_2NH_2$) ($50cm^3$)

[This solution can be made by taking $6.65cm^3$ of $1:2$ diaminoethane per dm^3 of solution]

Apparatus required:

6 test tubes to fit a colorimeter and of minimum capacity $15cm^3$

3 graduated pipettes (or the use of three burettes)

1 x $5.0cm^3$ pipette

4 x $150cm^3$ beakers

Colorimeter (one per 8 students is adequate). The EEL Portable Colorimeter is suitable, but a cheaper instrument can be built from a $0-50\mu$ A ammeter with an auxiliary logarithmic scale (obtainable from British Physical Laboratories, Radlett, Hertfordshire) and an EEL colorimeter block (obtainable from Evans Electroselenium Limited, Halstead, Essex.) This instrument can be built for a total cost of about £15.

Notes on questions and typical results

Use of colorimeter

The time which each student spends at the colorimeter is very short, and thus one colorimeter is quite adequate for at least eight students. We have found it quite satisfactory to take readings without using a filter, but colorimeters do vary and a suitable filter may be necessary. Students should record all six readings and plot the results, before discarding any mixture, since they may wish to repeat a result, or add an extra mixture to the list, and they will need to check the calibration of the colorimeter before taking further readings. Readings should be taken on a logarithmic scale.

Results of part (I)

Volume of approx. $1.5M(NH_4)_2SO_4$ solution/cm^3	5.0	5.0	5.0	5.0	5.0	5.0
Volume of $0.10M$ $CuSO_4$ solution/cm^3	7.5	5.0	2.5	2.0	1.5	1.0
Volume of $0.10M$ NH_3 solution/cm^3	2.5	5.0	7.5	8.0	8.5	9.0
Colorimeter reading	0.00	0.65	2.65	3.00	2.65	1.80

1. The ammonium sulphate produces a high concentration of ammonium ions in the solution, which suppresses the ionisation of the ammonia solution so that the hydroxide concentration in the solution is kept at such a low value that the solubility product of the copper(II) hydroxide is not reached.

$$NH_3 + H_2O = NH_4^+ + OH^-$$

73

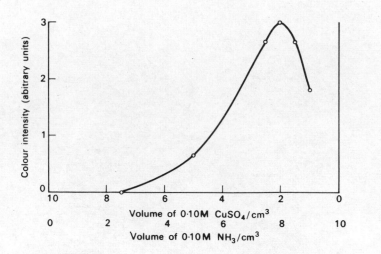

Fig. 13.1

Graph of colorimeter reading against composition for mixtures of 0·10M CuSO₄ and 0·10M NH₃ solution

2. Maximum colour intensity is obtained when $2·0cm^3$ of $0·10M$ $CuSO_4$ solution is mixed with $8·0cm^3$ of $0·10M$ NH_3 solution.

3. Since the two solutions are equimolar, the ratio of the number of moles of ammonia molecules to the number of moles of copper(II) ions is 4 : 1
Hence $x = 4$, and the formula of the complex ion is $[Cu(NH_3)_4]^{2+}$

Results of part (II)

Volume of 0·10M CuSO₄ solution/cm³	7·5	5·0	4·0	3·3	3·0	2·0
Volume of 0·10M 1 : 2 diaminoethane solution/cm³	2·5	5·0	6·0	6·7	7·0	8·0
Colorimeter reading	0·00	2·70	5·20	5·85	5·30	3·35

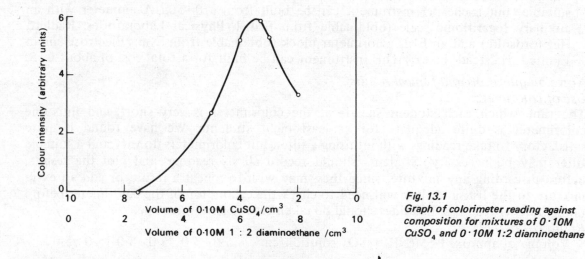

Fig. 13.1

Graph of colorimeter reading against composition for mixtures of 0·10M CuSO₄ and 0·10M 1:2 diaminoethane

4. The maximum colour intensity is produced when $3·4cm^3$ of $0·10M$ $CuSO_4$ solution is mixed with $6·6cm^3$ of $0·10M$ 1 : 2 diaminoethane solution.

5. The number of moles of 1 : 2 diaminoethane which produces the maximum colour intensity on mixing with one mole of copper(II) ions is $\frac{6·6}{3·4} = 1·94 \simeq 2$

Thus $y = 2$, and the formula of the complex ion is $[Cu(H_2NCH_2CH_2NH_2)_2]^{2+}$

6. A ligand is an ion, or molecule, which possesses one, or more, lone pair of electrons, which may be donated to a metal ion. The atoms frequently involved in this donation of lone pairs of electrons are nitrogen, or oxygen atoms, or the negatively charged carbon atoms of, for example, cyanide ions.

7. The commonest numbers of links formed from the ligands to the metal ion (coordination numbers) are 2, 4 or 6. In the case of copper(II) ions, this number is usually four. Each ammonia molecule has *one* lone pair of electrons available for donation to the copper(II) ion and so *four* molecules of ammonia will be needed for each copper(II) ion. Each molecule of 1 : 2 diaminoethane has *two* lone pairs of electrons, (one on each nitrogen atom), available for donation to the copper(II) ion and so *two* molecules of 1 : 2 diaminoethane are needed for each copper(II) ion.

Assignment 14

Complex Formation - A Study of Competition for Cations

INTRODUCTION

Complexes are formed between cations and neutral molecules, or ions of opposite charge i.e. anions. The neutral molecules, or anions, surrounding the central cation are called ligands, and each contains at least one atom bearing a pair of electrons, which can be donated to the central cation, forming a dative, (co-ordinate), bond. The ligand is said to co-ordinate to the central ion.

If only one atom, per ligand molecule or ion, has a pair of electrons which can be donated to the central ion, the ligand is said to be unidentate; if each ligand can form two dative bonds it is called bidentate, and so on. Some ligands can form as many as six dative bonds, with the central ion. A ligand, which has two, or more atoms each capable of forming a dative bond with the same central ion, is called a chelate ligand, and the complex formed is called a chelate complex.

The names and structures of the ligands studied in these experiments are as follows:

ethylenediamine tetracetate ion (EDTA)
1 : 2 diaminoethane (ethylenediamine)
oxalate ion

$$^-OOCCH_2 \diagdown N-CH_2CH_2-N \diagup CH_2COO^- $$
$$^-OOCCH_2 \diagup \qquad \diagdown CH_2COO^- $$

$H_2NCH_2CH_2NH_2$

$^-OOC-COO^-$

salicyclic acid

thiocyanate ion

water

$^-S-C\equiv N$

Some ligands can co-ordinate more strongly to the central ion than others, and the point of these experiments is to determine the relative strength of co-ordination of these ligands.

EXPERIMENTAL WORK

I. Complexes with Cu^{2+} as the central ion

(a) Place $2cm^3$ of aqueous copper sulphate solution in a test tube and add a solution of oxalate ions (e.g. aqueous ammonium oxalate), until no further change occurs.
Add aqueous 1 : 2 diaminoethane to the above until no further change occurs
Add aqueous EDTA to this solution

1. Record your observations and suggest an order of increasing strength of coordination of these ligands.

2. What is coordinated to the copper(II) ion in the solution you started with? Add this to your list in its correct position in the order.

76

(b) Confirm the order by starting with a strong co-ordinating ligand, and adding what you think is a weaker one.

3. How does this confirm the order?

4. What features do the strongest co-ordinating ligands have in common?

5. How do these features lead to the formation of very stable complexes?

II. Complexes with Fe^{3+} as the central ion

Devise experiments to find the relative strength as co-ordinating ligands of:
(a) water, (b) the thiocyanate ion, (c) the oxalate ion, and others you wish to use.

III. Competition between cations

Take about $2cm^3$ of aq. copper(II) sulphate and add 1 : 2 diaminoethane until the colour intensity is a maximum. Then add dilute sulphuric acid.

6. Explain your observations.

IV. Determination of the formula of a complex ion using competitive complexing

To about $2cm^3$ of an aqueous solution of iron(III) ions add a few drops of a solution of salicylic acid in acetone. Then add aqueous EDTA until no further change occurs.
Pipette $10.0cm^3$ of $0.10M$ Fe^{3+} solution into a $250cm^3$ titration flask, add about $100cm^3$ of distilled water, followed by about $1cm^3$ of salicyclic acid in acetone. Titrate against $0.10M$ EDTA until a clear yellow solution is obtained.

7. What is the formula of the Fe^{3+}/EDTA complex?

8. Explain how the salicylic acid can be used to indicate the end-point of this titration?

Notes 14

Standard: **

Reagents required:
    approx. 0·1M aqueous sodium, or ammonium oxalate (10cm³)
    approx. 0·1M aqueous 1 : 2 diaminoethane (10cm³)
    approx. 0·1M aqueous ethylenediamine tetracetic acid disodium salt (10cm³)
    approx. 0·1M aqueous potassium thiocyanate (10cm³)
    1% w/v salicylic acid in acetone, made by dissolving 1g of salicylic acid in 100cm³ of
    acetone (5cm³)
    distilled water (300cm³)
    0·10M aqueous ethylene diamine tetracetic acid disodium salt-EDTA (40cm³)
    0·10M iron(III) ions, which can conveniently be a 0·05M solution of ammonium
    iron(III) sulphate, $(NH_4)_2 SO_4.Fe_2(SO_4)_3.24H_2O$
    Weigh out 96·4g per dm³ of solution (30cm³)

Time required: 1½ hours
Apparatus required:
    250cm³ titration flask
    test-tubes
    10·0cm³ pipette

Notes on introduction, questions and results

The treatment given to the study of the relation between the structure of the ligand and the number of dative bonds it can make with the central ion, will depend on the standard and background of the students. It may be that students could be asked to mark the donor atoms in each ligand with an asterisk and hence predict the number of 'teeth' per ligand, or teachers may wish to discuss this with the class.

I(a) and questions 1 and 2. The aqueous copper sulphate contains the tetraquo copper(II) complex ion $[Cu(H_2O)_4]^{2+}$, which is blue. On addition of oxalate ions, a white or pale blue precipitate of CuC_2O_4 is formed and this dissolves to form a blue solution as more oxalate ions are added. This suggests displacement of the water, as the ligand, by oxalate ions.

The addition of 1 : 2 diaminoethane to this oxalate copper(II) complex forms a violet colour, suggesting that the 1 : 2 diaminoethane has displaced the oxalate ions as the ligand.

The addition of EDTA removes the violet colour and suggests the displacement of 1 : 2 diaminoethane as ligand by EDTA. Thus the changes can be summarised:

$$[Cu(H_2O)_4]^{2+} \xrightarrow{2C_2O_4^{2-}} [Cu(C_2O_4)_2]^{2-} \xrightarrow{2H_2NCH_2CH_2NH_2} [Cu(H_2NCH_2CH_2NH_2)_2]^{2+}$$
$$+ 4H_2O \qquad\qquad\qquad + 2C_2O_4^{2-}$$

$$\xrightarrow{EDTA} [Cu(EDTA)]^{2-}$$
$$+2H_2NCH_2CH_2NH_2$$

78

and the order of increasing strength of co-ordination is:

$$H_2O < C_2O_4{}^{2-} < H_2NCH_2CH_2NH_2 < EDTA$$

I(b) If the order of addition is reversed so that EDTA is added first, then 1 : 2 diaminoethane does not produce a violet colour, nor does the oxalate ion form a precipitate. If 1 : 2 diaminoethane is added, followed by oxalate ions, again no precipitate occurs.

3. Thus EDTA is not displaced by any of the other ligands, and so must be the most strongly co-ordinated.
1 : 2 diaminoethane is not displaced by oxalate ions and so must be more strongly co-ordinated.

4. It seems from these results that the strongly co-ordinated ligands are the multidentate ones, and that the more co-ordinating atoms per ligand, the more strongly it is attached to the central ion.
It should be realised that this is one factor determining the stability of complexes, but not the only one — the extent to which the electron pairs are available for bond-formation is another, and in the case of different ligands with the same number of co-ordinating atoms, this will be much more important.

5. The stability of the chelate complexes formed by multidentate ligands can be explained if one assumes that the dative bonds are only broken by collisions with other particles. If a unidentate ligand has the dative bond broken, it may be displaced from the vicinity of the central ion, whereas if a multidentate ligand has one bond broken, (one tooth removed!), the others will hold the ligand to the central ion and the bond may be re-formed. Thus unless all the bonds are broken simultaneously the multidentate ligand is unlikely to be displaced.
Another way of looking at this problem, also statistical, is to consider the entropy change accompanying complex formation. In general, reactions involving great increases in molecular disorder (i.e. large entropy increases) are more probable than others, assuming that energy considerations are not paramount.
A reaction in which a unidentate ligand reacts with a hydrated ion to displace a water molecule involves no net change in the number of molecular species in solution. On the other hand, when a multidentate ligand replaces many water molecules there will be an increase in entropy, e.g.

$$[Ni(H_2O)_6]^{2+} + EDTA^{4-} \rightarrow [Ni(EDTA)]^{2-} + 6H_2O$$

II. Similar experiments can be performed with solutions of iron(III) ions. The yellow hexaquo iron(III) ion forms a blood-red complex with thiocyanate ions, but the solution loses its red colour as oxalate ions are added.

So this suggests the order of increasing strength of co-ordination as:

$$H_2O < {}^-CNS < C_2O_4{}^{2-}$$

III. The violet colour of the complex formed between copper(II) ions and 1 : 2 diaminoethane is removed as hydrogen ions are added.

6. This suggests that 1 : 2 diaminoethane co-ordinates more readily with hydrogen ions than it does with copper(II) ions.
Here the similarity between complexing and acid/base reactions may be mentioned. The reaction may be represented as follows:

$$2H^+{}_{(aq)} + [Cu(H_2NCH_2CH_2NH_2)_2]^{2+} \rightarrow Cu^{2+}_{(aq)} + {}^+H_3NCH_2CH_2NH_3^+$$

1 : 2 diaminoethane is a stronger base than water, so will tend to displace the water molecules co-ordinating with the proton. Presumably the small proton, with the intense field surrounding it, is more strongly co-ordinated with 1 : 2 diaminoethane than is the much

larger copper(II) ion, in spite of the extra formal charge. The screening effect of the other electrons in the copper(II) ion plays a large part in determining the strength of the field surrounding it.

IV. In the titration, 10.0cm^3 of 0.10M EDTA is needed to produce the yellow colour, using 10.0cm^3 of 0.10M solution of iron(III) ions.

7. Hence the formula of the complex is $[\text{Fe(EDTA)}]^-$

8. Salicylic acid forms a violet complex with iron(III)ions, but co-ordinates less strongly than does EDTA with iron(III) ions. If a little salicyclic acid is added to the solution of iron(III) ions, some violet complex is formed, but this will not be broken until the EDTA has complexed with all the iron(III) ions present in the hexaquo iron(III) complex. Since salicylic acid complexes more strongly than water, the violet colour will not disappear until all the iron(III) ions have complexed with EDTA, i.e. at the end-point.

Assignment 15

A Study of The Ag^+-Cl^- System in the Presence of a Large Excess of Chloride ions

You are provided with a concentrated solution of sodium chloride in water. Use it to prepare the mixtures given in Table 1:

Table 1

Flask	Volume of concentrated NaCl solution (V/cm^3)	Volume of distilled water/cm^3
1	50·0	0·0
2	45·0	5·0
3	40·0	10·0
4	35·0	15·0
5	30·0	20·0

Titrate the contents of each flask with 0·010M $AgNO_3$ solution until a slight turbidity is noticed which persists after 30 seconds of shaking (N.B. It is worth retaining the turbid contents of the first flask to act as a reference in judging the end-points of the remaining four titrations). Record your titration results in Table 2:

Table 2

Flask	Burette Readings (i)	(ii)	Volume of 0·01M $AgNO_3$ solution used (T/cm^3)
1			....
2			....
3			....
4			....
5			....

The faint turbidity which marks the end-point is caused by the precipitation of AgCl; the fact that it dissolves in the presence of a very large excess of chloride ion suggests that the following reactions are taking place in the course of titration:

$$Ag^+_{(aq)} + Cl^-_{(aq)} \rightleftharpoons AgCl_{(s)} \ldots . \text{ (i)}$$

$$AgCl_{(s)} + (n-1) Cl^-_{(aq)} \rightleftharpoons AgCl^{(n-1)-}_{n(aq)} \ldots \text{ (ii)}$$

or overall

$$Ag^+_{(aq)} + n Cl^-_{(aq)} \rightleftharpoons AgCl^{(n-1)-}_{n(aq)} \ldots \text{ (iii)}$$

1. *If* there are only three silver species in the titration flasks ($Ag^+_{(aq)}$, $AgCl_{(s)}$ and $AgCl^{(n-1)-}_{n(aq)}$) explain why it is a reasonable approximation to assume that effectively all

of the silver ions added during titration are converted into the last of these species, $AgCl_{n(aq)}^{(n-1)-}$. (You will be told the concentration of the original NaCl solution.)

2. If a flask containing $V \text{cm}^3$ of the concentrated NaCl solution needed $T \text{cm}^3$ of 0·010M $AgNO_3$ solution to produce a permanent turbidity, what must the formal concentration of $AgCl_{n(aq)}^{(n-1)-}$ have been in terms of T?

3. Show that, providing n is a small integer, the *free* chloride ion concentration at the end-point of a titration is effectively equal to the *total* chloride ion concentration in the flask.

4. In terms of T and V (See question 2), what is the effective concentration of free chloride ions at the end-point of the titration? (Make the assumption given in question 3). Using the expressions you have derived in answering questions 2 and 4, calculate values for $[AgCl^{(n-1)-}]$ and $[Cl_{free}^-]$ at the onset of turbidity in each of your five titrations. Tabulate your results below and complete Table 3.

Table 3

Flask	$[AgCl_n^{(n-1)-}]$ /mol dm^{-3}	$[Cl_{free}^-]$ /mol dm^{-3}	$lg[AgCl_n^{(n-1)-}]$ /mol dm^{-3}	$lg[Cl_{free}^-]$ /mol dm^{-3}
1	....	....	....	....
2	....	....	....	....
3	....	....	....	....
4	....	....	....	....
5	....	....	....	....

Plot a graph of $lg[AgCl_n^{(n-1)-}]$ /mol dm^{-3} against $lg[Cl_{free}^-]$ /mol dm^{-3}

5. What is the expression for the equilibrium constant K for reaction (iii) in terms of the concentrations of the three species involved?
Assuming that the solubility product for silver chloride is a constant K_s for a fixed temperature and that it is given by the expression:

$$K_s = [Ag_{free}^+] \cdot [Cl_{free}^-]$$

substitute a value for $[Ag^+]$ in the expression for K and derive a relation between $lg[Cl_{free}^-]$ and $lg[AgCl^{(n-1)-}]$

From the gradient of this graph and its intercept when $lg[Cl_{free}^-] = 0$, calculate values for n and K. Assume that $K_s = 8·8 \times 10^{-11}$ mol^2 dm^{-6} at room temperature (18°C).
In general, when a cation forms complexes containing two or more ligands per ion, complexing occurs in a stepwise manner. In this case, studies by many different workers using a variety of different methods suggest that at *least* four successive steps are involved:

(a) $Ag_{(aq)}^+ + Cl_{(aq)}^- \rightleftharpoons AgCl_{(s)}$ $\quad K_a = 2750$ mol^{-1} dm^3

(b) $AgCl_{(s)} + Cl_{(aq)}^- \rightleftharpoons AgCl_{2(aq)}^-$ $\quad K_b = 72$ mol^{-1} dm^3

(c) $AgCl_{2(aq)}^- + Cl_{(aq)}^- \rightleftharpoons AgCl_{3(aq)}^-$ $K_c = 1·5$ mol^{-1} dm^3

(d) $AgCl_{3(aq)}^{2-} + Cl_{(aq)}^- \rightleftharpoons AgCl_{4(aq)}^{3-}$ $\quad K_d = 0·83$ mol^{-1} dm^3

And all four silver-chloro species indicated above will co-exist in any mixture containing $Ag_{(aq)}^+$ and $Cl_{(aq)}^-$ ions, although unless there is a high chloride ion concentration the second, third and fourth steps will not occur to any significant extent.

6. How are the equilibrium constants K_a, K_b, K_c and K_d related to K_o, the equilibrium constant for the overall reaction:

$$Ag^+_{(aq)} + 4\,Cl^-_{(aq)} \rightleftharpoons AgCl^{3-}_4(aq)$$

Calculate a value for K_o by assuming values for K_a K_b, K_c and K_d given above.

7. Assuming the value of K_s already quoted and the value of K_o which you have just obtained, calculate a value for the $AgCl^{3-}_4(aq)$ ion concentration in a solution for which the free chloride ion concentration is 4.0 mol dm^{-3}.

8. Which of the following sequences represents the order of increasing concentration of the silver-chloro complex ions in a solution which has a chloride ion concentration of 4.0 mol dm^{-3} and which is saturated with respect to AgCl? (Assume the given values of K_a, K_b, K_c and K_d)

$$[AgCl^{3-}_4(aq)] > [AgCl^{2-}_3(aq)] > [AgCl^-_2(aq)]$$

$$[AgCl^-_2(aq)] > [AgCl^{2-}_3(aq)] > [AgCl^{3-}_4(aq)]$$

9. The lengthy extrapolation necessary in order to obtain the value of $\lg[AgCl^{(n-1)-}_{n(aq)}]$ when $\lg[Cl^-_{free(aq)}]$ is zero is open to criticism. Why was it not suggested that the experimental study should be extended to include lower chloride ion concentrations?

10. It is probable that if measurements could be made at lower chloride ion concentrations, it would be found that the log-log graph would not remain linear. If this proved to be so, would you expect to get greater or smaller intercepts when $\lg Cl^-_{free}$ is zero? Would non-linearity of this graph imply that the value of n which you have determined is of no real significance?

11. By considering the whole experiment critically, including experimental errors, briefly discuss whether you believe that your results afford reliable evidence of silver-chloro complex ions containing more than four chloride ions per silver ion.

12. Suggest further experiments which might establish whether such species ($AgCl^{4-}_5$, $AgCl^{5-}_6$) can exist.

Notes 15

Standard: ***
Time required: 1½ hours practical work
Reagents required:
Nearly saturated aqueous sodium chloride solution of known concentration [N.B. a saturated solution works well, but in this case care must be taken to avoid conveying solid sodium chloride into the titration flasks] ($250cm^3$)
    1.0×10^{-2} M silver nitrate solution ($100cm^3$)
    Distilled water ($100cm^3$)
Apparatus required:
    5 titration flasks of 150-250cm^3 capacity (small, glass-stoppered reagent bottles are ideal)
    burette
    $25cm^3$, $20cm^3$, $10cm^3$ and $5cm^3$ pipettes (one of each). Alternatively, extra burettes provided for measuring out $10cm^3$ and $5cm^3$ portions of concentrated sodium chloride solution and distilled water.

Notes on questions and experimental results

There is likely to be some confusion as to the exact end-point. However, each student should be able to titrate to a certain fixed turbidity using the end-point of his first titration as a reference.

Typical results are shown below. They were obtained using a 5·34M solution of sodium chloride (The latter was standardized by diluting $10.0cm^3$ of the solution to $500cm^3$ and titrating with 0·10M silver nitrate solution to a chromate end-point)

Tables 1 and 2

Flask	Volume of concentrated NaCl solution/cm³	Volume of distilled water/cm³	Volume of 1×10^{-2} M AgNO₃ solution needed /cm³
	(V/cm³)		(T/cm³)
1	50·0	0·0	18·65
2	45·0	5·0	15·05
3	40·0	10·0	11·60
4	35·0	15·0	8·20
5	30·0	20·0	5·60

1. The solubility product of silver chloride is approximately 1×10^{-10} mol² dm⁻⁶. This indicates that the concentration of dissolved, free $Ag^+_{(aq)}$ ions must be *very* small under the conditions of the experiment.

$$\text{In fact} \quad [Ag^+_{free}] \simeq \frac{10^{-10}}{4} \simeq 2.5 \times 10^{-11} \text{ mol dm}^{-3}$$

in the presence of a free chloride ion concentration of 4 mol dm^{-3}. Thus, the free silver ion concentration must be entirely negligible compared with the concentration of the chlorosilver complex species. If the titration is stopped on the appearance of the first visible amount of solid silver chloride, the fraction of the added silver ions which are precipitated as $AgCl_{(s)}$ can also be neglected.

2. Assuming
(i) that all the added silver ions are used in forming the chlorosilver complex ions
(ii) that the chlorosilver complex ions contain only one silver ion
then:

$$[AgCl_n^{(n-1)-}] = \frac{T}{(50 + T)} \times 1 \cdot 0 \times 10^{-2} \text{ mol dm}^{-3}$$

3. The greatest concentration of $AgCl^{(n-1)-}$ will occur at the end-point of the titration of flask 1 when:

$$[AgCl^{(n-1)-}] = \frac{18 \cdot 65}{68 \cdot 65} \times 1 \cdot 0 \times 10^{-2} \simeq 2 \cdot 5 \times 10^{-3} \text{ mol dm}^{-3}$$

Thus, even if n is as large as 10, the concentration of complexed chloride ions will be insignificant compared with the total chloride ion concentration, which is never less than $2 \cdot 5$ mol dm^{-3} throughout any of the titrations.

4. Assuming that

$$[Cl_{free}^-] = [Cl_{total}^-] \text{ then at the end-point of a titration:}$$

$$[Cl_{free}^-] = \frac{V}{(50+T)} \times \text{concentration of the NaCl solution used}$$

Sample data for Table 3

Flask	$[AgCl_n^{(n-1)-}]$ /mol dm^{-3}	$[Cl_{free}^-]$ /mol dm^{-3}	$[AgCl^{(n-1)-}]$ /mol dm^{-3}	lg$[Cl_{free}^-]$ /mol dm^{-3}
1	$2 \cdot 72 \times 10^{-3}$	3·89	−2·57	0·590
2	2·31	3·69	−2·64	0·568
3	1·88	3·47	−2·74	0·540
4	1·41	3·21	−2·85	0·507
5	1·01	2·88	−3·00	0·460

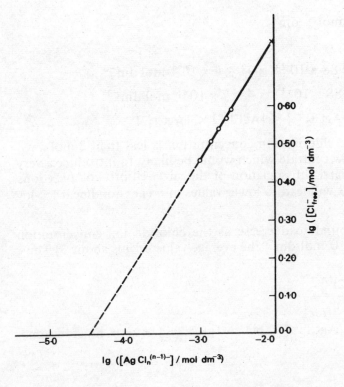

Fig. 15.1 Graph of lg [Cl⁻ free] against lg [AgCl_n^(n-1)-]

85

5. $K = \dfrac{[AgCl_n^{(n-1)-}]}{[Ag_{free}^+] \, [Cl_{free}^-]^n}$ Thus $K = \dfrac{[AgCl_n^{(n-1)-}]}{\dfrac{K_s}{[Cl_{free}^-]} \times [Cl_{free}^-]^n}$

$$= \dfrac{[AgCl_n^{(n-1)-}]}{K_s \times [Cl_{free}^-]^{(n-1)}}$$

Therefore: $K.K_s \, [Cl_{free}^-]^{(n-1)} = [AgCl_n^{(n-1)-}]$

and so: $\lg(K.K_s) + (n\text{-}1) \lg[Cl_{free}^-] = \lg[AgCl_n^{(n-1)-}]$

Thus, a graph of $\lg[Cl_{free}^-]$ against $\lg[AgCl^{(n-1)-}]$ should be linear providing n is a constant. This graph should have a gradient of $(n\text{-}1)$ and an intercept of $\lg(K.K_s)$ when $\lg[Cl_{free}^-] = 0$ (i.e. when the free chloride ion concentration is 1 mol dm^{-3})

The data quoted in Table 3 suggest values of 4·30 and $3\cdot3 \times 10^5$ mol^{-n}dm^{-3n} for n and for K, respectively.

6. The values for K_a, K_b, K_c and K_d are for a temperature of 18°C

$$K_a \times K_b \times K_c \times K_d = \dfrac{[\cancel{AgCl}]}{[Ag^+]\,[Cl^-]} \times \dfrac{[\cancel{AgCl_2^-}]}{[\cancel{AgCl}]\,[Cl^-]} \times \dfrac{[\cancel{AgCl_3^{2-}}]}{[\cancel{AgCl_2^-}]\,[Cl^-]} \times \dfrac{[AgCl_4^{3-}]}{[\cancel{AgCl_3^{2-}}]\,[Cl^-]}$$

$$= \dfrac{[AgCl_4^{3-}]}{[Ag^+]\,[Cl^-]^4} = K_0$$

Therefore $K_0 = K_a \times K_b \times K_c \times K_d = 2750 \times 72 \times 1\cdot5 \times 0\cdot83 = 2\cdot5 \times 10^5$ mol^{-4}dm^{12}

7. $[AgCl_4^{3-}] = K_0 \, [Ag^+]\,[Cl^-]^4 = K_0 \dfrac{K_s}{[Cl^-]} [Cl^-]^4 = K_0 \times K_s \times [Cl^-]^3$

$$= 2\cdot5 \times 10^5 \times 0\cdot88 \times 10^{-10} \times 4^3$$

$$= 1\cdot4 \times 10^{-3} \text{ mol dm}^{-3}$$

8. $\dfrac{[AgCl_3^{2-}]}{[Ag^+]\,[Cl^-]^3} = 2750 \times 72 \times 1\cdot5 \text{ mol}^{-3} \text{ dm}^9$

Thus $[AgCl_3^{2-}] = 2750 \times 72 \times 1\cdot5 \times 0\cdot88 \times 10^{-10} \times 4^2 \simeq 4 \times 10^{-4}$ mol dm^{-3}

Similarly $[AgCl_2^-] = 2750 \times 72 \times 0\cdot88 \times 10^{-10} \times 4 \simeq 7 \times 10^{-5}$ mol dm^{-3}

Thus, sequence of concentrations is $[AgCl_2^-] < [AgCl_3^{2-}] < [AgCl_4^{3-}]$

9. Studies of solutions for which the chloride ion concentration is less than 2 mol dm^{-3} would involve very small titres of silver nitrate which would be likely to introduce a very high experimental error. Moreover, partial dissociation of the silver-chloro complex ions as the chloride ion concentration falls will lead to lower values of n (i.e. non-linear log-log plots).

10. (i) The average value of n is bound to decrease as the chloride ion concentration decreases. (In fact, when $[Cl^-] = 1\cdot0$ mol dm^{-3} the average value of n is about 3) Thus, the gradient of the graph

$$\dfrac{\lg[AgCl_n^{(n-1)-}]}{\lg[Cl_{free}^-]}$$

will decrease, and so the value of $\lg[AgCl_n^{(n-1)-}]$when $\lg[Cl_{free}^-]$ is zero, must become less negative. This will result in the overall value of K becoming bigger. However, this does not invalidate the method used to determine n.

(ii) The gradient of the log-log plot will give the *mean* value of n *over the range of chloride ion concentrations studied*

11. Taking into account titration errors (difficulty in titrating to a fixed turbidity, etc.) and errors in making up solutions, it is probable that the experimentally determined mean value of n for solutions of chloride ion concentration in the range $3 \cdot 0 - 4 \cdot 0$ mol dm^{-3} will not differ from 4 by an amount which is of any theoretical significance.

12. Significant concentrations of $AgCl_5^{4-}$ and $AgCl_6^{5-}$, if such species can exist, will only be formed at very high chloride ion concentrations. It would be interesting to study this reaction in concentrated solutions of hydrochloric acid.

REFERENCE

Full tabulation of equilibrium constants can be found in *Stability Constants* (Chemical Society Special Publication 17). The values of K_a, etc. quoted here are taken from the work of Mironov, Radiokhimiya 4, 707 (1962).

FURTHER PROJECTS

1. Repeat this experiment using concentrated hydrochloric acid instead of brine.

2. Using the K values quoted here, calculate the percentage silver existing in the form of each of the silver-chloro complexes at each of the following chloride ion concentrations:

$$10^{-3}, 10^{-2}, 10^{-1}, 1 \cdot 0 \ 10 \cdot 0 \text{ mol dm}^{-3}$$

For each complex ion plot a graph of the percent silver existing as such against the logarithm of the chloride ion concentration.

3. Write a paragraph explaining why the existence of chlorosilver complex ions is ignored in most silver nitrate — chloride ion titrations.

Assignment 16
Determination of a Partition Coefficient

INTRODUCTION

1. What do you understand by the term *immiscible liquids*?

When a solute which is significantly soluble in two immiscible solvents is shaken up in the presence of both of these solvents, it does not dissolve exclusively in the solvent in which it is most soluble, but distributes itself between both solvents. The purpose of this experiment is to investigate the relationship between the equilibrium concentrations of the solute in the two immiscible solvents.

Succinic acid, $HO.\overset{O}{\underset{}{C}}.CH_2.CH_2.\overset{O}{\underset{}{C}}.OH$, is used as the solute and the immiscible solvents are water and diethyl ether, $CH_3.CH_2.O.CH_2.CH_3$

EXPERIMENTAL WORK

(i) Using a measuring cylinder, pour $25cm^3$ of distilled water into a separating funnel. Weigh out a portion of succinic acid of mass $0.5-1.5g$ and add this to the separating funnel followed by about $25cm^3$ of diethyl ether. Shake the mixture well (N.B. Since diethyl ether is both very volatile and inflammable, be careful to release pressure in the separating funnel from time to time, and make certain that there are no flames near at hand) and continue shaking until all the acid has dissolved. Then leave the separating funnel and its contents to stand for some minutes in order to allow the layers to separate as fully as possible.

(ii) Run off the lower layer (aqueous solution) into a clean beaker. Pipette $10.0cm^3$ of this solution into a conical flask and titrate it with $0.5M$ NaOH solution using phenolphthalein as an indicator. Record your results in the table below. Repeat the titration with a further $10.0cm^3$ portion of the aqueous solution. Since there is insufficient solution to allow more than two titrations to be done, great care should be taken with both titrations.

(iii) Discard the boundary layer from the separating funnel and then, using a clean pipette and a pipette-filler, transfer $10.0cm^3$ of the ethereal solution into a clean conical flask. Add a small volume of distilled water and then titrate this with $0.1M$ NaOH solution to a phenolphthalein end-point, shaking thoroughly after each addition of alkali. Titrate a second $10.0cm^3$ portion of the ether solution in the same way. All readings should be recorded in the table below:

	Aqueous Layer (0.5M NaOH used)	Ether Layer (0.1M NaOH)
Final Burette Reading/cm³		
Initial Burette Reading/cm³		
Result/cm³		
	Mean Titre:	Mean Titre:

88

CALCULATION AND EXPERIMENTAL INTERPRETATION:

2. How many moles of OH⁻ ion were needed to react with (a) 10cm³ of the aqueous layer? (b) 10cm³ of the ether layer?

3. Assuming that succinic acid is a dibasic acid, how many moles of the acid must there have been in 10cm³ of (a) the aqueous layer? (b) the ether layer?

4. What must have been the molarities of the acid solutions in both layers?
Tabulate each student's results for the concentrations of acid at equilibrium in each phase, and plot a graph of the equilibrium concentration of the succinic acid in ether against that in water.

5. Would you expect this plot to go through the origin? (Comment in the light of the introduction to this experiment)

6. What does the shape of this graph suggest about the ratio of the equilibrium concentrations of the acid in each phase, under the conditions of the experiment? Does this ratio, known as the distribution ratio or partition coefficient, depend upon the amount of succinic acid used in the experiment?

7. Would you expect the partition coefficient (a) to be related to the respective solubilities of succinic acid in the separate solvents? (b) to vary with temperature?

8. Explain why the amounts of water, ether and succinic acid placed in the separating funnel need not be measured out accurately, whereas the volumes of the aqueous and ethereal solutions used in the titrations must be known as accurately as possible.

9. If you repeated your experiment using 50cm³ of diethyl ether, but with the amount of all else unchanged, which of the following would be altered?
(a) the concentration of acid in the ether
(b) the concentration of the acid in the water
(c) the partition coefficient

10. Suppose that 8g of succinic acid are dissolved in a litre of ether and that a litre of water is available. Assuming that the partition coefficient of succinic acid between water and ether is 7, show whether more acid would be extracted from the ether by shaking it with the whole litre of water at once, or with two separate 500cm³ portions of water.

Notes 16

Standard: *

Time required: 1½ hours should be ample

Reagents required:
   succinic acid (2g)
   diethyl ether (30cm^3)
   0·5M NaOH (50cm^3)
   0·1M NaOH (50cm^3)
   distilled water (100cm^3)

Apparatus required:
   measuring cylinder (100cm^3 or 50cm^3)
   separating funnel
   beaker (50cm^3)
   pipette (10cm^3)
   conical flasks
   burette

Specimen results and notes on questions

1. Immiscible liquids: two or more liquids which, when shaken together, do not form an homogeneous mixture but remain as distinct, pure phases. In fact, this is an ideal definition and no actual system conforms exactly to it.

Experimental Notes

(i) It is advisable to specify a different amount of succinic acid for each student as it is important to study as wide a range of concentrations as possible. Less than 0·5g of acid results in inaccuracies from low titres, while more than 1·5g of acid is very difficult to dissolve in the quantities of solvent used.

(ii) It is very important that the pipette should be cleaned after it has been used for the aqueous layer.

Typical Results: (Room Temperature 19°C)

Mass of succinic acid used:	0·52g	1·00g	1·53g
Mean titre of 0·5M NaOH/10cm^3 aqueous layer	5·5cm^3	10·8cm^3	16·2cm^3
Mean titre of 0·1M NaOH/10cm^3 ether layer	4·3cm^3	7·9cm^3	12·0cm^3
Partition Coefficient	6·4	6·9	6·8

N.B. Answers to the next three questions are based on the above data for the experiment using 1·00g of succinic acid

2. Amounts of hydroxide ion needed:

(a) $\frac{10 \cdot 8}{1000}$ x 0·5 = 0·0054 moles/10cm^3 aqueous layer

(b) $\frac{7 \cdot 9}{1000}$ x 0·1 = 0·00079 moles/10cm^3 ether

3. Amounts of acid
(a) 0·0027 moles/10cm³ of aqueous layer.
(b) 0·000395 moles/10cm³ of ether layer.

4. Molarities of acid
0·0027 x (1000/10) = 0·27 mol dm⁻³ of aqueous layer
0·000395 x (1000/10) = 0·0395 mol dm⁻³ of ether layer

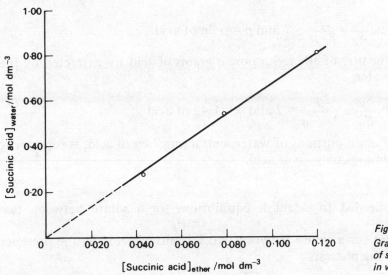

Fig. 16.1
Graph of the equilibrium concentration of succinic acid, in ether, against that in water

5. Yes. If it did not go through the origin it would signify that in dilute solutions the acid dissolved exclusively in one solvent.

6. The graph should be linear and pass through the origin. Thus, it is described by the equation:

$$\text{Constant} = \text{Partition Coefficient} = \frac{[\text{Succinic acid in water}]}{[\text{Succinic acid in ether}]}$$

(Of course, the concentration quotient could be inverted)
Since the gradient of the graph is independent of the concentration of acid in either phase, the partition coefficient must be independent of the acid concentration. Hence, it must also be independent of the amount of acid used.

$$\text{Thus, Partition Coefficient} = \frac{[\text{Solute}] \text{ in phase 1}}{[\text{Solute}] \text{ in phase 2}} = \frac{\text{Solubility of solute in phase 1}}{\text{Solubility of solute in phase 2}}$$

7. (a) Consider separate portions of ether and water at the same temperature, each saturated with respect to succinic acid. When a saturated solution is shaken with excess solute no net change of solute concentration can take place. Thus, if the two separate saturated solutions, ethereal and aqueous, are shaken together, no change of solute concentration is to be expected in either solvent.

(b) It is known that solubilities vary with temperature. Assuming that the solubilities of a solute in two different solvents do not vary with temperature in exactly the same proportion, then the partition coefficient is to be expected to vary with temperature.

8. and 9. If the amounts of water, ether and succinic acid are varied then the concentrations of solute in both solvents must change. However, the ratio of the equilibrium concentrations of the solute in both solvents (i.e. the partition coefficient) will not change. Thus, in order to determine the partition coefficient accurately, it is only necessary to determine the acid concentrations in the separate solvents with accuracy.

91

10. Single extraction with 1 litre of water: Let S_w and S_e represent the concentrations of succinic acid in water and ether respectively.

Thus: $\dfrac{S_w}{S_e} = \dfrac{7}{1}$ and, since only 8 grams of acid are present altogether, it is clear that 7g of acid will be extracted into the litre of water

Two separate 500cm³ portions of water: Let p grams of acid be extracted by the first 500cm³ of water.

$$\text{Thus: } \frac{S_w}{S_e} = \frac{2p}{8-p} = 7 \text{ and } p = 6 \cdot 2 \text{g of acid}$$

This leaves 1·8g of acid in the litre of ether. Suppose q grams of acid are extracted by the second 500cm³ portion of water,

$$\text{Thus, } \frac{S_w}{S_e} = \frac{2q}{1 \cdot 8 - q} = 7 \text{ and } q = 1 \cdot 4 \text{g of acid}$$

Thus, extraction by two separate portions of water, extracting 7·6g of acid, is superior to a single extraction, which removes only 7g of acid.

FURTHER PROJECT

1. How much shaking is needed to establish equilibrium for a solute between two solvents?
2. Is the partition coefficient for a solute between two solvents affected by the presence of a second solute in one of the phases?

Assignment 17

A Study of the Partition of Acetic Acid Between Water and Carbon Tetrachloride

INTRODUCTION

If a solute is shaken with two mutually immiscible solvents until equilibrium is established, then the ratio of the total equilibrium concentrations of the solute in the two phases is usually a constant for a fixed temperature. This constant, the partition coefficient, (or distribution ratio) is independent of both the volumes of either solvent and the total mass of solute used. However, it is important to note that it must be the *equilibrium* concentrations of the *same solute species* in the two solvents which are used in calculating a partition coefficient.

e.g. For an acid, HA, which is considerably ionized in water: $HA \rightleftharpoons H^+ + A^-$
but which exists completely as undissociated monomers, HA, in benzene, then

$$\frac{[HA] \text{ total at equilibrium in } H_2O}{[HA] \text{ total at equilibrium in } C_6H_6} \neq \text{a constant}$$

whereas $\dfrac{[HA] \text{ undissociated at equilibrium in } H_2O}{[HA] \text{ total at equilibrium in } C_6H_6} = \text{Partition Coefficient}$

It should thus be apparent that partition studies can be used to investigate equilibria existing in solution. If the ratio of the total equilibrium concentrations of a solute in two phases varies with the overall mass of solute used, then it is almost certain that the solute is involved in a further equilibrium (e.g. association, dissociation or solvolysis) in at least one of the solvents, i.e. the solute does not exist totally as the same species in the two solvents. By careful study, in such cases, it is usually possible to infer the identities of the other species.

EXPERIMENTAL WORK

1. Using the microburette provided, run 1·0, 1·5, 2·0, 2·5 or 3·0cm³ of glacial acetic acid, as directed, into a separating funnel containing 25cm³ of distilled water and 25cm³ of carbon tetrachloride (it is sufficient to use a measuring cylinder to dispense the two solvents). Shake the resulting mixture for about 3 minutes at room temperature. At the end of this time the system should have reached equilibrium and the layers should be allowed to separate.
2. Run off the carbon tetrachloride layer (lower phase) into a clean boiling tube, discarding the smallest possible quantity of the boundary layer. Titrate 10·0cm³ portions of this carbon tetrachloride layer (use a pipette filler), in duplicate, with the 0·02 M NaOH solution provided, having the alkali in the burette. Use phenolphthalein as an indicator. The alkali should be added slowly and the contents of the titrating flask should be shaken *well* after each addition of alkali.
3. Titrate 10·0cm³ portions of the aqueous layer, again in duplicate and with phenolphthalein as an indicator, but this time with 1·00 M NaOH solution in the burette.

INTERPRETATION OF DATA

1. Why is it comparatively unimportant to take care in measuring out the $25 cm^3$ portions of the solvents and the volume of glacial acetic acid, whereas the $10.0 cm^3$ portions of the two phases used in the titrations must be dispensed as accurately as possible?

2. What is the equation for the reaction of acetic acid with sodium hydroxide?

3. Why is phenolphthalein chosen as the indicator?

4. Why is it necessary to titrate the carbon tetrachloride layer slowly and with thorough shaking?

Exchange results with other students and complete Table 1.

Table 1

Volume of glacial acetic acid used $(/cm^3)$	1.0	1.5	2.0	2.5	3.0
Volume of 0.02 M NaOH used $(/cm^3)$ per $10 cm^3$ of CCl_4 layer					
Volume of 1.00 M NaOH used $(/cm^3)$ per $10 cm^3$ of H_2O layer					
$[CH_3CO_2H]$ total H_2O $(/mol\ dm^{-3})$					
$[CH_3CO_2H]$ total CCl_4 $(/mol\ dm^{-3})$					

$[CH_3CO_2H]_{total\ H_2O}$ and $[CH_3CO_2H]_{total\ CCl_4}$ represents the total acetic acid concentrations at equilibrium in the water and carbon tetrachloride phases respectively. Plot a graph of the total acetic acid concentration in water against that in the carbon tetrachloride layer. (Graph 1)

5. Should Graph 1 go through the origin?

6. Is the expression: $\dfrac{[CH_3CO_2H]\ total\ H_2O}{[CH_3CO_2H]\ total\ CCl_4}$ a constant at room temperature? (Inspect Graph 1)

7. Given that the acid dissociation constant K_a for acetic acid in water is $10^{-4.8}\ mol\ dm^{-3}$, is it possible that the non-linearity of Graph 1 could be caused by dissociation of acetic acid in the aqueous layer? (calculate the percentage ionization of 1.0 and 2.0 M acetic acid solutions)

8. Perhaps the non-linearity of Graph 1 is the result of some phenomenon taking place in the carbon tetrachloride phase. It is to be expected that acetic acid is far more likely to associate in carbon tetrachloride than to dissociate into ions. Why?

Let it be assumed that acetic acid associates in the CCl_4 phase into single aggregate species containing n monomers:

$$nCH_3CO_2H \rightleftharpoons (CH_3CO_2H)_n$$

Thus, the significant equilibria in the two-phase system are as shown in Figure 17.1

Thus $[CH_3CO_2H]_{total\ H_2O} \simeq [CH_3CO_2H]$ undissociated in H_2O ... (i) (See question 7)

and $[CH_3CO_2H]_{total\ CCl_4} = [CH_3CO_2H]$ unass. in $CCl_4 + n[(CH_3CO_2H)n]$ ... (ii)

If it is further assumed (this will be justified later) that

$[CH_3CO_2H]_{unass.\ in\ CCl_4} \ll n[(CH_3CO_2H)n]$, then equation (ii) can be rewritten

$$[CH_3CO_2H]_{total\ CCl_4} \simeq n[(CH_3CO_2H)n] \ ... \ (iii)$$

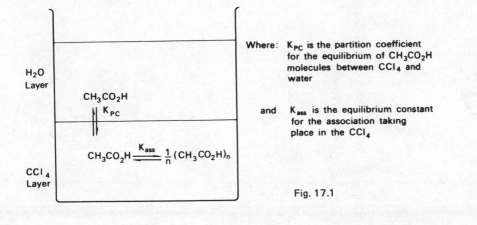

Where: K_{PC} is the partition coefficient for the equilibrium of CH_3CO_2H molecules between CCl_4 and water

and K_{ass} is the equilibrium constant for the association taking place in the CCl_4

Fig. 17.1

9. What is the expression linking K_{ass} with $[CH_3CO_2H]_{unass.\ in\ CCl_4}$ and $[(CH_3CO_2H)n]$?

10. Using your answer to question 9, rewrite equation (iii) in terms of K_{ass} and $[CH_3CO_2H]_{unass\ in\ CCl_4}$

11. Assuming that $K_{PC} = \dfrac{[CH_3CO_2H]_{unass.\ in\ CCl_4}}{[CH_3CO_2H]_{undiss.\ in\ H_2O}}$, obtain an expression for $[CH_3CO_2H]_{unass.\ in\ CCl_4}$ in terms of $[CH_3CO_2H]_{total\ H_2O}$ and K_{PC}.

12. Using your answers to questions 10 and 11, derive a relation between $[CH_3CO_2H]_{total\ CCl_4}$, n, K_{ass}, K_{PC} and $[CH_3CO_2H]_{total\ in\ H_2O}$

Plot a graph of $lg[CH_3CO_2H]_{total\ H_2O}$ against $lg[CH_3CO_2H]_{total\ CCl_4}$ (Graph 2) and from it, together with your answer to question 12, determine a value for n.

13. From your value for n, suggest a structure for $(CH_3CO_2H)_n$.

14. What sort of forces are responsible for holding the n acetic acid molecules together as an aggregate?

The linearity of Graph 2 is a justification for the assumption that:

$$[CH_3CO_2H]_{unass.\ in\ CCl_4} \ll n\ [(CH_3CO_2H)_n]$$

It is also possible to determine a value of n by a more rigorous procedure which does not involve making this assumption.

95

Notes 17

Standard: ***

Time required: 1½ hours practical time is ample (A further hour for interpretation of results)

Reagents required:
- 1·00 M NaOH (50cm³)
- 0·02 M NaOH (50cm³)
- carbon tetrachloride (30cm³)
- glacial acetic acid (3cm³)
- phenolphthalein solution
- distilled water (100cm³)

Apparatus required:
- 100cm³ separating funnel with stopper
- a pipette filler
- 10cm³ pipette
- a burette
- a boiling tube
- 50cm³ measuring cylinder
- a microburette for communal use

Sample data and comments on questions

1. All that need be known with accuracy are the *equilibrium* total concentrations of acetic acid in the two phases. These will be affected by the volumes of the two phases used and by the amount of glacial acetic acid taken, but the final equilibrium concentrations are determined by experiment. Specific quantities of water, acetic acid and carbon tetrachloride are prescribed to ensure that the class study is carried out over a reasonable range of concentration. They need not be measured out to greater than 90% accuracy.

2. The reaction which occurs during the titrations is:

$$CH_3CO_2H_{aq} + OH^-_{aq} = CH_3CO_2{}^-{}_{aq} + H_2O_l$$

3. Sodium acetate, the product of the titration, is hydrolyzed by water to give an alkaline solution. Thus, the pH at the end-point of the titration will be greater than 7 and phenolphthalein is used as its transition range is pH 8·3 - 10·0

4. Since sodium hydroxide is ionic it will not dissolve in carbon tetrachloride to any extent. Accordingly, slow titration and thorough shaking will be necessary to promote maximum contact between the two phases, thus minimizing the chances of over-shooting the end-point of the titration.

5. Graph 1 must go through the origin. If equilibrium exists between the two phases, the concentration in one phase can only be zero if that in the other phase is zero.

6. Graph 1 is quite definitely non-linear. Thus, $\dfrac{[CH_3CO_2H] \text{ total } H_2O}{[CH_3CO_2H] \text{ total } CCl_4}$ is not a constant for all the solutions studied.

Table 1:

Volume of glacial acetic acid used (/cm³)	1·0	1·5	2·0	2·5	3·0
Volume of 0·02 M NaOH used per 10cm³ of CCl₄ layer (/cm³)	3·5	5·5	8·5	16·0	22·5

96

Volume of 1·00 M NaOH used per 10cm³ of H₂O layer	(/cm³)	6·8	9·2	12·0	15·8	18·5
$[CH_3CO_2H]$ total H₂O	(/mol dm⁻³)	0·68	0·92	1·20	1·58	1·85
$[CH_3CO_2H]$ total CCl₄	(/mol dm⁻³)	0·007	0·011	0·017	0·032	0·045

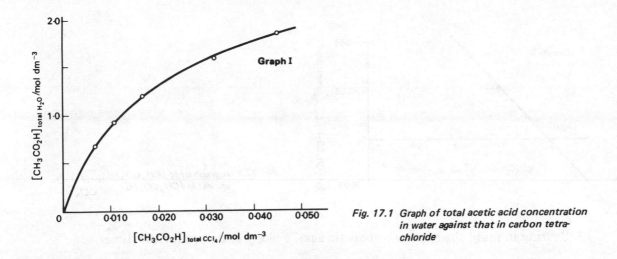

Fig. 17.1 Graph of total acetic acid concentration in water against that in carbon tetra-chloride

7. $K_a = \dfrac{[H_{aq}^+][CH_3CO_2^- aq]}{[CH_3CO_2H_{aq}]} = 10^{-4\cdot8}$ mol dm⁻³ Assuming that the hydrogen ion and the

acetate ion concentrations are equal and that the concentration of undissociated acetic acid molecules is effectively equal to the total concentration of acetic acid in the aqueous layer, it can be shown that 1 M and 2 M aqueous acetic acid solutions are approximately 0·4% and 0·3% ionized, respectively. Inspection shows that the curvature of Graph 1 could not be the result of assuming that:

$$[CH_3CO_2H]_{undiss} = [CH_3CO_2H]_{total\ H_2O}$$

8. Carbon tetrachloride is a non-polar liquid of low dielectric constant. As such there can be little attraction between CCl₄ molecules and ions and so carbon tetrachloride will not encourage ionization of the acetic acid.

9. The expression for the equilibrium constant of the association reaction is:

$$K_{ass} = \frac{[(CH_3CO_2H)_n]^{\frac{1}{n}}}{[CH_3CO_2H]_{unass\ in\ CCl_4}}$$

10. From question 9: $[(CH_3CO_2H)_n] = K_{ass}^n [CH_3CO_2H]_{unass.\ in\ CCl_4}^n$

Substituting this value for $[(CH_3CO_2H)_n]$ in equation (iii) (See Assignment Sheet)

we get $[CH_3CO_2H]_{total\ CCl_4} = n\,K_{ass}^n [CH_3CO_2H]_{unass.\ in\ CCl_4}^n$

11. From the partition coefficient expression

$[CH_3CO_2H]_{unass\ in\ CCl_4} = K_{PC}[CH_3CO_2H]_{unass.\ in\ H_2O} = K_{PC}[CH_3CO_2H]_{total\ in\ H_2O}$

12. Substituting the above value for $[CH_3CO_2H]_{unass.\ in\ CCl_4}$ in the expression obtained in answering question 10:

$$[CH_3CO_2H]_{total\ CCl_4} = n\,K_{ass}^n (K_{PC}[CH_3CO_2H]_{total\ H_2O})^n$$

Taking logarithms:

$$\lg[CH_3CO_2H]_{\text{total } CCl_4} = \lg(n\, K_{\text{ass}}^{n} K_{PC}^{n}) + n\, \lg[CH_3CO_2H]_{\text{total } H_2O}$$

Thus, since $\lg(n\, K_{\text{ass}}^{n} K_{PC}^{n})$ will be constant for a fixed temperature, Graph 2 should be linear with a gradient of n. Typical results give a value of about 1·9 for n, suggesting that acetic acid is largely dimerized in carbon tetrachloride.

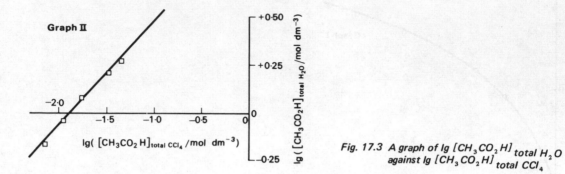

Fig. 17.3 A graph of $\lg[CH_3CO_2H]_{\text{total } H_2O}$ against $\lg[CH_3CO_2H]_{\text{total } CCl_4}$

13. Bearing in mind the structure of acetic acid, a likely structure for the dimer is:

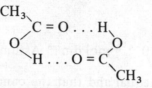

14. Hydrogen bonding is thought to be responsible for holding the two acetic acid molecules together. Hydrogen bonds rarely have strengths in excess of 10% of the strength of a normal covalent O—H bond.

More rigorous procedure for determining n

$[CH_3CO_2H]_{\text{total } CCl_4} = [CH_3CO_2H]_{\text{unass. in } CCl_4} + n\,[(CH_3CO_2H)_n] \ldots$ Equation (ii)

Using the expressions developed in answering questions 9 - 12, it can be shown that

$[CH_3CO_2H]_{\text{total } CCl_4} = K_{PC}[CH_3CO_2H]_{\text{total } H_2O} + nK_{\text{ass}}^{n}K_{PC}^{n}[CH_3CO_2H]_{\text{total } H_2O}^{n}$

Thus $\dfrac{[CH_3CO_2H]_{\text{total } CCl_4}}{[CH_3CO_2H]_{\text{total } H_2O}} = K_{PC} + n\, K_{\text{ass}}^{n}K_{PC}^{n}[CH_3CO_2H]_{\text{total } H_2O}^{n-1}$

By plotting the left-hand side of this equation against $[CH_3CO_2H]_{\text{total } H_2O}$, $[CH_3CO_2H]^2_{\text{total } H_2O}$ etc., it can be shown that the experimental data are consistent with a small value for K_{PC} together with a value of 2 for n.

Since this procedure rests on trial-and-error reasoning, it was felt that the Assignment Sheet should be based on the log-log graph treatment. The latter method is useful in solving the great majority of more advanced problems.

FURTHER PROJECTS

Predict the effects of repeating the experiment:
(a) using a 1 M solution of sodium acetate in water instead of pure water.
(b) using chloroform or dichloromethane instead of carbon tetrachloride.

REFERENCE

Chemical Principles in Practice Experiment 10, Ed. Jerry A. Bell, Addison-Wesley (1967).

Assignment 18

Determination of an Equilibrium Constant-A Partition Coefficient Study

INTRODUCTION

Iodine is very soluble in the covalent solvent benzene, but has a very low solubility in pure water. Water and benzene are mutually immiscible. At 18°C it can be shown that when iodine is shaken up with any volumes of water and benzene, the ratio of the equilibrium concentration of iodine in benzene to that in water is always 130.

If some iodide ions are added to the water then it is found that much more iodine will dissolve in the aqueous layer than in the same volume of pure water. This is generally assumed to be due to the following equilibrium being set up in the aqueous layer:

$$I_{2 aq} + I_{aq}^- \rightleftharpoons I_{3 aq}^-$$
$$\text{triiodide ion}$$

If this explanation is correct the expression:

$$\frac{[I_{3 aq}^-] eq}{[I_{2 aq}] eq [I_{aq}^-] eq}$$

should be a constant for any fixed temperature, no matter what *initial* concentrations of iodine molecules and iodide ions are employed. This experiment sets out to establish whether this is so.

1. A mixture of solid iodine and solid potassium iodide is shaken with some benzene and some water. Assuming that the only solute species present in the system are I_2, K^+, I^- and I_3^-, which of these will you expect to dissolve to a significant extent in both solvents? Why?

2. By what physical methods would it be possible to check up on the exact identity of the solute species in the benzene layer?

3. Consider a solute in equilibrium with two immiscible solvents. If some of the solute is removed from one of the solvents and the system is again shaken up until equilibrium is reestablished, what is the relation between the ratio of the solute concentrations in the two solvents in the first place and the ratio when equilibrium is reestablished?

EXPERIMENTAL PROCEDURE

Solution X consists of iodine dissolved in benzene (approximately $40g \, dm^{-3}$)
Solution Y is an aqueous solution of potassium iodide the exact concentration of which you will be told

Table 1:

Mixture	Solution X/cm³	Pure benzene/cm³	Solution Y/cm³	Distilled water/cm³
A	25	0	25·0	0·0
B	20	5	20·0	5·0
C	15	10	15·0	10·0
D	10	15	10·0	15·0
E	5	20	5·0	20·0

You will be instructed to prepare one of the above mixtures. In doing so a measuring cylinder is accurate enough for dispensing both Solution X and pure benzene. However, both Solution Y and the distilled water must be carefully measured out from the burettes provided directly into a separating funnel. Shake the mixture thoroughly in the stoppered separating funnel for at least two minutes and then allow the two layers to separate.

(a) Using a pipette and a pipette filler (benzene is both inflammable and toxic), run 10·0cm³ of the benzene layer into a small conical flask and titrate this with 0·1 M sodium thiosulphate solution. Thorough shaking (it is best to stopper the flask) is necessary throughout this titration and the sodium thiosulphate should be added very slowly. The end-point is reached when the red colour of iodine in benzene suddenly goes pale after the addition of one drop of the thiosulphate solution and thorough shaking. Starch indicator should *not* be used. The titration should be repeated. Record your results in Table 2.

(b) Pipette two 10·0cm³ portions of the aqueous layer into conical flasks and titrate these against 0·02 M sodium thiosulphate solution, this time adding a little starch solution shortly before the end-point. Again, record your readings in Table 2.

4. What is the equation for the reaction of iodine molecules with thiosulphate ions? Knowing this, use your experiment data to complete Table 2.

Table 2:
Mixture studied: ....

	Benzene Layer		Aqueous Layer	
Titration...............................	(a)i	(a)ii	(b)i	(b)ii
Burette readings				
Burette readings				

Volume of 0·1 M $S_2O_3^{2-}$
solution used /cm³   Vol of 0·02 M
                                            $S_2O_3^{2-}$ /cm³

Moles of $S_2O_3^{2-}$ used per titration

Moles of iodine per 10cm³ of layer

Iodine concentration of benzene
layer ($[I_{2(ben)}]_{eq}$ /mol dm⁻³) $[Iodine_{(aq)}]_{eq}$ /mol dm⁻³

5. Assuming: (i) your data from titration (a), (ii) that the iodine exists solely as free I_2 molecules in the benzene layer and (iii) the value of the partition coefficient for I_2 between benzene and water (see Introduction):
calculate the free I_2 molecule concentration in the aqueous layer, $[I_{2(aq)}]_{eq}$

6. Why does your answer to question 5 differ from $[Iodine_{(aq)}]_{eq}$, calculated in Table 2?

7. Which of the following expressions represents the total iodine concentration in the aqueous layer, $[Iodine_{(aq)}]_{eq}$, which you calculated in Table 2:

(i) $[I_{2(aq)}]_{eq} + [I^-_{(aq)}]_{eq}$? (ii) $[I_{2(aq)}]_{eq} + [I_3^-_{(aq)}]_{eq}$? (iii) $[I^-_{(aq)}]_{eq} + [I_3^-_{(aq)}]_{eq}$?

8. From your answers to question 5 and question 7, calculate a value for the equilibrium concentration of the triiodide ion in the aqueous phase, $[I_3^-_{(aq)}]_{eq}$.

9. Knowing the volume and concentration of Solution Y which you used, calculate the *total* iodide concentration in your aqueous layer, $[I^-_{(aq)}]$ total:

10. Which of the following expressions will equal $[I^-_{(aq)}]$ total:

(i) $[I^-_{(aq)}]$ eq? (ii) $[I^-_{(aq)}]$ eq + $[I_{2(aq)}]$ eq? (iii) $[I^-_{(aq)}]$ eq + $[I^-_{3(aq)}]$ eq?

(iv) $[I^-_{(aq)}]$ eq + $3[I^-_{3(aq)}]$ eq?

11. Using your answers to questions 8–10, together with the suggested equation for the iodine-iodide-triiodide equilibrium, calculate a value for the free iodide ion concentration at equilibrium in the aqueous phase of your mixture, $[I^-_{(aq)}]$ eq.

12. What is your value for the equilibrium constant K for the reaction of iodine molecules with iodide ions to form the triiodide ion? (Use answers to questions 8, 5 and 11). Collect data from other students and complete Table 3.

Table 3:

Mixture	A	B	C	D	E
Volume of 0·02 M $S_2O_3^{2-}$ needed for 10cm³ of H_2O layer /cm³					
Volume of 0·10 M $S_2O_3^{2-}$ needed for 10cm³ of C_6H_6 layer /cm³					
$[I_{2(ben)}]$ eq /mol dm⁻³					
$[I_{2(aq)}]$ eq /mol dm⁻³					
$[Iodine_{(aq)}]$ eq /mol dm⁻³					
$[I^-_{3(aq)}]$ eq /mol dm⁻³					
$[I^-_{(aq)}]$ total /mol dm⁻³					
$[I^-_{(aq)}]$ eq /mol dm⁻³					

Equilibrium Constant, $K = \dfrac{[I^-_{3(aq)}]\,eq}{[I_{2(aq)}]\,eq\,[I^-_{(aq)}]\,eq}$ /mol⁻¹ dm³

13. Try to assess the accuracy of the experimental results. Are you justified in reaching the conclusion that, within experimental error, the above values for K are constant?

14. Why was more care needed in measuring out Solution Y and the distilled water than Solution X and benzene?

Notes 18

Standard: **

Time required: 1½ hours for the practical work; a further hour for calculation and answering questions

Reagents required:

benzene

Solution X: Iodine dissolved in benzene [approx, $40g\ dm^{-3}$]. The exact strength need not be known. ($250cm^3$)

N.B. This volume is adequate for the preparation of 10 mixtures.

Solution Y: An aqueous solution of potassium iodide containing $20\cdot0g$ of KI per dm^3 of solution. The total volume needed will be equal to that of Solution X. ($250cm^3$)

$0\cdot10$ M sodium thiosulphate solution. [$24\cdot8g\ Na_2S_2O_3 . 5H_2O$ per dm^3 of solution] ($75cm^3$)

$0\cdot02$ M sodium thiosulphate solution. [$4\cdot96g\ Na_2S_2O_3 . 5H_2O$ per dm^3 of solution] ($50cm^3$)

Distilled water ($100cm^3$)

Apparatus required:

$25cm^3$ measuring cylinder

$100cm^3$ separating funnel with stopper

$10cm^3$ pipette

pipette filler

2 conical flasks with bungs

a burette

It is convenient to have a further 4 burettes for communal use (2 for distilled water and 2 for Solution Y)

Introduction and notes on experimental procedure

The practical work here is fundamentally very simple, though, unless care is taken to ensure reasonable technique, it is not difficult to get erratic results. Experience shows that most students find the calculation difficult and so, in the interests of simplicity, no attempt has been made to present this experiment as an open-ended study of the equilibrium principle. It is assumed that students will have met the equilibrium law and discussed equilibrium constants before they undertake this experiment.

The experimental procedure could be improved by

(i) direct measurement of the partition coefficient of I_2 between pure water and benzene

(ii) determination of the total iodine concentration in the aqueous layer by oxidation of iodide ions to iodine with nitrous acid, followed by titration with sodium thiosulphate. This latter procedure would avoid the less desirable operation of adding exact volumes of water and standard potassium iodide solution. It would, however, prolong the practical work and make the calculation slightly more difficult.

After shaking the mixtures until equilibrium has been established, it may be found useful to run off the bottom layer from the separating funnel into a boiling tube or a small beaker.

102

Sample data and notes on questions

1. I_2 molecules should be the only species found in significant concentration in both water and benzene. Ionic solutes have very low solubilities in non-polar, covalent solvents.

2. Conductance studies of solutions of iodine in benzene should establish the absence of ionic solutes. The depression of the freezing point of benzene, induced by dissolving a known mass of iodine in a known mass of benzene, should show that the solute has a molecular weight of 254, i.e. I_2.

3. The first paragraph of the introduction to the students' sheets gives sufficient information to deduce that the removal of some solute from one phase *should* have *no* effect on the ratios of the solute concentrations in the two phases at equilibrium. This question is asked in the hope that it will subsequently help students to appreciate that the removal of some I_2 from the aqueous phase by forming I_3^- will have no effect on the I_2 partition coefficient.

4. The equation for the reaction taking place during the titration is:

$$2 \, S_2O_3^{2-}{}_{(aq)} + I_{2\,(aq)} = S_4O_6^{2-}{}_{(aq)} + 2 \, I^-_{(aq)}$$

5. If $\dfrac{[I_2\,(ben)]_{eq}}{[I_2\,(aq)]_{eq}} = 130$ then $[I_2\,(aq)]_{eq} = \dfrac{[I_2\,(ben)]_{eq}}{130}$

6. As $S_2O_3^{2-}$ ions are added to a mixture of I_2 and I_3^-, the I_2 molecules react according to the equation noted in the answer to question 4. Removal of I_2 results in the dissociation of some I_3^- to form more I_2. Thus, the colour of the I_2 molecules will not disappear until enough sodium thiosulphate has been added to shift the equilibrium:

$$I_2\,(aq) + I^-_{(aq)} \rightleftharpoons I_3^-\,(aq)$$

entirely to the left.

7. Thus $[\text{Iodine}_{(aq)}]_{eq} = [I_2\,(aq)]_{eq} + [I_3^-\,(aq)]_{eq}$

8. It follows that $[I_3^-\,(aq)]_{eq} = [\text{Iodine}_{(aq)}]_{eq} - \dfrac{[I_2\,(ben)]_{eq}}{130}$

9. If the mixture studied involved y cm³ of Solution Y and if the latter contained 20·0g of KI per dm³ of solution, then:

$$[I^-_{(aq)}]_{total} = \frac{y}{25} \cdot \frac{20 \cdot 0}{166} \text{ mol dm}^{-3}$$

10. Since the formation of each I_3^- ion involves only one iodide ion:

$$[I^-_{(aq)}]_{total} = [I^-_{(aq)}]_{eq} + [I_3^-\,(aq)]_{eq}$$

11. Thus: $[I^-_{(aq)}]_{eq} = [I^-_{(aq)}]_{total} - [I_3^-\,(aq)]_{eq}$ and values for $[I^-_{(aq)}]_{total}$ and for $[I_3^-\,(aq)]_{eq}$ have been calculated in answering questions 9 and 8, respectively.

12. Values for the equilibrium constant K are listed at the foot of Table 3

Sample Data for Table 3
These data were obtained on a day when room temperature was about 292 K

Mixture	A	B	C	D	E
Volume of 0·02 M $S_2O_3^{2-}$ needed for 10cm³ of the H_2O layer (/cm³)	24·0	16·2	9·8	4·7	1·5
Volume of 0·10 M $S_2O_3^{2-}$ needed for 10cm³ of the C_6H_6 layer (/cm³)	25·0	21·2	16·0	10·8	9·4
$[I_{2(ben)}]_{eq}$ (/mol dm⁻³)	0·125	0·106	0·080	0·054	0·047
$[I_{2(aq)}]_{eq}$ (/mol dm⁻³)	0·00096	0·00082	0·00062	0·00041	0·00036
$[Iodine_{(aq)}]_{eq}$ (/mol dm⁻³)	0·024	0·0162	0·0098	0·0047	0·0015
$[I_{3(aq)}^-]_{eq}$ (/mol dm⁻³)	0·023	0·0154	0·00918	0·00429	0·00114
$[I_{(aq)}^-]_{total}$ (/mol dm⁻³)	0·121	0·0968	0·0726	0·0484	0·0242
$[I_{(aq)}^-]_{eq}$ (/mol dm⁻³)	0·098	0·0814	0·0634	0·0441	0·0231

Equilibrium Constant $K =$

$$\frac{[I_{3(aq)}^-]_{eq}}{[I_{2(aq)}]_{eq}[I_{(aq)}^-]_{eq}} \quad \text{(/mol dm}^{-3}\text{)}$$

	A	B	C	D	E
	245	231	233	234	(137)

13. The accuracy of the experimental results varies from mixture to mixture, being least for Mixture E because of the extremely small titres for the aqueous layer. For mixtures A–D, however, the experimental values for K usually vary by less than 5%. In most cases it would seem reasonable to ascribe this variation to experimental error.

14. Unless the initial composition of the aqueous phase is known with reasonable precision, it is impossible to calculate a value for the equilibrium iodide ion concentration in the aqueous phase. (See question 11)
The literature (*Stability Constants*, Chem. Soc. Sp. Pub. 17(1964) suggests values of K of the order of 800, and it would be interesting to establish why values of K found by this experiment are low and yet usually constant. A colorimetric study of the system at greater dilutions should give useful data for comparison.
At lower temperatures K becomes bigger (263 mol⁻¹ dm³ at a temperature of about 288K) showing that the formation of the triiodide ion is an exothermic reaction.

FURTHER PROJECTS

1. Can the equilibrium constant K be determined colorimetrically?
2. Determine the enthalpy of the equilibrium by studying the variation of K with temperature.

REFERENCE

Chemical Principles in Practice, Experiment 11, Ed. Jerry A. Bell, Addison-Wesley (1967).
This reference contains a very useful discussion of the iodine-complex iodide system.

Assignment 19

An Investigation of the Variation of Boiling Point, With Composition, for Different Mixtures of Two Immiscible Liquids

INTRODUCTION

The boiling point of a liquid depends upon its molecular weight and the forces of attraction between the molecules. If two different liquids are mixed, the forces of attraction between different molecules may be, (a) greater than the forces between identical molecules in the pure liquids, (b) weaker than the forces between identical molecules or (c) approximately the same as the forces between identical molecules.

1. What effect do you think the three different results of mixing two miscible liquids, (a), (b) and (c) outlined above, will have on the boiling points of the liquids?

EXPERIMENTAL WORK

(I) Variation of Boiling Point, with Composition, using Chloroform/Acetone Mixtures

Place 10·0cm³ of chloroform, with a few pieces of pumice, in a 50cm³ round-bottomed flask, fitted with a thermometer and reflux condenser (as shown in the diagram).

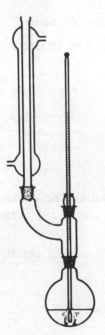

Figure 19.1

Determine the boiling point of the liquid by warming the flask over a flame, just large enough to cause the liquid to boil. Record the boiling point as the temperature shown on the thermometer after it has become steady. Remove the flame to a safe distance and add 2·0cm³ of acetone, mix, and determine the boiling point of this mixture. After this determination, add a further 3·0cm³ of acetone and determine the boiling point of this

105

mixture. Add a further 5·0cm³ of acetone and determine the boiling point of this mixture.

Empty the flask, well away from any flames, allow the flask to dry and add to it 10·0cm³ of acetone. Determine the boiling point of this liquid and of the mixtures obtained by adding, in succession, 2·0cm³ and 3·0cm³ of chloroform. Record the results as shown below:

Volume of chloroform/cm³	10·0	10·0	10·0	10·0	5·0	2·0	0·0
Volume of acetone/cm³	0·0	2·0	5·0	10·0	10·0	10·0	10·0
Percentage of acetone, by volume							
Boiling point/°C							

Plot the boiling point of the mixtures, and the pure liquids, against the percentage composition, by volume.

2. In the literature on the subject, boiling point is normally plotted against mole %. How could your values of percentage composition, by volume, be converted to mole %.

3. What explanation can you give for the shape of your graph, in terms of the forces of attraction between the molecules?

4. If there is this interaction between the molecules of these compounds, what temperature changes would you expect to observe on mixing the two liquids?

Devise, and carry out an experiment to investigate the variation of change in temperature (or heat change) on mixing, with the percentage composition by volume, of chloroform/ acetone mixtures.

5. How do these results compare with those for the variation of boiling point with composition?

6. What explanation can you give for this?

(II) Variation of Boiling Point, with Composition, using *n*-Hexane/Acetone Mixtures

Repeat the experiment, as above, but substituting normal hexane for the chloroform throughout. Record the results as shown below:

Volume of *n*-hexane/cm³	10·0	10·0	10·0	10·0	5·0	2·0	0·0
Volume of acetone/cm³	0·0	2·0	5·0	10·0	10·0	10·0	10·0
Percentage of acetone, by volume							
Boiling point/°C							

7. Plot the boiling point of the mixtures, and the pure liquids, against the percentage composition by volume. What does the shape of the graph suggest about the forces between the molecules?

8. Predict what temperature changes you would expect to observe on mixing the two liquids in different proportions?

Devise and carry out an experiment to test your predictions.

Notes 19

Standard: *

Time required: 1½ hours is sufficient for each part of the experiment. If done as a class co-operative experiment 1½ hours is sufficient for the whole.

Reagents required:
chloroform	$(50cm^3)$
acetone	$(120cm^3)$
n-hexane (not mixed hexanes)	$(50cm^3)$

pumice or suitable anti-bumping granules

N.B. The volumes of reagents specified are sufficient to produce one complete set of results

Apparatus required:

1 x $50cm^3$ flask, round-bottomed (Quickfit B14/23 Cat. no. FR 50/1S)

1 x flaskhead adaptor (Quickfit B14/23   Cat. no. MA 1/11)

1 x thermometer pocket (Quickfit B14/23   Cat. no. SH 4A)

1 x Liebig water condenser (Quickfit B14/23   Cat. no. C1/11)

1 x thermometer covering the range 0–100°C

2 x $10cm^3$ measuring cylinders

2 x boiling tubes

Notes on questions and typical results

1(a) If two miscible liquids, A and B, are mixed, and the forces of attraction between molecules of A and molecules of B are greater than the forces of attraction between molecules of A, and also greater than the forces of attraction between molecules of B, then the addition of one liquid to the other will raise its boiling point. The boiling point/composition graph will show a maximum value of boiling point, greater than that of either of the two liquids.

(b) If the forces of attraction between molecules of A and molecules of B are weaker than the forces between identical molecules, the addition of one liquid to the other will lower its boiling point, and the boiling point/composition graph will show a minimum value of boiling point, lower than the boiling point of either of the two liquids.

(c) If the forces of attraction between molecules of A and molecules of B are approximately the same as the forces between identical molecules, then the addition of the more volatile liquid to the less volatile liquid will lower its boiling point, and the addition of the less volatile liquid to the more volatile one will raise its boiling point. The boiling point/composition graph will show that the boiling point of the mixture is between the values for the two pure liquids.

It is important to emphasise the need for *caution* in handling the liquids, some of which are highly inflammable. All flames, in the vicinity, should be extinguished when the liquids are placed in the apparatus, and when the condenser is removed. It is important to emphasise that a small flame must be used if the temperature reading on the thermometer is to be close to the boiling point of the mixture, originally placed in the flask. If the liquid is boiling strongly, and a large amount of it is thus in the vapour state, the composition of the liquid in the flask will differ from that originally produced.

(I) Results

Volume of chloroform/cm³	10·0	10·0	10·0	10·0	5·0	2·0	0·0
Volume of acetone/cm³	0·0	2·0	5·0	10·0	10·0	10·0	10·0
% of acetone, by volume	0·0	16·7	33·3	50·0	66·7	83·3	100·0
Boiling point/°C	59·5	62·5	63·5	62·0	60·0	57·5	55·5

2. To convert from percentage, by volume, to mole percent, one needs to know the density and molecular weight of each liquid.
Then taking the 10·0cm³ chloroform/5·0cm³ acetone mixture as an example,

Density of chloroform = 1·4 g cm⁻³   M.W. of chloroform = 119·5
Density of acetone   = 0·8 g cm⁻³   M.W. of acetone   = 58

Hence number of moles of chloroform $= \dfrac{10\cdot0 \times 1\cdot4}{119\cdot5} = 11\cdot7 \times 10^{-2}$ moles

number of moles of acetone $= \dfrac{5\cdot0 \times 0\cdot8}{58} = 6\cdot9 \times 10^{-2}$ moles

Total number of moles $= 18\cdot6 \times 10^{-2}$ moles

Hence mole percent of chloroform $= \dfrac{11\cdot7}{18\cdot6} \times 100\%$; Mole percent of acetone $= \dfrac{6\cdot9}{18\cdot6} \times 100\%$

Mole percent of chloroform $= 63\%$; mole percent of acetone $= 37\%$

3. The graph shows a maximum boiling point mixture of composition approximately 33% by volume of acetone (i.e. approximately 37 mole percent of acetone). This suggests that the forces of attraction between acetone and chloroform molecules are greater than those between identical molecules, and that maximum interaction occurs in a mixture in which the molar ratio is slightly less than 2 of chloroform: 1 of acetone. Both acetone and chloroform are polar molecules, and it may be that hydrogen bonding occurs between the oxygen atom in acetone and the hydrogen atom in chloroform.

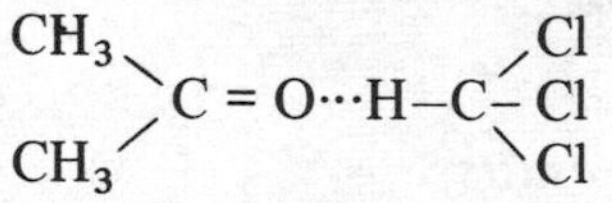

$$\begin{array}{c} CH_3 \\ \diagdown \\ \diagup \\ CH_3 \end{array} C = O \cdots H - C \begin{array}{c} \diagup Cl \\ - Cl \\ \diagdown Cl \end{array}$$

Furthermore, it may be that each of the lone pairs of electrons on the oxygen atom of the acetone is able to interact with a separate chloroform molecule to some extent. This would explain why the molar ratio is nearly 2 : 1.

4. If this interaction occurs, one would expect energy, in the form of heat, to be liberated as the formation of a hydrogen bond is an exothermic process. Thus, on mixing, a temperature rise would be expected.
It is possible to investigate the temperature change, on mixing different proportions of acetone and chloroform, using a boiling tube and a total volume of 10cm³ of the mixed liquids, in each case. Rapid mixing is essential in order to achieve the maximum temperature change.

Results

% acetone, by volume	20	40	50	60	80
temperature rise/°C	7·5	9·5	9·5	8·0	4·0

5. The graph of temperature rise against percentage composition by volume shows a similar pattern to that obtained with the variation of boiling points, although the peak is slightly displaced.

108

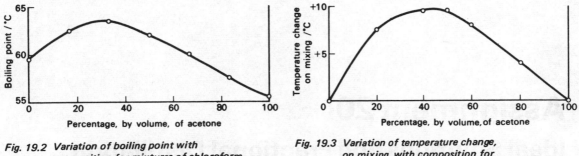

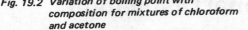

Fig. 19.2 *Variation of boiling point with composition for mixtures of chloroform and acetone*

Fig. 19.3 *Variation of temperature change, on mixing, with composition for mixtures of chloroform and acetone*

6. The two graphs suggest that, on mixing these two liquids, interaction between molecules of acetone and molecules of chloroform occurs, releasing energy as the stronger bonds are formed. This is the type of interaction described in question 1(a)

(II) Results

Volume of n-hexane/cm^3	10·0	10·0	10·0	10·0	5·0	2·0	0·0
Volume of acetone/cm^3	0·0	2·0	5·0	10·0	10·0	10·0	10·0
Percentage of acetone by volume	0·0	16·7	33·3	50·0	66·7	83·3	100·0
Boiling point/°C	67·0	51·0	49·5	48·5	49·5	50·5	55·5

7. The graph shows a minimum boiling point at approximately 50% of acetone by volume. This suggests that the forces of attraction between molecules of acetone and n-hexane are weaker than the forces between identical molecules.

8. If the forces of attraction between molecules of acetone and n-hexane are weaker than those of the pure liquids, one would expect that on mixing the thermal motion of the molecules would cause rupture of some of the links between identical molecules, and this may require energy, so that the net result of mixing would be a fall in temperature.

Results:

% acetone by volume	20	40	50	60	80
temperature drop/°C	2·5	3·5	3·8	3·3	2·0

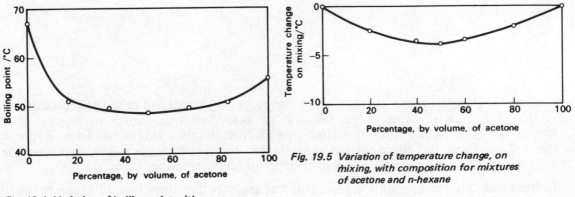

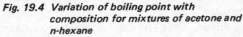

Fig. 19.4 *Variation of boiling point with composition for mixtures of acetone and n-hexane*

Fig. 19.5 *Variation of temperature change, on mixing, with composition for mixtures of acetone and n-hexane*

Assignment 20
Ideal Solutions and Fractional Distillation

Place 12·0cm³ of toluene in a 50cm³ round-bottomed flask, add a few pieces of pumice and set up the apparatus as shown in Figure 19.1. Determine the boiling-point of the toluene, by warming the flask over a flame just large enough to cause the liquid to boil. Record the temperature shown on the thermometer, as soon as it becomes steady, and estimate the possible error in the determination of the boiling-point of the toluene.

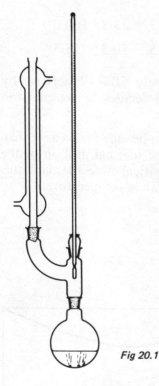

Fig 20.1

Remove the flame to a safe distance, allow the contents to cool and raise the thermometer so that the bulb is opposite the side-arm of the adapter as shown in Figure 20.1. Reheat the flask with a flame just large enough to maintain a ring of condensing vapour about 2cm above the thermometer bulb. Record the steady temperature shown on the thermometer and estimate the possible error in this determination.

1. What does this temperature represent if one assumes that there is equilibrium between the vapour and the liquid condensed on the thermometer bulb?
Add 3·0cm³ of benzene to the toluene in the flask, ensure that the two liquids are mixed and repeat the procedure as described above for toluene. Record the results in the chart on the next page.
Complete the experiment by following the same procedure for each of the mixtures. In

110

the case of mixture 5, add the benzene first and determine the results for pure benzene before adding the toluene.

Plot a graph of boiling-point of the original mixture (and the pure liquids) against the percentage by volume of benzene.

2. What property of pure liquids is illustrated by the results you have obtained?

3. How does the boiling point of each distillate compare with that of the original mixture from which it came?

4. What does this suggest about the composition of the distillate? Express your answer in terms of the proportion of the more volatile component relative to the proportion of it in the original mixture.

5. What determines the boiling point (at constant pressure, of course) of a mixture of benzene and toluene?

6. Well then, does the boiling point of a mixture of benzene and toluene enable the composition of it to be determined?

Add to your first graph a plot of the temperature at which each distillate is produced (i.e. the boiling point of the mixture from which it was obtained) against its composition, expressed as percentage by volume of benzene.

7. What can you say about the boiling point of mixtures of benzene and toluene relative to the values for the pure liquids?

8. Two liquids are said to behave like an ideal solution if the boiling points of all mixtures of the two liquids, in any proportions, are between the values for the pure liquids. How would you classify mixtures of benzene and toluene on this criterion?

Mixture number	1	2	3	4	5		
Vol. of benzene/cm^3	3·0	6·0	7·5	9·0	12·0	pure	pure
Vol. of toluene/cm^3	12·0	9·0	7·5	6·0	3·0	benzene	toluene
b.p. of original mixture/°C							
b.p. of distillate/°C							
% by volume of benzene in original mixture							
% by volume of benzene in distillate							

Ideal solutions are also characterized by obeying Raoult's law over the whole range of concentrations and at all temperatures.

The expression of Raoult's law which enables the calculation of the vapour pressure above an ideal solution is:

$$p_s = (\frac{n_a}{n_a + n_b}) p_a + (\frac{n_b}{n_a + n_b}) p_b \quad \text{where,}$$

$$p_s = x_a.p_a + (1-x_a).p_b$$

p_s = saturated v.p. of the solution
p_a, p_b = saturated v.p. of components a and b
n_a, n_b = amounts of a and b, usually expressed in moles.
x_a, x_b = mole fractions of a and b

9. Using this expression of Raoult's law, calculate the mole % of benzene in the vapour above a liquid mixture of 25mol % benzene and 75mol % of toluene at 40°C.

S.V.P. of benzene at 40°C = 178mm of Hg or 23·7kN m^{-2}

S.V.P. of toluene at 40°C = 59mm of Hg or 7·8kN m^{-2}

(N.B. 1N m^{-2} is sometimes called a pascal and written 1 Pa)

10. The adherence to Raoult's law would suggest that mixing two liquids, which form an ideal solution does not alter the tendency of the molecules of each liquid to change into the vapour state. What does this imply about the forces of attraction between the molecules of these liquids? Express your answer in terms of the forces of attraction between identical molecules, and between molecules of one substance and those of the other.

Determine whether or not a heat change occurs on mixing equal volumes of benzene and toluene.

11. Does this agree with your answer to question 10? Explain.

12. Define the term 'ideal solution', incorporating the relevant results of your experiments.

Fractional Distillation

13. Using the graph you have drawn, explain what happens if a mixture of equal volumes of benzene and toluene is distilled, and the distillate is then re-distilled.

14. How many successive distillations would have to be performed to produce a sample of benzene which is more than 99% pure?

Each effective distillation stage in which equilibrium has been reached between liquid and vapour is referred to as a theoretical plate. In some fractionating columns, there are plates across the column, with holes in the plates so that vapour bubbles up through liquid which is running down the column.

15. Assuming that equilibrium is reached on each plate (i.e. one actual plate represents one theoretical plate) how many plates would be needed in the column if a mixture of benzene and toluene consisting of equal volumes of each is heated at the bottom of the column, and 99% pure benzene is wanted at the top of the column?

Some fractionating columns are packed uniformly with an inert material to provide a surface on which vapour condenses, and frequently in the case of columns with plates more than one actual plate is needed to achieve one effective distillation stage. For these situations it is more convenient to refer to the height of the column which is equivalent to one theoretical plate.

Fractionating columns are sometimes used for a process called 'topping and tailing', in which the liquid mixture to be separated is fed in to a position on the column, corresponding to the composition of the mixture. Heat is supplied at the bottom of the column the more volatile component is taken off at the top of the column and the less volatile at the bottom.

Let us assume you have a fractionating column, and can feed into it, at a constant rate, a supply of a benzene/toluene mixture consisting of 30% benzene–70% toluene, by volume, and that 95% pure benzene and 95% pure toluene are required from this. If the theoretical plate height, at this rate of feeding is 2 metres:

16. What height should the column be?

17. At what height should the mixture be introduced?

18. If the rate of supplying the original mixture were altered, what effect do you think this would have on the height equivalent to one theoretical plate?

Notes 20

Standard: **

Time required: 1½ hours practical work; 1½ hours interpretation and questions.

Reagents required:

   benzene (50cm^3)

   toluene (50cm^3)

   pumice (or suitable anti-bumping granules)

Apparatus required:

   1 x 50cm^3 round-bottomed flask (Quickfit B14/23   Cat. no. FR 50/1S)

   1 x flaskhead adapter (Quickfit B14/23   Cat. no. MA 1/11)

   1 x stirrer gland for thermometer (Quickfit B14/23) Cat. no. ST 5/2)

   1 x Liebig water condenser (Quickfit B14/23)   Cat. no. C 1/11)

   1 x thermometer covering range 0−100°C.

   2 x 10cm^3 measuring cylinders

   2 x boiling tubes

Notes on questions, practical details and typical results

It is important to adopt a standard technique for determining the boiling point of the mixture. If the flask is heated too strongly, a large proportion of the mixture will be in the vapour state and this will lead to inaccurate values for the boiling point. It is a good idea to have the highest ring of condensing vapour in the same place in each experiment.

1. If there is equilibrium between the liquid on the thermometer bulb and the vapour around it, this temperature represents the boiling point of the mixture with the composition of the vapour produced by boiling the mixture in the flask. If a large volume of vapour is produced, the composition of the mixture in the flask will not be the same as it was at the beginning of the experiment, hence the necessity not to boil too strongly.

Results:

Mixture number	1	2	3	4	5	6	7
Vol. of benzene/cm^3	3·0	6·0	7·5	9·0	12·0	pure benzene	pure toluene
Vol. of toluene/cm^3	12·0	9·0	7·5	6·0	3·0		
b.p. of original mixture/°C	101±1	92·5±1	91·5±1	87·5±1	83·0±1	79·5±1	108·5±1
b.p. of distillate/°C	96·0±1	89·0±1	86·0±1	83·5±1	80·5±1	80·5±1	108·5±1
% by volume of benzene in original mixture	20·0%	40·0	50·0	60·0	80·0	100·0	0·0
% by volume of benzene in distillate	30%	54	66	76	92	100	0

113

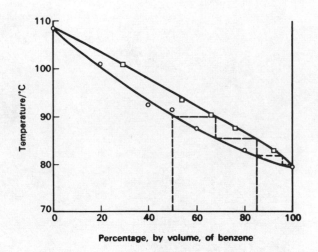

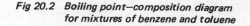

Fig 20.2 *Boiling point—composition diagram for mixtures of benzene and toluene*

2. The boiling point of the distillate is the same as the boiling point of the liquid from which it distilled. Thus on distillation, the temperature at which the pure liquid boils remains the same throughout the distillation.

3. The boiling point of the distillates (other than from the pure liquids) is, in each case lower than the boiling point of the mixture from which it distilled.

4. This suggests that the distillate contains a larger proportion of the more volatile component than does the mixture from which it distilled.

5. The boiling point of the mixture of benzene and toluene is determined by the proportions of the two components.

6. Yes. If a boiling point/composition graph has been drawn, the composition of a benzene-toluene mixture can be read from it, if the boiling point of the mixture is known.

7. The boiling point of mixtures of benzene and toluene have values between the boiling point of benzene and that of toluene.

8. In this respect mixtures of benzene and toluene behave like an ideal solution.

9. Using the form of Raoult's law.

$p_S = x_a. p_a + (1-x_a). p_b$

$p_S = (0.25 \times 178) + (0.75 \times 59)$mm of Hg or $p_S = (0.25 \times 23.7) + (0.75 \times 7.8)$kN m^{-2}

$p_S = 44.5 + 44.3$mm of Hg or $p_S = 5.9 + 5.9$kN m^{-2}

$p_S = 88.8$mm of mercury   or $p_S = 11.8$kN m^{-2}

Since the vapour pressure contribution of each component is proportional to the number of molecules of that component in the vapour phase, the mole % of benzene in the vapour is

$$x_{a_{vap}} \times 100 = \frac{44.5}{88.8} \times 100 \text{ or } \frac{5.9}{11.8} \times 100 \%$$

mole % of benzene in vapour = 50%

10. As ideal solutions obey Raoult's law it implies that the forces between identical molecules are very similar to the forces between benzene molecules and toluene molecules.

11. Only a very small heat change is observed on mixing benzene and toluene and this is in agreement with the implication referred to in question 10. If the forces of attraction between the molecules are not altered very much on mixing, one would not expect much energy in the form of heat to be evolved or absorbed.

12. The term 'ideal solution' is applied to a mixture of liquids, which obeys Raoult's law, has boiling points between the values for the pure liquids and is formed from the pure liquids without evolution or absorption of heat.

13. If a mixture of equal volumes of benzene and toluene is distilled, the mixture boils at 90°C and gives a distillate of 68% benzene. If this is distilled, the mixture boils at 85°C and gives a distillate of 85% benzene.

14. In order to produce a sample of benzene, greater than 99% purity, from the 50% mixture four successive distillations would be needed.

15. Assuming that one plate of a fractionating column represents one distillation stage, a column with four plates would be needed to obtain 99% benzene from a 50% mixture.

16. A total of nine theoretical plates would be needed, so the height of the column should be 18 metres.

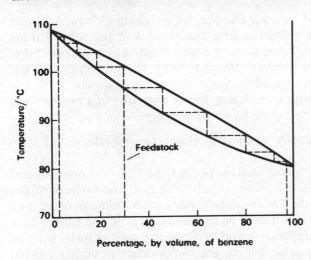
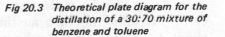

Fig 20.3 Theoretical plate diagram for the distillation of a 30:70 mixture of benzene and toluene

17. The 30% benzene–70% toluene mixture should be fed in at the height equivalent to the fourth theoretical plate i.e. at a height of 8 metres.

18. Increasing the rate of supply of the original mixture would probably mean that a greater height would be needed for equilibrium to be reached i.e. the height equivalent to one theoretical plate would be increased. Likewise a decrease in the rate of supply would decrease the height equivalent to one theoretical plate.

FURTHER PROJECT

Construct a fractionating column and investigate theoretical plate height, etc.

Assignment 21

Phase Diagram for the Naphthalene/ p-Nitrotoluene System - Eutectic Mixtures

Make up one of the mixtures as instructed by your teacher, by weighing a clean, dry, soft glass test tube (5 x 5/8inch) and then weighing the first component in the tube. Taking care not to contaminate the reagents, weigh the second component into the same tube. Warm the tube plus contents over a small bunsen flame to melt the mixture, cork the tube, and shake to make the mixture homogeneous. Cool the mixture slowly until it is about to crystallize, then cool rapidly under a cold tap. Break the tube in a mortar, and after separating the broken glass, crush the mixture to a fine powder.

1. Explain why the mixture is cooled slowly until it is about to crystallize and then cooled rapidly.

Introduce a sample of one of the mixtures into a melting point tube sealed at one end and tap down the mixture until a column of solid about 1-2cm long is at the bottom of the tube (N.B. Do not handle the tubes more than is absolutely essential as some melting may occur below blood temperature; in some cases it may be necessary to hold the tube with a cloth) Place the tube in a melting point apparatus, and arrange the rate of heating to be about 3°C rise per minute. Record in the table below, the temperature at which melting commences (this is usually indicated by the mixture settling down against the side of the tube) and the temperature at which the last particles of solid disappear. Follow the same procedure for pure samples of naphthalene and 1-methyl-4-nitrobenzene.

Sample number	1	2	3	4	5	6	7	8	9	10
Wt. of naphthalene/g	1·0	2·0	3·0	4·0	4·5	5·0	6·0	8·0	pure	pure
Wt. of 1-methyl-4-nitrobenzene/g	8·0	7·0	6·0	5·0	4·5	4·0	3·0	1·0	naphthalene	1-methyl-4-nitro-benzene
Temp. melting starts/°C										
Temp. solid disappears/°C										
Percentage by wt. of naphthalene										

Plot a graph of temperature at which melting starts, and temperature at which solid disappears against the percentage by weight of naphthalene. Use the same axes, but indicate the different plots in different colours.

2. What difference did you notice between the melting of pure solids and the melting of mixtures?

3. Does your graph suggest that mixtures of a certain composition will behave in a similar way to pure substances on melting? Explain.

4. The mixture which melts 'sharply' over a small temperature range is called the eutectic mixture. What composition do you predict for the eutectic mixture?

5. Since pure substances and eutectic mixtures have sharp melting points, how might one distinguish between a pure substance and a eutectic mixture?

6. Acetanilide (m.p.114°C) and o-acetotoluidide (m.p.112°C) are of similar appearance. If you were provided with a sample of a compound known to be either acetanilide or o-acetotoluidide, how could you identify it? You have available a known sample of acetanilide.

7. Using your graph explain what would happen if you started with a mixture of naphthalene and 1-methyl-4-nitrobenzene containing 20% of naphthalene at a temperature of 60°C and cooled it to 20°C?

8. From your graph predict the conditions under which you could have solid naphthalene, solid 1-methyl-4-nitrobenzene and the liquid in equilibrium.

9. Different types of solder can be made from mixtures of tin and lead. Assuming that the phase diagram of the tin/lead system is of similar shape to the one for the naphthalene/1-methyl-4-nitrobenzene system, what composition would you recommend for (a) plumber's solder (b) solder for use in electrical work? Give your reasons.

10. What other applications of eutectic mixtures can you think of?

Notes 21

Standard: *

Time required: This depends on how the practical is organised. It would take about 1½ hours if each student made up one mixture and determined its m.p. and that of the pure substances. If time is short the mixtures may be prepared beforehand and kept in stoppered bottles.

Reagents required:
- naphthalene (40g)
- 1-methyl-4-nitro-benzene (p-nitrotoluene) (40g)

N.B. (1) It may be necessary to recrystallize these substances in order to illustrate the sharp melting point of pure substances.

(2) The quantities specified are sufficient to produce a complete set of mixtures.

Apparatus required:
- soft-glass test tubes, with corks
- mortar and pestle
- chemical balance (preferably direct-reading)
- melting point tubes
- melting point apparatus (Gallenkamp electrically-heated apparatus works well, but the tradition oil-bath, or even a beaker of distilled water will do)
- cloth or insulated gloves to prevent warming melting-point tubes during filling

Notes on questions and typical results

1. Rapid crystallization of the whole sample is required to produce small crystals, so that, after crushing an intimate mixture of the two substances is obtained. If the tube is cooled rapidly, from well above the temperature at which it crystallizes, solid forms around the sides of the tube, and being a poor conductor of heat, the centre of the sample cools slowly, forming large crystals.

Results

Sample number	1	2	3	4	5	6	7	8	9	10
Wt. of naphthalene/g	1·0	2·0	3·0	4·0	4·5	5·0	6·0	8·0	pure	pure
Wt. of 1-methyl-4-nitrobenzene/g	8·0	7·0	6·0	5·0	4·5	4·0	3·0	1·0	naphthalene	1-methyl-4-nitrobenzene
Temp. melting starts/°C	28	28	27	28	27	28	29	29	79	50
Temp. solid disappears/°C	49	43	36	42	48	53	61	75	81	53
Percentage by wt. of naphthalene	11.1	22.2	33.3	44.4	50.0	55.5	66.7	88.9	100.0	0.0

118

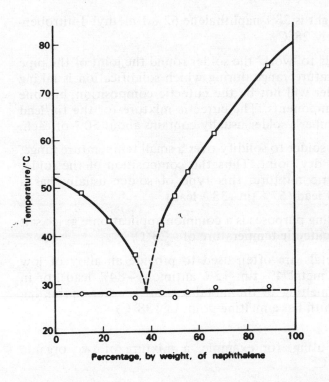

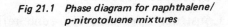

Fig 21.1 *Phase diagram for naphthalene/ p-nitrotoluene mixtures*

2. The pure substances melt over a small temperature range (2 or 3°C) whereas the mixtures melt over a large temperature range (9 to 46°C). The addition of small amounts of a second substance, lowers the melting-point of the first substance.

3. Continuation of the curves suggests that there are mixtures which melt over a small temperature range, as do pure substances.

4. The composition of the mixture which, according to the graph, should have a sharp melting-point is approximately 38% by weight of naphthalene.

5. To distinguish between a pure substance and a eutectic mixture, one could recrystallize from a suitable solvent. Recrystallization of a pure substance can only make its melting-point sharper; recrystallization of a eutectic mixture will alter its composition and thus the melting-point of the mixture will become less sharp.

6. To identify a sample which may be either acetanilide or *o*-acetotoluidide, one could add a sample of the acetanilide to the unknown sample. If the melting-point remained sharp, the sample must have been acetanilide; if the sample melted over a large temperature range, it must have been *o*-acetotoluidide. To eliminate the unlikely possibility that the eutectic mixture had been produced (giving a sharp melting-point), one could add a further quantity of acetanilide. If in both cases the melting-point remained sharp the sample must without doubt, have been acetanilide.

7. If a mixture of 20% naphthalene-80% 1-methyl-4-nitrobenzene at 60°C was cooled, the liquid would cool to about 45°C whereupon solid 1-methyl-4-nitrobenzene would start to separate and the rate of cooling of the mixture would decrease as the latent heat of freezing of the *p*-nitrotoluene was given out. As solid 1-methyl-4-nitrobenzene separates, the liquid mixture becomes richer in naphthalene and the temperature at which the solid 1-methyl-4-nitrobenzene separates becomes lower, until the composition of the liquid reaches that of the eutectic mixture. At this temperature and liquid composition, both solids separate out together, and the temperature remains steady until the mixture is entirely solid, the temperature then starts to drop again.

8. The conditions under which solid naphthalene, solid 1-methyl-4-nitrobenzene and the liquid mixture are in equilibrium are those when the composition is that of the eutectic mixture and the temperature is the melting-point of the mixture of this composition. This

will occur when the composition by weight is 38% naphthalene-62% 1-methyl-4-nitrobenzene and the temperature is approximately 28°C.

9. (a) Plumber's solder. A plumber needs to 'work' the solder round the joint of the pipe so he will require a fairly large temperature range during which solidification is taking place. Thus the composition of the solder will not be the eutectic composition, but one which contains more of one of the components. The eutectic mixture for the tin/lead system is about 62% tin—38% lead; plumber's solder usually contains about 50% of each.

(b) For electrical work, one requires the solder to solidify over a small temperature range, so that a shaky hand will not cause a 'dry' joint. Thus the composition of the solder should be close to that of the eutectic mixture; this type of solder usually has a composition of 2 parts of tin to 1 part of lead (67% tin—33% lead)

10. The use of eutectic mixtures for cooling purposes is a common application e.g. ice salt 23·6% sodium chloride—76·4% ice has a eutectic temperature of −23°C.

Eutectic mixtures of two or three metals are often used to provide an alloy of low melting-point for use in printing (type metal 4% tin—12% antimony—84% lead), or in automatic fire-extinguishers where the melting of the metal sets off a water- sprinkling system (fusible alloy; 43% tin—57% bismuth has a melting-point of 138°C)

FURTHER PROJECT

Construct apparatus for zone refining using, for example, a mixture of two organic compounds of melting point about 100 °C.

120

Assignment 22
Steam Distillation - Principles and Practice

INTRODUCTION
Fractional Distillation

If two liquids mix and form an ideal solution, it can be shown with the help of Raoult's Law that distillation will yield a distillate that will be richer in the more volatile component than the original mixture was. If this distillate is itself redistilled, the boiling point will be lower and the second distillate will be richer again than the first in the more volatile of the two liquids. In fact, for ideal solutions the boiling point depends on the composition of the mixture being distilled, and successive distillations (fractional distillation in effect) will result in the mixture being separated, the most volatile component being distilled off first.

1. What are the characteristics of an 'ideal' solution?

For an 'ideal' mixture of two volatile liquids, A and B, the total vapour pressure of the mixture, P_m, at any given temperature is given by the expressions:

$$P_m = p_A + p_B = m_A p_A^o + m_B p_B^o$$

where:

p_A^o and p_B^o are the saturated vapour pressures of the *pure* liquid A and B at the given temperature

p_A and p_B are the partial vapour pressures of A and B in the mixture at the given temperature

m_A and m_B are the mole fractions of A and B in the mixture

Now, if A and B are *mutually immiscible*, two liquid phases exist, pure A and *pure B*, each of which must have a mole fraction of one, irrespective of the relative amounts of A and B in the mixture.

In this case the above expression can be rewritten:

$$P_m = p_A^o + p_B^o$$

It follows that the vapour pressure of a mixture of immiscible liquids, at any given temperature, ought to be independent of the relative proportions in which the immiscible liquids are present.

By way of illustrating the principles of steam distillation, consider the following data:

20g of a pure, water immiscible substance, Y, and 80g of water were placed in a flask. Steam was passed continuously into the flask and the mixture was found to distil at a steady temperature of $t°C$ throughout the experiment. The distillate was collected in fractions, the first three of which had the following compositions:

	1st Fraction	2nd Fraction	3rd Fraction
Mass of water:	4·5g	1·8	4·5g
Mass of Y:	7·2g	2·9g	7·3g

Atmospheric pressure on the day was 101·3 kN m^{-2} (i.e. 760 mm of Hg). The saturated vapour pressure of water at t°C is 85·3 kN m^{-2} (i.e. 640 mm of Hg).
(N.B. 1 N m^{-2} is sometimes called a pascal and written 1 Pa)

2. What is the saturated vapour pressure of Y at t°C?

3. During the distillation, did the composition of (a) the distillate change? (b) the liquid left in the flask change?

4. Write down expressions for the ratio of the number of moles of water to the number of moles of $\dot{Y}$ in the distillate: (a) using the vapour pressure data only. (b) using the distillate compositions given above.

5. Calculate a rough value for the molecular weight of Y.

6. Was the boiling point of the distillate, t°C, greater or less than 100°C? Explain.

7. The vapour pressures show that Y is much less volatile than water (actually, pure Y boils at 157°C at standard atmospheric pressure) and yet the distillate contains nearly 70% of Y by weight. Try to explain why.

EXPERIMENTAL WORK

Weigh out about 2g of 1-hydroxy-2-nitrobenzene (o-nitrophenol) and 2g of 1-hydroxy-4-nitrobenzene (p-nitrophenol). Place these, together with about 50cm^3 of water in the distilling flask of the steam distillation apparatus. Connect the flask to the steam generator and turn on the water supply to the condenser. Carefully observe all changes taking place inside the condenser and check the temperature of distillation from time to time.

8. What was the appearance of the distillate in the condenser?

9. What was the temperature of distillation and did it remain more or less steady?
Solid material, which will collect in the condenser, can be allowed to accumulate there provided that the condenser does not become blocked. When most of the solid has been collected, it may be removed from the condenser by letting the water drain from the cooling jacket and allowing the steam to melt the solid in the condenser. The condenser jacket can then be refilled and distillation should be continued until there is little or no sign of solid or oil in the condenser. Keep the combined distillate C and pour the hot solution D which remains in the distilling flask into a beaker in order to allow it to cool.

10. What was the appearance of C?

11. What was the appearance of D after it had been allowed to cool?
Make solutions A and B by dissolving a crystal or two of 1-hydroxy-2-nitrobenzene and 1-hydroxy-4-nitrobenzene, respectively in 1-2cm^3 of distilled water. Add 2—3 drops of iron (III) chloride solution to each and record your observations. Repeat these tests using small portions of the liquor from C and D instead of A and B. Record these observations also.

12. What can you conclude as a result of testing, A, B, C and D with iron(III) chloride?
Filter both C and D and allow the two solids to dry at room temperature. Determine the melting point of these solids and compare them with the literature values for the two starting materials.

13. What can you conclude about the purity of the two solids?

14. In this experiment two solids of very similar formulae are separated by steam distillation. Suggest why one of these solids should be steam volatile while the other is not.

15. What other simple evidence (literature or personal observation) suggests that the intermolecular forces between the molecules of the steam volatile solid are weaker than those between molecules of the other solid?

16. What criteria dictate whether a substance can be steam distilled?

17. What other substances are commonly purified by steam distillation?

18. It is possible to achieve steam distillation by merely boiling the substance with excess water. Why is it conventional to pass steam into the distilling flask?

19. What are the advantages of steam distillation over ordinary distillation?

20. What are the main differences between steam distillation and fractional distillation?

Notes 22

Standard: **
Note:
Obtaining the quantitative data necessary to gain a thorough understanding of steam distillation is a time consuming and a somewhat tedious operation demanding a lot of care. Accordingly, the Assignment Sheets give sample data which can be analysed as a homework before the practical work is done.

Time required for experimental work: About an hour for the distillation, followed by about 30 minutes for the filtration and the iron(III) chloride tests. The solids can be left to dry at room temperature and their melting points determined in the next laboratory period.

Reagents required:
   1-hydroxy-2-nitrobenzene (*o*-nitrophenol) (2·5g)
   1-hydroxy-4-nitrobenzene (*p*-nitrophenol) (2·5g)
   iron(III) chloride solution (5cm^3)

Apparatus required:
   steam generator and steam delivery tube
   150cm^3 round-bottomed flask
   distilling apparatus
   thermometer (−10 to 110°C to read 1°C)
   150cm^3 beaker
   test-tubes
   filtration apparatus (preferably a small Buchner Funnel)
   Melting-point apparatus

Notes on experimental work and questions
Brief fractional distillation notes are provided on the Assignment Sheets by way of preliminary revision. It is very important to have the essential details of the former clear before steam distillation is tackled.

1. An 'ideal' solution is such that when the components are mixed, no volume change occurs and no heat is evolved or absorbed. Further, the solution obeys Raoult's Law.
The data analysis section is intended to be done for homework. Teachers may well wish to give a brief qualitative demonstration of the steam distillation of chlorobenzene (the data given are approximately typical of bromobenzene) immediately before the homework assignment is set.

2. The s.v.p. of Y at t°C must be 16·0 kN m^{-2} (i.e. 120 mm of Hg) as a solution or mixture will boil when the total vapour pressure becomes equal to the atmospheric pressure. Draw attention to the assumption that for immiscible liquids (or solids) each component in the mixture exerts its own characteristic vapour pressure. This vapour pressure is independent of the composition of the mixture (*cf.* fractional distillation) and depends only on the temperature.

3. (a) No. The ratio of the mass of water to the mass of Y is effectively constant for each fraction.

(b) Yes. The liquid in the flask becomes steadily depleted of Y.

4. (a) Since pressure is directly proportional to the number of molecules per unit volume:

$\dfrac{n_w}{n_y}$ in distillate $= \dfrac{p_w}{p_y} = \dfrac{85 \cdot 3}{16 \cdot 0}$ where n_w and n_y are the numbers of moles of water and of Y, respectively, in the distillate and p_w and p_y are their respective saturated vapour pressures at $t\,^\circ$C

(b) $\dfrac{n_w}{n_y} = \dfrac{1 \cdot 8}{18} \bigg/ \dfrac{2 \cdot 9}{\text{M.Wt. of } Y}$

5. By combining the two expressions for n_w/n_y:

$$\text{Molecular weight of } Y = \frac{85 \cdot 3}{16 \cdot 0} \times 2 \cdot 9 \times \frac{18}{1 \cdot 8} = 155$$

6. $t\,^\circ$C must be less than 100°C and always will be for any steam distillation carried out at a pressure of 101·3 kN m^{-2} (i.e. 760 mm of Hg). This is because distillation will always occur at a total pressure of 101·3 kN m^{-2} (if external pressure is standard) and pure water itself boils at 100°C (See also note to question 2)

7. The vapour pressures indicate the relative molar content of the distillate, but since the molecular weight of water is so low compared to the molecular weights of most other liquids, the composition of the distillate in terms of mass is less rich in water than we might have supposed. Compare the composition of the distillate in terms of mass with the corresponding initial composition in the distilling flask.

EXPERIMENTAL WORK

Check that:

(i) the steam generator has a long safety tube and that the generator is not more than half full of water. Ensure that the steam is supplied to the distilling flask by a short tube, with no loops in it where water might condense and get trapped.

(ii) steam is supplied steadily and that the flow is not so rapid that liquid may spray into the condenser

(iii) the rate of distillation does not exceed about 1 cm^3 minute^{-1}.

(iv) the volume of mixture in the distilling flask does not exceed about 100 cm^3

(v) the steam generator is disconnected immediately the distillation is completed

8. Pale yellow, oily drops are seen at the top of the condenser, congealing to give lumps of an orange-yellow solid in the condenser. Some of the material will crystallize in the receiving flask.

9. About 98°C ± 0·5°C. Steadiness depends on draughts etc.

10. A mixture of bright yellow lumps and pale yellow crystals.

11. Ideally, D should be allowed to cool overnight, whereupon beautiful, lemon-yellow, needle-like crystals will be deposited. If time is short, D may be cooled under the tap.
Solutions B and D should give violet colourations with iron(III) chloride (*cf.* phenol) whereas A and C should appear unaffected by the iron (III) chloride.

12. Steam distillation *seems* to have separated these two phenols, the 1-hydroxy-4-nitrobenzene remaining in the distilling flask. However, while the iron(III) chloride tests show that little or no 1-hydroxy-4-nitrobenzene has distilled over with C, they do not show whether there is any 1-hydroxy-2-nitrobenzene left in D. In order to check up on this the melting points are determined.

Typical values (obtained after drying the crystals for an hour by drawing air through them on a Buchner Funnel)

Solid C: 1·85g (filtered from 40cm³ of aqueous solution) with a melting point of 40–43°C (*cf.* 1-hydroxy-2-nitrobenzene 44°C)

Solid D: 0·45g (filtered from 100cm³ of aqueous solution) with a melting point of 107–111°C. (*cf.* 1-hydroxy-4-nitrobenzene 114°C)

13. The melting points should show that the samples are reasonably pure. If it is desired to recrystallize solid C, alcohol or methylated spirits should be used. Details can be found in most standard organic practical books.

The fact that steam distillation has resulted in a reasonable separation of these two compounds can be further checked by comparing the original masses of the compounds used with the masses of crystals obtained and taking their solubilities into account:

Approximate solubilities in water at room temperature:

1-hydroxy-2-nitrobenzene 0·25g/100g

1-hydroxy-4-nitrobenzene 1·60g/100g

14. If one solid is more volatile than another under the same conditions it is likely that the former has weaker intermolecular forces than the latter. In the case in question, *intra*molecular hydrogen bonding is possible in the 1-hydroxy-2-nitrobenzene isomer only. This causes a weakening of the *inter*molecular forces in this compound relative to those existing in the 1-hydroxy-4-nitro isomer, and results in the latter isomer being the most soluble in water and the least volatile of the two.

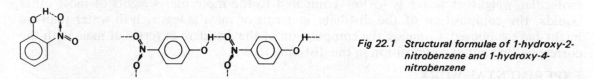

Fig 22.1 Structural formulae of 1-hydroxy-2-nitrobenzene and 1-hydroxy-4-nitrobenzene

15. The steam volatile isomer has a lower melting point and a lower boiling point than the other isomer. Also, it has a much more noticeable smell than 1-hydroxy-4-nitrobenzene. The latter, however, is only circumstantial evidence.

16. The substance to be steam distilled must be insoluble in water (or only slightly soluble) and should be appreciably volatile (i.e. have a vapour pressure at 100°C of not less than about 0·5 kN m⁻²).

17. Aminobenzene (aniline); nitrobenzene etc.

18. The steam bubbles prevent undue 'bumping' so that it is unnecessary to use pumice, etc. Furthermore, the steam replaces the water lost from the distilling flask. This last point is especially important if a large sample is being steam distilled. In semi-micro scale steam distillations, however, the steam generator is usually omitted, the aqueous suspension plus anti-bumping granules being heated directly.

19. Steam distillation is used to separate substances which have the characteristics listed in the notes on question 16 from non-volatile byproducts (e.g. salts and the tars which are an unwanted feature of many organic syntheses). It has the advantage over ordinary distillation in that the process occurs well below the boiling point of most substances. This is a very valuable property in the cases of substances which are very sensitive to oxidation or decomposition on heating (e.g. iodobenzene).

20. In steam distillation the composition of the distillate and the temperature of distillation remain constant, whereas in fractional distillation the temperature of distillation usually increases steadily throughout the process and the distillate becomes steadily richer in the less volatile component.

FURTHER WORK

It would be interesting to study the nitration of phenol with a view to determining:
(i) the ratio of the yields of the two isomeric products
(ii) the effect of the conditions of nitration (temperature, strength of acid, presence of urea etc.) on the ratio of the products

REFERENCE

For further discussion of steam distillation see:
Elementary Practical Organic Chemistry, Part 1: Small Scale Preparations. Arthur I. Vogel; Longman (2nd Edition; 1966)

Assignment

Investigation of the Heat Change (Enthalpy) and Entropy Change during the Fusion of Naphthalene

INTRODUCTION

Theoretical reasoning (based on the Boltzmann Distribution) and experimental observation are both compatible with the view that the rate of a chemical process should be governed by a relation of the form:

$$\text{Rate} = P Z e^{-E/RT}$$

where P, Z, E and R are factors which are either independent of the Kelvin Temperature T, or relatively insensitive to small changes in it. Z, the collision number, represents the the total number of collisions between reactant molecules per unit time. It is directly related to the reactant concentrations.

For a system in chemical equilbrium, the rates of forward and reverse reactions must be equal.

i.e. $P_f Z_f e^{-E_f/RT} = P_b Z_b e^{-E_b/RT}$ where the subscripts f and b refer to the forward and reverse reactions.

Thus $(P_b Z_b / P_f Z_f) = (e^{-E_f/RT}) / (e^{-E_b/RT}) = e^{-(E_f - E_b)/RT} = e^{-\Delta H/RT}$.

1. What do the symbols P, Z, E and R represent?

2. What is ΔH ? Draw a simple energy diagram illustrating the relation between E_f, E_b and ΔH.

Now, because of the nature of Z, the factor $(P_b Z_b)/(P_f Z_f)$ will be proportional to the equilibrium constant, K for the reaction.

Thus:

K x a constant $= e^{-\Delta H/RT}$

and it follows that:

$\ln K = $ a constant $- \Delta H/RT$

and so: $2 \cdot 303 \lg K = $ a constant $- \Delta H/RT$ (Equation 1)

Therefore a graph of $\lg K$ against the reciprocal of the Kelvin Temperature should be linear.

3. What will be the gradient of this graph?

4. What factor could be determined from the gradient of a plot of log reaction rate against the reciprocal of the Kelvin Temperature?

Equation 1 applies not only to chemical reactions but to physical situations such as solid–liquid and liquid–vapour equilibria. The following experiment attempts to investigate the effect of a solute on the equilibrium between solid and liquid naphthalene.

EXPERIMENTAL WORK

Weigh out accurately about 12·8g of pure, dry naphthalene into a clean boiling tube and immerse the tube in a beaker of water heated to about 90°C. When the naphthalene has all melted, insert a thermometer in the tube and place the tube in a small beaker filled with cotton wool. Stir with the thermometer and record the temperature at 30 second intervals. A graph of temperature against time should be plotted while the readings are being taken and readings should be continued for several minutes after solid naphthalene is seen.

Add 3–5g (accurately weighed) of diphenylamine to the solidified naphthalene, remelt the naphthalene and stir thoroughly to ensure that the diphenylamine dissolves and forms an homogeneous solution. Repeat the cooling procedure, again plotting a cooling curve. A further weighed portion of diphenylamine (in the range 3–13g) should now be added to the tube and the whole procedure repeated again.

Study the appearance of your three cooling curves. In each case the temperature probably rose immediately crystals of naphthalene first appeared and then either remained more or less constant or fell only very slowly.

5. What explanation can you offer for this?
From the cooling curves, determine the freezing points of pure naphthalene and the two solutions of diphenylamine.

6. How well does your value for the freezing point of pure naphthalene agree with the melting point for this compound quoted in the literature?

7. What is meant by the term 'mole fraction'?
Determine the mole fractions of naphthalene for each of the solutions you studied and tabulate mole fractions of naphthalene together with freezing points of solutions, collecting data from the other students.

Interpretation of results

We are considering the equilibrium:

$$C_{10}H_8 \text{(solid)} \rightleftharpoons C_{10}H_8 \text{(solution)}$$

8. What is the connection between the equilibrium constant for this system and the mole fractions of (i) pure naphthalene and (ii) naphthalene in a naphthalene-diphenylamine solution?

9. What is the mole fraction of a pure solid? Rewrite your answer to question 8 accordingly.

10. What must $1/T$ be plotted against in order to get a linear graph from which the enthalpy of fusion ($\Delta H°$) of pure naphthalene can be determined? (Consider your answer to question 9 together with Equation 1). Plot this graph.

11. If two liquids form an *ideal* solution with each other, what can be said about their enthalpy of mixing?

12. If we assume that diphenylamine forms an ideal solution with naphthalene, what must be the relationship between the enthalpy of fusion of pure naphthalene ($\Delta H°$) and the enthalpy of fusion of naphthalene in the presence of molten diphenylamine (ΔH)?

13. What is the relationship between the Free Energy Change (ΔG), the Enthalpy Change (ΔH) and the Entropy Change (ΔS) for any process? (Equation 2)

14. What can be said about ΔG for any system that has reached equilibrium?

15. Bearing in mind your answer to question 14, what is the simplified form of Equation 2 which governs the conditions under which solid and liquid naphthalene are in mutual equilibrium in the presence of diphenylamine?

16. In general, are enthalpies of reaction particularly sensitive to temperature changes?

17. Calculate the Entropy Change for the fusion of:
(a) pure naphthalene ($\Delta S°$)
(b) naphthalene in a mixture with mole fraction of 0·25 of diphenylamine (ΔS)

18. In terms of the molecular interpretation of ΔS, suggest:
(i) why ΔS is greater than $\Delta S°$?
(ii) why solutes lower the freezing point of solvents

129

Notes 23

Standard: ***

Time required: 1½ hours practical work

Reagents required:
  naphthalene (15g)
  diphenylamine (15g)

Apparatus required:
  Dry boiling tube
  500cm³ beaker (for water bath)
  250cm³ beaker
  cotton wool
  Thermometer (-10 to 110°C)

Typical results and notes on questions

1. R is the Gas Constant; $R \simeq 2$ cals. deg C^{-1} mol $^{-1} \simeq 8 \cdot 3$ J deg C^{-1} mol $^{-1}$
E is the Activation Energy for the process; i.e. the minimum energy necessary before reaction will occur.
P is the 'steric factor'; i.e. a measure of the fraction of the total collisions which occur with the correct geometrical orientation for reaction to be possible.

Thus, the equation:

$$\text{Rate} = P Z e - E/RT \ \ldots (1) \text{ can be interpreted as:}$$

Rate ∝(Total collisions/second with correct orientation for reaction) x (fraction of total collisions with the minimum energy needed for reaction to occur.)

2. ΔH, the enthalpy change during a reaction, is the difference between the heat contents of the products and the reactants. It is related to the activation energies of the forward and reverse reactions as shown in the diagram:

$$\text{i.e. } \Delta H = E_f - E_b$$

3. The gradient of a graph of lg K against T^{-1} should be $- \Delta H/2 \cdot 303 \, R$

4. Rate $= P Z e^{-E/RT}$
Thus: ln rate $= \ln P Z - E/RT$
Since $P Z$ is relatively insensitive to temperature changes, a graph of log Rate against T^{-1} should be linear. From the gradient of this graph, E, the activation energy, can be calculated.

5. A sharp rise in temperatures as the first crystals appear (this may not always be observed) indicates that the molten compound had supercooled. In such cases, once crystallization begins it occurs very rapidly, the latent heat of fusion thereby released raising the temperature of the substance to its true freezing point. Crystallization then continues at a rate governed by the rate of loss of heat to the surroundings and so no temperature drop is observed until all the substance has crystallized.

130

In the case of mixtures of naphthalene and diphenylamine the temperature does not remain steady during crystallization. As the naphthalene freezes out, the remaining molten mixture becomes more concentrated and, since the depression of freezing point is proportional to the solute concentration, the freezing point steadily drops during crystallization.

A typical set of class data is as follows:

Mole Fraction of Naphthalene (m_N)	1	1	0·766	0·784	0·784	0·579	0·547
Freezing Point/deg C (T-273)	79·0	80·2	66·8	70·0	64·9	54·5	50·0
lg m_N	0	0	−0·116	−0·106	−0·106	−0·237	−0·262
$10^3 \times (T/K)^{-1}$	2·84	2·83	2·95	2·92	2·96	3·06	3·10

6. The actual freezing point of the naphthalene depends on its purity. Bearing this in mind, the above data are in reasonable agreement with the figure of 81°C quoted in the literature as the freezing point of pure naphthalene.

7. If n_N and n_D are the numbers of moles of naphthalene and diphenylamine respectively in a mixture then the mole fraction of naphthalene, m_N, is given by

$$m_N = \frac{n_N}{n_N + n_D}$$

The mole fraction is clearly a measure of the concentration of a species in a mixture.

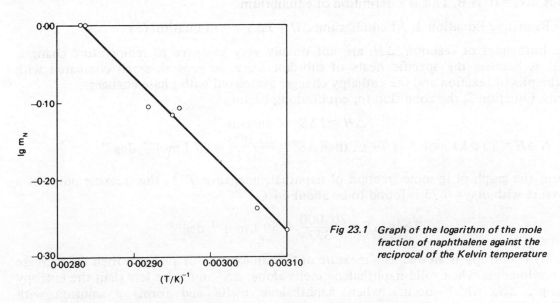

Fig 23.1 *Graph of the logarithm of the mole fraction of naphthalene against the reciprocal of the Kelvin temperature*

8. Applying the usual equilibrium expression to the equilibrium:

$$C_{10}H_8 \text{(solid)} \rightleftharpoons C_{10}H_8 \text{(solution)}$$

we get $K = \dfrac{[C_{10}H_8 \text{(solution)}]}{[C_{10}H_8 \text{(solid)}]} = \dfrac{\text{mole fraction of naphthalene in solution.}}{\text{mole fraction of naphthalene in solid.}}$

9. The mole fraction of a pure solid must be unity and so:

$$K = \text{Mole fraction of naphthalene in solution} = m_N$$

10. A graph of lg m_N against T^{-1} should be linear with gradient $- \Delta H^\circ/2\cdot303$ R.

In this way, the data given above suggest a value of 20·0 kJ mol^{-1} for ΔH° as opposed to the literature value of 18·7 kJ mol^{-1}

11. An 'ideal' solution is defined as a solution for which the enthalpy of mixing is zero.

12. By Hess' Law: $\Delta H + \Delta H_{mixing} = \Delta H°$

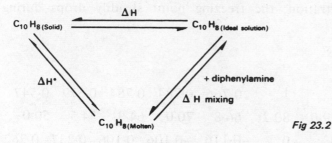

Fig 23.2

But $\Delta H_{mixing} = 0$ if we assume that naphthalene and diphenylamine form an ideal mixture.

Therefore, $\Delta H = \Delta H°$ and so the reasoning used in determining $\Delta H°$ as outlined in the answer to question 10 is correct providing that we are dealing with an ideal system. The close agreement between the experimental value for ΔH and that quoted in the literature suggests that this is a permissible assumption.

13. $\Delta G = \Delta H - T\Delta S$ (Equation 2)

14. ΔG, the free energy change for the process, is a measure of the useful work which the process can do. At equilibrium, no net change is occurring and no useful work can be derived from the system.

Thus, $\Delta G = 0$. N.B. This is a definition of equilibrium

15. Rewriting Equation 2: At equilibrium $\Delta H = T\Delta S$ Equation (3)

16. Enthalpies of reaction, ΔH, are not usually very sensitive to temperature changes. This is because the specific heats of substances are, in general, small compared with enthalpies of reaction and the enthalpy changes associated with phase changes.

Thus, Equation 3, the condition for equilibrium, becomes:

$$\Delta H = T\Delta S \simeq \text{Constant}$$

17. If $\Delta H = 20\cdot0$ kJ mol^{-1} at 79°C, then $\Delta S° = \dfrac{20\ 000}{337} \simeq 57$ J mol^{-1} deg^{-1}

From the graph of lg mole fraction of naphthalene against T^{-1}, the freezing point of a mixture with $m_N = 0\cdot75$ is found to be about 64°C

$$\text{Thus, } \Delta S = \frac{20\ 000}{337} \simeq 59 \text{ J mol}^{-1} \text{ deg}^{-1}$$

18. (i) If entropy is viewed as a measure of the randomness of a system then the increase in randomness when solid naphthalene melts alone, $\Delta S°$, must be less than the entropy change, ΔS, which occurs when naphthalene melts and forms a solution with diphenylamine.

i.e. a naphthalene-diphenylamine molten mixture is more disordered than molten naphthalene alone.

(ii) In general, it is true that

(a) $\Delta S^{freezing}_{solution} > \Delta S^{freezing}_{pure\ solvent}$

and that

(b)   the condition for freezing is:

$\Delta H \simeq \text{constant} = T\Delta S$

$\simeq$ Freezing Point in °K $\times \Delta S^{freezing}$

132

Thus, if $\Delta S^{freezing}$ is increased by adding a solute, then the freezing point of the solution must drop if $T\Delta S$ is to remain constant.

REFERENCES

B.H. MAHAN, *J.Chem Ed.* 40, 293 (1963) *Chemical Principles in Practice,* Ed. J.A. BELL p98, Addison Wesley (1967).

FURTHER ASSIGNMENTS

1. The saturated vapour pressure of water varies with temperature as shown below:

Temperature (°C)	0	10	20	30	40	50	60
s.v.p. H_2O(mm of Hg)	4·58	9·21	17·54	31·82	55·32	92·51	149·4

Show how these data can be handled in order to yield a value for the Enthalpy of Evaporation (alias Latent Heat of Evaporation) for water.
N.B. The data must be treated in an entirely analogous fashion to the way in which the naphthalene mole fraction data were processed.
2. Explain (i) why the term *Enthalpy of Evaporation/Boiling Point (in °K)* is approximately constant for many liquids.
(ii) why water is anomalous in this respect.

Assignment 24
Investigation of the Order of the Reaction of Iodine with Acetone

INTRODUCTION

Chemical kinetics, the investigation of the rates at which chemical reactions occur, is of great importance as it enables the exploration of reaction mechanism. Even the simplest chemical reactions may consist of a complex sequence of events. Thus, it is customary practice to simplify matters by devising experiments in which, effectively, the concentration of one species only is changing.

The following solutions are provided:

0·02M I_2 dissolved in aqueous KI solution.

1·0M acetone dissolved in water.

1·0M sulphuric acid.

0·5M sodium bicarbonate solution.

Very dilute sodium thiosulphate solution.

Using these, each pair of students should prepare one of the combinations of solutions indicated below. Clean, dry conical flasks, A and B, should be used for this purpose:

Student pair:	1.	2.	3.	4.	5.
Flask A:					
Volume of I_2 solution/cm³	50·0	50·0	50·0	50·0	50·0
Flask B:					
Volume of H_2SO_4 soln/cm³	25·0	25·0	25·0	25·0	25·0
Volume of Acetone soln/cm³	25·0	20·0	15·0	12·5	6·25
Volume of distilled H_2O/cm₃	0	5·0	10·0	12·5	18·75

The flasks should be stoppered and placed in a thermostat at 25°C. It is necessary to wait 10-15 minutes for the solutions to reach the temperature of the bath and during this time fill a burette with the sodium thiosulphate solution and pipette 10cm³ portions of the $NaHCO_3$ solution into each of three clean conical flasks. Make sure that you have a stopclock and a clean 10cm³ pipette.

When you are ready, mix the contents of the flasks, A and B, thoroughly and at once start the clock. Reclamp the flask containing the reaction mixture in the thermostat. Check the temperature of the mixture carefully. After about 5 minutes, pipette 10cm³ of the reaction mixture into one of the flasks containing the $NaHCO_3$ solution, noting the time at which this was done. The contents of the flask should be mixed thoroughly and then titrated with the sodium thiosulphate solution. When the mixture is nearly colourless two or three drops of a fresh starch solution should be added and then titration is continued until one drop of sodium thiosulphate solution discharges the blue starch-iodine complex colour.

After about 10, 15, 20 and 30 minutes withdraw further 10cm³ portions of the reaction mixture from the thermostat and carry out the above procedure each time. Record all times and titration data as follows:

Time sample of reaction mixture
added to NaHCO₃ solution/mins.

Burette reading (ii). . . . .
Burette reading (i) . . . .

Volume of sodium thiosulphate
solution needed/cm³

Temperature of mixture/°C . . . .

GRAPH 1.

Plot the times at which $10 cm^3$ samples of reaction mixture were added to NaHCO₃ solution against the volumes of sodium thiosulphate needed to react with the remaining iodine.

Answer the following questions:

1. What are the formulae of sodium thiosulphate and acetone?
2. What is the equation for the reaction between sodium thiosulphate and iodine?
3. The reaction between acetone and iodine is catalysed by acid. What is the function of the sodium bicarbonate?
4. Did the iodine concentration in the reaction mixture fall throughout the expt.?
5. How can the rate of the reaction be determined from Graph 1?
6. Did the iodine concentration change at a uniform rate throughout the experiment?
7. Is the rate of change of the iodine concentration dependent on the iodine concentration?
8. What is the order of the reaction with respect to iodine?
i.e. What is the value of x in the equation:

$$\text{Rate of reaction} = \text{constant.} \ [I_2]^x \ ?$$

9. Does iodine take part in the rate determining step of this reaction?
10. What is the significance of the intercept of Graph 1?
11. What must the concentration of the sodium thiosulphate solution have been?

Record the gradients of GRAPHS 1 obtained by the whole class:

Pair number: 1.   2.   3.   4.   5.

Gradient of Graph $1/cm^3 \ mins^{-1}$:

Since the total volume of the reaction mixture was in every case the same ($100 cm^3$) the initial concentration of acetone in each case is proportional to the total volume of acetone solution added.

12. Will the acetone concentration have varied significantly in the course of any of the above experiments?

GRAPH 2

Plot the gradients of Graphs 1 against the initial volume of acetone solution added.

13. How did the rate of reaction depend on the acetone concentration?
14. What is the order of the reaction with respect to acetone?

Notes 24

Standard: *

Time required: 1½ hours should be ample if the class is briefed before the practical session.

Reagents required:

   0·02M I_2 in 0·2M KI [5·08g of I_2 and 33·2g of KI per dm^3]   (250cm^3)
   1·0M acetone solution [73·3cm^3 of acetone per dm^3 of aqueous solution](150cm^3)
   1·0M H_2SO_4 (150cm^3)
   0·5M $NaHCO_3$ solution [approx. 42g dm^{-3}]   (1000cm^3)
   0·01M $Na_2S_2O_3$ solution [4·96g of $Na_2S_2O_3.5H_2O$ per 2dm^3 of solution](750cm^3)
   Distilled water   (600cm^3)
   Fresh starch solution

   N.B. the quantities specified are sufficient to produce one complete set of results

Apparatus required:

  1 burette
  5 x 250cm^3 conical flasks
  2 x 10cm^3 pipettes
  1 x 50cm^3 and 1 x 25cm^3 pipettes
  thermometer (0 to 50°C preferably)
  2 x 100cm^3 beakers to contain spare $NaHCO_3$ and $Na_2S_2O_3$ solutions.
  2 communal burettes for dispensing distilled water and acetone solutions.
  1 communal thermostat. This is very desirable but not essential providing that reaction mixtures are kept well away from radiators or sun. The reaction is rather sensitive to temperature changes.
  N.B. The product of this reaction has lachrymatory properties. Care should be taken to see that flasks are well stoppered.

Typical Results

Graphs 1

Good straight lines extrapolating back to indicate 20cm^3 titres of $Na_2S_2O_3$ at time zero. There appears to be no advantage in trying to take an initial sample before 5 minutes have elapsed after mixing.

At 22·9°C

Negative slope of Graph 1/cm^3 min^{-1}	0·070	0·100	0·116	0·200	0·255
Volume of 1M acetone in original mixture/cm^3	6·25	10·0	12·5	20·0	25·0

Graph 2

Our typical results show a slight scatter, probably due to minor temperature fluctuations. It is not difficult to be persuaded that the plot should be linear and that it should pass through the origin. i.e. reaction is first order with respect to acetone. The above slopes are probably accurate to within ± 0·005cm^3.min^{-1}.

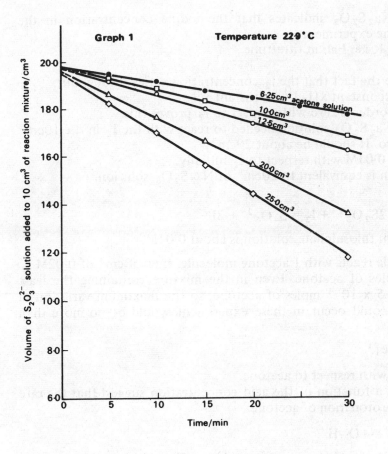

Graph 1　　　　　　　　Temperature 22·9°C

Fig 24.1
Graph 1: Volume of $Na_2S_2O_3$ solution
needed at various times

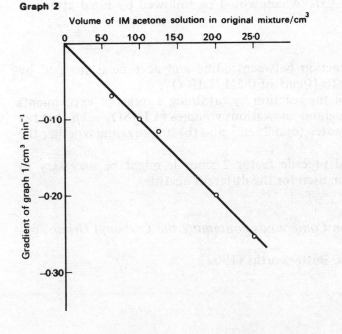

Graph 2

Fig 24.2
Graph 2: Gradient of Graph 1 as a
function of acetone concentration in
the original mixture

Notes on Questions

1. The formula of sodium thiosulphate is $(Na^+)_2S_2O_3^{2-}$. That of acetone is $CH_3-\overset{\displaystyle O}{\overset{\displaystyle \|}{C}}-CH_3$.

2. The equation for the reaction between sodium thiosulphate and iodine is quoted in the answer to question 11.

3. The function of the $NaHCO_3$ is to neutralise the acid catalyst, the reaction being effectively stopped thereby.

4. Yes, the falling titre of $Na_2S_2O_3$ indicates that the iodine concentration in the reaction mixture falls during the experiment.

5. From the gradient of Graph 1. i.e. Fall in titre/time.

6. Yes, since Graph 1 is linear.

7. No, Graph 1 is linear despite the fact that the I_2 concentration varies throughout.

8. Zero. i.e. Rate of reaction = constant $x[I_2]^0$ = constant x 1

9. It cannot. The fact that the order is zero with respect to I_2 proves this.

10. This gives the volume of $Na_2S_2O_3$ solution needed to react with the I_2 in the $10cm^3$ of reaction mixture at time zero. It should be about $20cm^3$.

11. All the mixtures should be 0·01M with respect to I_2 initially.

i.e. $10cm^3$ of 0·01M I_2 solution is equivalent to $20cm^3$ of $Na_2S_2O_3$ solution.

Hence, from the equation:

$$2S_2O_3{}^{2-} + I_2 = S_4O_6{}^{2-} + 2I^-$$

it can be shown that the sodium thiosulphate solution is about 0·01M.

12. Assuming that 1 I_2 molecule reacts with 1 acetone molecule, then $50cm^3$ of 0·02M I_2 can react with 1×10^{-4} moles of acetone. Even in the mixture containing the least acetone, $6·25cm^3$, there is $62·5 \times 10^{-4}$ moles of acetone, so the maximum variation in acetone concentration which could occur in these experiment would be no more than 1–2%.

13. Rate = constant x $[acetone]^1$

14. Reaction rate is first order with respect to acetone.

Studies of the reaction rate as a function of the acid concentration suggest that the rate determining step involves the protonation of acetone:

$$CH_3-\overset{O}{\overset{\|}{C}}-CH_3 + H^+ \xrightarrow{\text{slow}} CH_3-\overset{+O-H}{\overset{\|}{C}}-CH_3$$ which would be followed by rapid attack of the protonated species by iodine.

FURTHER PROJECTS

1. Investigate how effectively the reaction between iodine and acetone is stopped by adding $10cm^3$ of the reaction mixture to $10cm^3$ of 0·5M $NaHCO_3$.

2. Investigate the acid dependence of the reaction by (a) doing a series of experiments with $25cm^3$ of acetone solution throughout and various volumes of H_2SO_4 such that the volume of acid plus that of distilled water total $25cm^3$ and (b) investigating whether the identity of the acid has any effect.

N.B. Investigation of factor 1 should precede factor 2 since it might be necessary to adjust the volumes of $NaHCO_3$ solution used for the different acidities.

REFERENCES

Lapworth, *The Action of Halogens on Compounds containing the Carbonyl Group*, pp. 30-41, J. Chem. Soc. (1904)

Latham, *Elementary Reaction Kinetics*, Butterworths (1962).

138

Assignment 25

Determination of the Activation Energy for the Iodination of Acetone

INTRODUCTION

It is the activation energy which dictates the way in which the rate of a reaction varies with temperature. Thus, in order to determine the activation energy for a reaction it is necessary to study the rate of that reaction as a function of temperature.

The experimental procedure in the case of this particular reaction is identical with that described for the previous experiment. However, on this occasion each pair work at a different temperature but with the same reaction mixture:

Flask A

Volume of I_2 solution $50 \cdot 0 cm^3$

Flask B

Volume of acetone solution $25 \cdot 0 cm^3$
Volume of $1 \cdot 0M\ H_2SO_4$ $25 \cdot 0 cm^3$

As explained in the previous experiment, Flasks A and B must be stoppered and left immersed in the relevant thermostat for about 10–15 minutes in order to allow their contents to reach the required temperature before the reaction is started.

In most cases it should not be necessary to take more than five $10 cm^3$ samples of the reaction mixture over a period of 30 minutes, but for reactions carried out below 10°C it may be desirable to continue for an extra 15 minutes or so. Record your results as before, being especially careful to check the temperature of the reaction mixture periodically.

Time sample of reaction mixture added to NaHCO₃ solution/min					
Burette reading (ii) Burette reading (i)					
Volume of $Na_2S_2O_3$ solution needed/cm³					
Temperature of mixture/°C					

GRAPH 3

Plot the times at which $10 cm^3$ portions of reaction mixture were added to sodium bicarbonate solution, against the volume of sodium thiosulphate solution needed to react with the iodine remaining.

Each pair should determine the rate of the reaction (expressed as cm³ of $Na_2S_2O_3$ solution.min⁻¹) from their Graph 3, and information from the whole class should be collected and recorded in the first three columns of the following table:

139

Pair Number	Temperature /°C	Rate of reaction /cm³ min⁻¹	lg(Rate/cm³ mins⁻¹)	T/K	(T/K)⁻¹
1					
2					
3					
4					
5					

1. How does the rate of reaction vary with temperature? Is it directly proportional to temperature?

Let us assume that in order for reaction to occur, the reacting molecules on collision must have a *minimum* energy of E.

2. What is the name normally given to this factor E?

Suppose A is the rate of reaction *if* every collision was successful in bringing about reaction (N.B. A is a measure of the *total* number of collisions per unit time and is often called the collision number). Now it can be proved that the fraction of collisions which have a minimum energy of E is given by $e^{-E/RT}$ where:

R is the Gas Constant ($8 \cdot 3$ J mol⁻¹ deg K⁻¹)
T is the Kelvin (Absolute) temperature
e is the base of natural logarithms (i.e. $2 \cdot 72$)

Thus, at any given temperature

$$\text{Rate of reaction} = A.e^{-E/RT} \dots \text{(i)}$$

Hence, taking logarithms

$$\text{lg Rate} = \text{lg } A - E/2 \cdot 3RT \dots \text{(ii)}$$

$$\text{(N.B. lg } 2 \cdot 72 = 1/2 \cdot 3)$$

When you have completed the tables of data you can test the validity of Equation (ii) by plotting:

GRAPH 4: lg Rate plotted against the reciprocal of the Kelvin temperature.

3. Graph 4 should be linear. If it is so, what does this signify about A and E?

4. What is the algebraic expression for the slope of Graph 4? (See Equation (ii))

5. What is the slope of Graph 4? From it $\left(\dfrac{\text{lg Rate}}{(T/K)^{-1}}\right)$ calculate a value for E in kJ mol⁻¹.

6. What sign should be given to E?

7. How is E related to the heat changes for the forward and reverse reactions?
Draw a simple energy diagram to make your answer clear.

8. What are the main sources of error in your experiment?

9. Try to decide how accurate you think your value for E is.

10. If the activation energy, E, for the reaction of iodine with acetone was changed (e.g. by adding a catalyst) what effect would this have on the equilibrium constant for the reaction?

11. What rise in temperature above room temperature (say 17°C) causes the rate of reaction of iodine with acetone to be doubled? (Estimate roughly from your measured rates and temperatures or calculate from your value of E using Equation (ii))

12. If E is 191 kJ mol⁻¹, what effect would this have on the answer to question 11?

Notes 25

Standard: ***

Time required: 1½ hours. If the class have recently done the previous experiment it is likely that this will allow time for the complete processing of the data.

Reagents and apparatus required:
These are exactly as specified for the previous experiment with the exception of thermostats.

Thermostats: It is desirable to study the reaction at four or five different temperatures but few teaching establishments will be able to boast as many thermostats. However, with care, a large reservoir (e.g. a large pneumatic trough) of water functions tolerably well as a thermostat for the periods of 45 minutes or so needed in this case. The typical results described here were obtained as follows:

3·2°C   ice/water in a pneumatic trough
19·7°C   room temperature
22·9°C   a small amount of warm water added to a pneumatic trough of tap-water
24·4°C   thermostat
29·0°C   thermostat

N.B. 1. The reaction is inconveniently rapid above 30°C

2. This reaction is sufficiently sensitive to temperature for it to be important that the temperatures of the water baths do not vary by more than 0·5°C during the reaction

3. Introductory note to the previous experiment

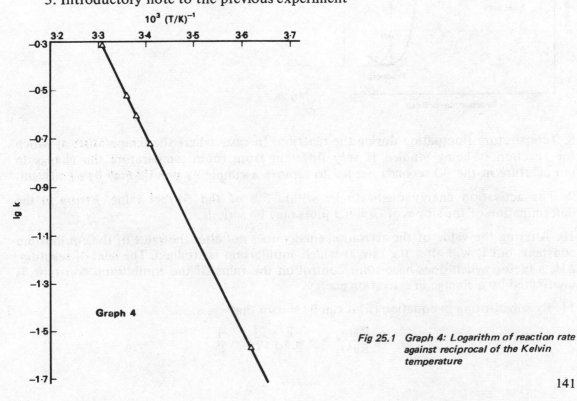

Fig 25.1 *Graph 4: Logarithm of reaction rate against reciprocal of the Kelvin temperature*

141

Typical Data

Both Graphs 3 and 4 should be linear; care must be exercised to determine the correct slopes of the Graph 3 plots.

Temperature/°C	k/cm^3 min^{-1}	$\lg(k$/cm^3 min$^{-1})$
3·2	0·0267	−1·573
19·7	0·190	−0·721
22·9	0·250	−0·603
24·4	0·300	−0·523
29·0	0·490	−0·310

Notes on questions

1. Although reaction rates increase with increasing temperature, the relationship is not a linear one.

2. The term E is normally called the activation energy of the reaction.

3. A and E either do not depend on temperature or are much less sensitive to it than is the factor $\exp(-E/RT)$.

4. The slope of Graph 4 is $-E/2 \cdot 303RT$ where R is 8·32 J mol^{-1} K^{-1} and T is expressed in degrees K.

5. The data quoted here indicate a value of 76·6 kJ mol^{-1} for E.

6. E must be positive; energy is supplied to activate the reacting molecules.

7.

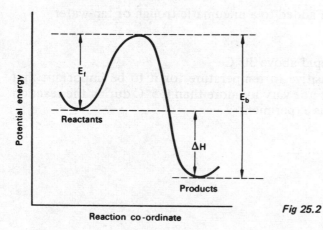

Fig 25.2

8. Temperature fluctuation during the reaction. In cases where the temperature at which the reaction is being studied is very different from room temperature the change in temperature in the 30 seconds needed to remove a sample by pipette may be significant.

9. The activation energy ought to be within 5% of the correct value. Errors in the determination of the slopes of Graph 3 plots may be serious.

10. Altering the value of the activation energy does not alter the value of the equilibrium constant, but it will alter the rate at which equilibrium is attained. The heat of reaction, ΔH, a factor which does have some control on the value of the equilibrium constant, is unaffected by a change in activation energy.

11. By substituting in equation (ii) it can be shown that

$$\lg \frac{\text{Rate}_2}{\text{Rate}_1} = -\frac{E}{2 \cdot 3R} \left(\frac{1}{T_2} - \frac{1}{T_1} \right)$$

142

Thus if $T_1 = 290K$ and T_2 is the temperature at which the reaction rate is twice that at 290K, then

$$\lg 2 = -\frac{76\cdot 6}{2\cdot 3R}\left(\frac{1}{T_2} - \frac{1}{290}\right)$$

whence $T_2 \simeq 296K$.

That is, on raising the temperature from 17°C to 23°C the reaction should be doubled.

12. A similar calculation to that shown above, taking T_1 as 290K and E as 191kJ mol^{-1}, suggests that the reaction rate would then be doubled by a temperature rise of about 2°C.

FURTHER PROJECTS

1. Look up as many activation energies as possible. Is there any difference between the magnitudes of the activation energies for gas reactions and reactions in solution?

2. Try to calculate the value of A, the collision frequency, from the experimental data. (For this it will be necessary to convert the intercept of Graph 4 into molar units). From the kinetic theory, try to assess the number of collisions per second that you would expect and compare this with the value of A.

REFERENCES

Principles of Reaction Kinetics, P.G. Ashmore, R.I.C. Monographs for Teachers (No. 9)
Elementary Reaction Kinetics, J.L. Latham, Butterworths (1962)

Assignment 26
Redox Reactions and Electrode Potentials

INTRODUCTION

Redox reactions can be defined as chemical changes involving the net transfer of one or more electrons from one molecule or ion to another. The species losing electrons is said to be 'oxidized', while that gaining electrons is 'reduced'. e.g. When chlorine is added to any solution containing iodide ions, the following reaction takes place:

$$Cl_{2(g)} + 2\ I^-_{(aq)} \rightarrow 2\ Cl^-_{(aq)} + I_{2(aq)}$$

This reaction involves the removal of an electron from each of the two iodide ions. i.e. The chlorine is behaving as an oxidizing agent and the iodide ions as reducing agents. The reaction can be considered to arise from a combination of two half-equations:

$$(a)\ Cl_2 + 2\ e^- \rightleftharpoons 2\ Cl^-\ \text{and (b)}\ I_2 + 2\ e^- \rightleftharpoons 2\ I^-$$

Because Cl_2 has a stronger affinity for electrons than I_2 has (i.e. half-equation (a) has a greater tendency to proceed from left to right than does (b)) Cl_2 can oxidize I^- ions, but I_2 cannot oxidize Cl^- ions.

EXPERIMENT (i)

Add a little of an aqueous solution containing iron (III) ions to about 2–3cm³ of an aqueous solution containing iodide ions. Describe your observations and carry out tests to establish the identity of the products.

1. Write an ionic equation for the reaction involved.

2. Place half-equations (b) and (c) in order of decreasing tendency to proceed to the right:

i.e. Either   (c) $Fe^{3+} + e^- \rightleftharpoons Fe^{2+}$ or   (b) $I_2 + 2\ e^- \rightleftharpoons 2\ I^-$

                (b) $I_2 + 2\ e^- \rightleftharpoons 2\ I^-$ (c) $Fe^{3+} + e^- \rightleftharpoons Fe^{2+}$

3. What reaction would you expect to occur between I_2 molecules and Fe^{2+} ions?
If the apparatus illustrated in Figure 26.1 is set up, it is found that no apparent change takes place as long as wires A and B are not touching each other. Within a few minutes of them being joined together, however, blue colourations can be detected close to both electrodes, but *nowhere else*. A reaction has taken place between two chemicals without them coming into direct contact with each other.

4. What chemical change takes place at the electrode in the iron (III) chloride beaker?

5. What chemical change takes place at the electrode in the potassium iodide beaker?

6. What is the equation for the overall reaction that has taken place?

7. Why is a salt-bridge needed?
In order to explain the fact that the above changes take place *only* at the two electrodes and only when A and B are joined, it is reasonable to assume that a flow of electrons occurs through the wire AB.

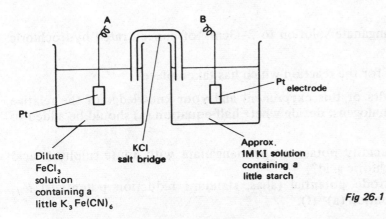

Dilute FeCl₃ solution containing a little K₃Fe(CN)₆

KCl salt bridge

Approx. 1M KI solution containing a little starch

Pt electrode

Pt

A

B

Fig 26.1

8. Do electrons flow through the wire from A to B, or *vice-versa*?

If a current flows through the wire then the two electrodes must be at different potentials. The intimate connection between test-tube redox reactions and electricity, illustrated by the above experiments, suggests that there might be a connection between electrode potentials and the tendency for redox reactions to take place.

Test-tube investigation of the relative strengths of oxidizing and reducing agents

In this practical the following half-equations should be considered, in addition to (a), (b) and (c) already given:

(d) $Br_2 + 2e^- \rightleftharpoons 2Br^-$

(e) $MnO_4^- + H^+ + e^- \rightleftharpoons Mn^{2+} + H_2O$

(f) $S_4O_6^{2-} + e^- \rightleftharpoons 2S_2O_3^{2-}$

N.B. Where necessary, add the correct numbers of electrons and protons.

EXPERIMENT (ii)

Add a *little* bromine water to a solution containing iron (II) ions. Describe your observations and investigate whether the iron (II) ions have been oxidized.

9. Write an ionic equation for the reaction involved.

10. Place half-equations (b), (c) and (d) in order of decreasing tendency to proceed to the right.

EXPERIMENT (iii)

Acidify some potassium bromide solution with a little dilute sulphuric acid. To this mixture add 2–3 drops of potassium permanganate solution.

11. Write an ionic equation which is consistent with your observations in Experiment (iii).

12. Add half-equation (e) to the table which you have constructed so far.

EXPERIMENT (iv)

Using your table of half-equations, predict whether permanganate ions, MnO_4^-, will oxidize iron (II) ions to iron (III) ions or whether iron (III) ions will oxidize manganous ions, Mn^{2+}, to permanganate ions. Carry out the appropriate reaction to test your theory and describe your results.

13. Why is it usual to carry out reactions involving the permanganate ion in acid solution?

EXPERIMENT (v)

Add a little of a solution of iodine to a little sodium thiosulphate solution, $Na_2S_2O_3$. Describe your observations.

14. Where should half-equation (f) be placed in your table?

EXPERIMENT (vi)

Add a little potassium permanganate solution to $2-3\,cm^3$ of concentrated hydrochloric acid. Identify the gas evolved.

15. What is the ionic equation for the reaction which has taken place?

16. Bearing in mind the results of this experiment and your knowledge of the relative oxidizing powers of the free halogens, decide where half-equation (a) should be added to your table.

17. Why is it customary to acidify potassium permanganate with dilute sulphuric acid rather than with dilute hydrochloric acid?

Look up the standard electrode potential (alias, standard reduction potentials) E_0, corresponding to each half-equation (a)–(f).

18. What is the relation between the E_0 values and the relative positions of half-equations (a)–(f) on your table?

19. In terms of E_0 values, what is the criterion which decides that, under standard conditions, the reaction:

$$Cl_2 + 2\,I^- \rightarrow 2\,Cl^- + I_2$$

takes place from left to right and not *vice-versa*

20. Given the following data:

$$Ce^{4+} \quad + \quad e^- \rightleftharpoons Ce^{3+} \quad E_0 = +1\cdot74\ V$$

$$Ag^+ \quad + \quad e^- \rightleftharpoons Ag \qquad\qquad +0\cdot80$$

$$Fe(CN)_6^{3-} + \quad e^- \rightleftharpoons Fe(CN)_6^{4-} \quad +0\cdot36$$

$$Sn^{4+} \quad + 2\,e^- \rightleftharpoons Sn^{2+} \qquad\quad +0\cdot15$$

$$2\,H^+ \quad + 2\,e^- \rightleftharpoons H_2 \qquad\qquad\ 0\cdot00$$

$$Ga^{3+} \quad + 3\,e^- \rightleftharpoons Ga \qquad\qquad -0\cdot56$$

$$Li^+ \quad + \quad e^- \rightleftharpoons Li \qquad\qquad -3\cdot05$$

which of the following reactions *should* take place under standard conditions:

1. $2\,Ag \ + 2\,H^+ \qquad\quad \rightarrow 2\,Ag^+ + H_2 \qquad$?
2. $Ce^{4+} + Fe(CN)_6^{4-} \rightarrow \quad Ce^{3+} + Fe(CN)_6^{3-}$?
3. $2\,Ga \ + 6\,H^+ \qquad\quad \rightarrow 2\,Ga^{3+} + 3\,H_2 \qquad$?
4. $Sn^{2+} + 2\,Li^+ \qquad\quad \rightarrow \quad Sn^{4+} + 2\,Li \qquad$?
5. $2\,Ce^{4+} + \ H_2 \qquad\quad \rightarrow 2Ce^{3+} + 2\,H^+ \qquad$?

21. Why is the word 'should' stressed in the previous question? Comment on this in the light of your knowledge of elementary chemistry in relation to the following data:

$$S \ + 2\,H^+ + 2\,e^- \rightleftharpoons H_2S \quad E_0 = +0\cdot14\ V$$

$$2\,H^+ \qquad\quad + 2\,e^- \rightleftharpoons H_2 \qquad\qquad\quad\ 0\cdot00$$

22. What are the 'standard' conditions to which E_0 values refer?

Notes 26

Standard: *
Time required: 1½ hours of practical work
Reagents required:
  concentrated hydrochloric acid (3cm³)
  chloroform (1cm³)
  starch-iodide papers
  The following 'bench' reagents: (exact concentration relatively unimportant):
  iron (III) chloride
  potassium iodide
  potassium hexacyanoferrate (III)
  potassium hexacyanoferrate (II)
  bromine water
  iron (II) sulphate
  potassium bromide
  dilute sulphuric acid
  potassium permanganate
  manganese (II) sulphate
  sodium thiosulphate
For the demonstration:
  dilute iron (III) chloride solution (100cm³)
  dilute potassium iodide solution (100cm³)
  starch solution (1cm³)
  potassium chloride and gelatine (for salt bridge)
Apparatus required:
  test-tubes
  droppers (convenient but not essential)
  For the demonstration: 2 small platinum electrodes
                           2 beakers (150cm³ to 250cm³)

This is an elementary study which is designed to establish:
(1) that it is possible to estimate the relative strengths of many oxidizing and reducing agents by carrying out simple test-tube reactions.
(2) that standard reduction potentials can be used to predict which redox reactions ought to be feasible.

Notes on Experiment (i) and Preliminary Demonstration

It is suggested that students do this first experiment and that, having answered questions 1—3, they are shown the demonstration which is described on the students' sheets.

Addition of iron (III) chloride to an aqueous solution of potassium iodide produces a brown colouration of iodine (strictly, the triiodide ion I_3^-) whose identity can be established either by shaking with a few drops of chloroform (violet solution) or by testing with starch (deep, blue-black colouration). The fact that hydrated iron (II) ions are also produced can be shown by testing some of the reaction mixture (and some of the

147

original iron (III) chloride as a 'control') with potassium hexacyanoferrate (III) solution. The latter forms a precipitate of prussian blue in the presence of iron (II) ions.

1. The ionic equation is $2 Fe^{3+} + 2 I^- \rightarrow 2 Fe^{2+} + I_2$

2. It follows that Fe^{3+} has a greater affinity for electrons than I_2 and that the order of decreasing tendency to proceed to the right is

(c) $Fe^{3+} + e^- \rightleftharpoons Fe^{2+}$

(b) $I_2 + 2 e^- \rightleftharpoons 2 I^-$

3. This being so, we would not expect any redox reaction to occur between I_2 molecules and Fe^{2+} ions.

The demonstration of iron (III) chloride solution reacting with potassium iodide solution even though the two do not come into direct physical contact (see students' sheets for details) is reliable and effective. It may take 15–30 minutes to produce convincing results, however. Attention must be drawn to the fact that initially, before wires A and B are joined, there is no sign of a blue colouration or precipitate throughout the whole apparatus. However, shortly after joining A and B, prussian blue can be seen forming at the electrode in the iron (III) chloride beaker, while deep-blue, starch-iodine complex forms at the other electrode. If the electrodes are inserted in small sample tubes, immersed in the solutions, it is easy to see that the coloured products are formed *only* at the electrodes.

4. At the electrode in the iron (III) chloride beaker, Fe^{3+} ions are reduced to form Fe^{2+} ions (which are precipitated as prussian blue).

5. At the electrode in the potassium iodide beaker, I^- ions are oxidized to I_2 molecules.

6. Thus, the same overall reaction has taken place as that discussed in answering question 1.

7. Initially, both the iron (III) chloride and potassium iodide solutions are electrically neutral. For every Fe^{3+} ion reduced, a positive charge is lost and the solution in the beaker containing the iron (III) chloride will contain an excess of Cl^- ions. Similarly, in the other beaker, as I^- ions are oxidized, an excess of K^+ ions is produced.

The salt bridge enables diffusion of ions to take place between the two beakers, thus compensating for the tendencies mentioned above. (A net drift of K^+ ions from the potassium iodide beaker and of Cl^- ions from the iron (III) chloride beaker). Unless electroneutrality is preserved, a back-emf would quickly prevent all further action at either electrode.

8. Electrons must flow through the wire from B to A.

Notes on the test-tube investigation of the relative strengths of oxidizing and reducing agents

Experiment (ii)

The fact that bromine is able to oxidize Fe^{2+} ions to Fe^{3+} ions can be shown by testing both the reaction mixture and some of the original iron (II) sulphate solution with potassium hexacyanoferrate (II) solution. More prussian blue should be seen in the former case.

9. $Br_2 + 2 Fe^{2+} \rightarrow 2 Br^- + 2 Fe^{3+}$

10. Experiment (ii) shows that bromine is a stronger oxidizing agent than iron (III) ions. Consequently, the order of decreasing tendency for the half-equations to proceed to the right is:

(d)   (c)   (b)

Experiment (iii)

Providing that only a few drops of potassium permanganate solution are added there will be excess potassium bromide and the formation of brown bromine will be clearly seen.

11. $2\,MnO_4^- + 16\,H^+ + 10\,Br^- \rightarrow 2\,Mn^{2+} + 8\,H_2O + 5\,Br_2$

12. The permanganate ion is a stronger oxidizing agent then the bromine molecule. Thus, the order of half-equations must be

$$(e)\quad (d)\quad (c)\quad (b)$$

Experiment (iv)

This sequence of half-equations indicates that the MnO_4^- ion is the strongest oxidizing agent encountered so far. Thus, it can certainly oxidize Fe^{2+} ions to Fe^{3+} ions. This can be verified by adding a few drops of potassium permanganate solution to some acidified ferrous sulphate solution. The discharge of the purple colour of the permanganate ion, together with a positive prussian blue test for simple iron (III) ions, is evidence for the reaction being:

$$MnO_4^- + 8\,H^+ + 5\,Fe^{2+} \rightarrow Mn^{2+} + 4\,H_2O + 5\,Fe^{3+}$$

13. Half-equation (e) shows that hydrogen ions must be present if the MnO_4^- ions are to be reduced to Mn^{2+} ions.

Experiment (v)

As drops of a solution of iodine in aqueous potassium iodide solution are added to sodium thiosulphate solution, the brown iodine colour is discharged.
Although the student may be allowed to guess that this implies that the thiosulphate ion can reduce iodine molecules to iodide ions, it makes a useful exercise to challenge the student to prove by experiment that the discharge of the brown colour is not due to oxidation of the iodine molecules.

14. If it is accepted that I_2 molecules oxidize $S_2O_3^{2-}$ ions, then half-equation (f) must be placed at the foot of the table

$$(e)\quad (d)\quad (c)\quad (b)\quad (f)$$

Experiment (vi)

If only a little potassium permanganate solution is added to $2-3\,cm^3$ of concentrated hydrochloric acid and the mixture warmed, the purple permanganate ion colour is discharged and chlorine gas (pale green, choking, turns starch-iodide paper blue) is evolved.

15. The above observations are consistent with the equation

$$2\,MnO_4^- + 16\,H^+ + 10\,Cl^- \rightarrow 2\,Mn^{2+} + 8\,H_2O + 5\,Cl_2$$

16. Experiment (vi) shows that the MnO_4^- ion is a stronger oxidizing agent than the Cl_2 molecule and so half-equation (a) must be placed *after* (e).
It is also known that chlorine is a stronger oxidizing agent than bromine. Thus, half-equation (a) must come *before* half-equation (d).
Thus, the final sequence of half-equations must be

$$(e)\quad (a)\quad (d)\quad (c)\quad (b)\quad (f)$$

17. Since the MnO_4^- ion can oxidize the Cl^- ion but not the SO_4^{2-} ion, dilute sulphuric acid is used in preference to hydrochloric acid to acidify solutions of potassium permanganate.

The potentials are

(e) $MnO_4^- + 8\,H^+ + 5\,e^- \rightleftharpoons Mn^{2+} + 4\,H_2O$ $E_0 = +1\cdot51\ V$

(a) Cl_2 $+ 2\,e^- \rightleftharpoons 2\,Cl^-$ $+1\cdot40$

(d) Br_2 $+ 2\,e^- \rightleftharpoons 2\,Br^-$ $+1\cdot09$

(c) Fe^{3+} $+ e^- \rightleftharpoons Fe^{2+}$ $+0\cdot77$

*(b) I_2	$+ 2 e^- \rightleftharpoons 2 I^-$		$+0.62$
(f) $S_4O_6^{2-}$	$+ 2 e^- \rightleftharpoons 2 S_2O_3^{2-}$		$+0.15$

*Actually the half-equation under consideration should be: $I_3^- + 2 e^- \rightleftharpoons 3 I^-$. However, the value of the standard reduction potential for this (0.54 V) does not affect the argument.

18. The above data show that the experimentally determined sequence of decreasing strength of oxidizing agent agrees with the sequence of decreasing reduction potentials.

19. The chlorine–chloride reduction potential is greater than that for the iodine–iodide system and so chlorine can oxidize iodide ions to iodine.
i.e. The general rule is that if:

$$\text{Oxidizing Agent}_1 + e^- \rightleftharpoons \text{Reducing Agent}_1 \quad E_0 = + P \text{ volts}$$
$$\text{Oxidizing Agent}_2 + e^- \rightleftharpoons \text{Reducing Agent}_2 \quad E_0 = + Q \text{ volts}$$

when P>Q, the reaction to be expected under standard conditions is:

$$\text{Oxidizing Agent}_1 + \text{Reducing Agent}_2 \rightarrow \text{Oxidizing Agent}_2 + \text{Reducing Agent}_1$$

20. Applying the above rule to the given data, it can be seen that the following reactions *should* occur under standard conditions:

2. $Ce^{4+} + Fe(CN)_6^{4-} \rightarrow Ce^{3+} + Fe(CN)_6^{3-}$

3. $2 Ga + 6 H^+ \rightarrow 2 Ga^{3+} + 3 H_2$

5. $2 Ce^{4+} + H_2 \rightarrow 2 Ce^{3+} + 2 H^+$

Reactions 1 and 4 are to be expected to occur in the reverse directions to those suggested.

21. The standard free energy change for a redox reaction is directly related to the standard reduction potentials of the half-equations involved. Thus, E_0 values merely enable us to decide whether a particular reaction is energetically feasible. They give us *no* information about the rate of reactions. Many redox reactions are theoretically possible and yet are so slow as to be deemed not to occur at all.
i.e. The E_0 values given suggest that the reaction

$$H_2 + S \rightarrow H_2S_{(aq)}$$

should be just as likely to occur as

$$2 MnO_4^- + 16 H^+ + 10 Cl^- \rightarrow 2 Mn^{2+} + 8 H_2O + 5 Cl_2$$

and yet, while Experiment (vi) shows that the second reaction occurs readily, most students know that it is not possible to prepare hydrogen sulphide by bubbling hydrogen through an aqueous suspension of sulphur.

22. The 'standard' conditions for electrochemical measurements are:
298K, unit activities of reactants (effectively 1 M solutions and 1 atmosphere pressure for gases) and for solids existing in allotropic or polymorphic forms, the standard form is that which is most stable at 298K.
All standard reduction potentials are relative to the standard reduction potential of the hydrogen electrode, which is arbitrarily assigned to be zero.

SUGGESTIONS FOR FURTHER WORK

Experiments (vii) and (viii) refer to the half-equations:

(g) $H_2O_2 + 2 H^+ + 2 e^- \rightleftharpoons 2 H_2O$

(h) $O_2 + 2 H^+ + 2 e^- \rightleftharpoons H_2O_2$

150

Experiment (vii)
Acidify a little potassium permanganate solution with some dilute sulphuric acid and add a few drops of dilute hydrogen peroxide solution. Identify the gas which is evolved.
How does hydrogen peroxide behave in this reaction? What deduction can you make concerning the position of half-equation (h) relative to half-equation (e)? What is the ionic equation for the reaction involved?

Experiment (viii)
Acidify a little potassium iodide solution with dilute sulphuric acid and add a little hydrogen peroxide solution. Establish what has happened to the iodide ions.
How does hydrogen peroxide behave in this reaction? What limits can you place on the value of the standard reduction potential for half-equation (g)? Write an equation for the catalytic decomposition of hydrogen peroxide; explain what is being oxidized and what is reduced.

Experiment (ix)
Put 2 clean copper turnings in each of two test-tubes and add about $2-3cm^3$ of dilute hydrochloric acid to each. To one tube add about the same volume of chlorine water and warm both tubes for about a minute. Then add excess ammonium hydroxide solution to both tubes.
What do you see? Use data books to suggest the identity of any coloured substances formed. Does dilute hydrochloric acid react with copper? Do reduction potentials support your conclusion? Why is the action of chlorine water on copper different from that of dilute hydrochloric acid alone?

Factors affecting reduction potentials
The Assignment Sheets deal exclusively with *standard* reduction potentials. For most purposes these are valuable guides in interpreting test-tube reactions, but if it is desired to investigate the factors affecting reduction potentials, the following experiments are useful:

Experiment (x)
Dissolve a few grains of solid potassium iodate in *pure* distilled water and add a little potassium iodide solution. What do you see? Add a little dilute acid. What do you see?
With the help of a table of electrode potentials, (and a knowledge of the Nernst equation) try to explain what you see. Are reduction potentials affected by acidity?

Experiment (xi)
To $2cm^3$ of iron (III) chloride solution add $2cm^3$ of potassium iodide solution. What do you see? How could you test for the formation of iodine? Repeat this experiment using $2cm^3$ of potassium hexacyanoferrate (III) solution instead of the iron (III) chloride. Does complexing of a cation affect its electrode potential? From the result of your experiment suggest whether $Fe(CN)_6^{3-}$ ions are dissociated into free iron (III) ions to any marked extent.
A further demonstration which illustrates the influence of complexing on reduction potentials is the copper-thiourea-hydrochloric acid reaction. (See Notes on Copper (I) Compounds).

REFERENCES

College Chemistry by Bruce H. Mahan, Addison-Wesley (1966)
Chemistry—A Structural View, D.R. Stranks *et al*, Cambridge University Press (1965).

Assignment 27
Chemical Periodicity - An Introductory Survey

'The more I study the arrangement of this zig-zag curve, the more I am convinced that he who grasps the key will be permitted to unlock some of the deepest mysteries of creation.'

Sir William Crookes, F.R.S.
Presidential Address to the Brit. Association in 1886.

PRELIMINARY CONSIDERATIONS

It seems logical to attempt to arrange the elements in order of increasing atomic weights, since we might guess that this would represent the order of increasing atomic complexity. How do the 'simple' physical properties of the elements vary for this sequence? Plot the following three graphs: (i) the volumes of gram atoms; (ii) atomic radii and (iii) the melting points for the twenty elements H–Ca, all against their atomic weights. (It will be convenient to plot the first two on the same axes).

The initial appearance of these three graphs does suggest a cyclic or periodic relation between these physical properties and the atomic weights of the elements.

1. How many elements do there seem to be in one cycle or 'period' of these graphs?

2. Do the elements which occupy relatively high volumes per gram atom owe this to having high atomic radii?

3. By studying the three graphs, try to decide which of these twenty elements exist as simple molecules and which have polyatomic lattices. Explain your reasoning.

4. How does the metal/non-metal character of these elements vary with atomic weight? (Draw on your general knowledge; do not base your decision solely on graphs (i)–(iii)).

5. Early chemists plotted physical properties against atomic weights, as in your first three graphs. What evidence can you produce to suggest that the properties discussed so far are periodic functions of *atomic number* rather than atomic weight.?

6. Why is it that atomic number is a more useful function for this purpose than atomic weight?

Since both the physical and the chemical properties of all substances depend on interatomic forces, which, in turn, depend on electronic interactions, your answers to questions 2, 3, 4 and 6 probably suggest that it might be worth investigating the manner in which electron energies and distributions vary with increasing atomic number. It is convenient to study *ionization energies* for this purpose.

7. The first ionization energy of an element is the energy associated with which of the following processes:
(a) the removal of one electron from a singly charged, negative ion?
(b) the removal of one electron from a gaseous atom?
(c) the addition of one electron to a gaseous atom?
(d) the removal of one electron from each of a mole of gaseous atoms?
(e) the addition of one electron to a positive ion in aqueous solution?

152

Look up values for the first ionization energy of the first twenty elements and plot these against atomic number (Graph (iv)). Also look up the first nine or ten ionization energies of sodium and fluorine and plot the logarithms of successive ionization energies for each element against the number of electrons removed (Graph (v)).

8. Do Graphs (iv) and (v) support your answer to question 1?

9. What will the shape of Graph (v) be for neon? Pencil it in on your graph.

10. Why are ionization energies chozen for graphs (iv) and (v) in preference to electrode potentials?
We must now consider whether the chemical evidence for periodicity is convincing.

SURVEY OF THE GENERAL PROPERTIES OF THE OXIDES AND CHLORIDES OF THE ELEMENTS Na–S

Write down the formulae for the oxides and chlorides of these elements.

11. Do principal valencies bear a periodic relation to atomic number or to atomic weight?

The Oxides

You will almost certainly know a lot about these compounds already. Fill in what you can of Table 1 and answer as many as possible of questions 12–16 before the practical session.

12. Which of the oxides under consideration (those of Na–S) could be prepared in reasonable purity by each of the following methods:
(a) by burning the element in excess oxygen? (b) by passing steam over the heated element?
(c) by adding just enough sodium hydroxide to a salt solution to precipitate the hydroxide followed by thermal decomposition of the insoluble hydroxide? (d) by stirring the anhydrous chloride with excess water? (e) by passing a limited supply of oxygen over the heated element, followed by distillation to remove the excess element?; (f) by heating the carbonate or nitrate in a bunsen burner flame?

Table 1 Oxide properties

Element	Na	Mg	Al	Si	P	S
Formula of oxide						
Appearance of oxide						
Volatility of oxide						
Effect of water on the oxide						
Effect of aqueous solution or suspension of oxide in water on universal indicator						

Use the data of Table 1 to answer the following questions. In each case explain how you reached your conclusions.

13. Which of the oxides concerned exist as simple molecules?

14. Which of the oxides concerned certainly contain oxide ions, O^{2-}?

15. Which of the oxides concerned is most likely to have a polyatomic, covalent lattice?

16. Which of the elements concerned form acidic oxides?

Carry out any experiments and make what observations are needed for you to complete Table 1.

The Chlorides

Each pair should observe the effect of passing chlorine over a small, heated sample of one of the elements: Na, Mg, Al, Si, P or S. (Remember: chlorine is very toxic and these experiments can be dangerous if the gas is allowed to escape or if the experiment is done on too large a scale. It is not necessary to use more than 0·2g of any of the elements). A diagram of the apparatus used should be drawn and a brief description should be made giving details of the ease of reaction, together with a note of the appearance and volatility of any product. If possible, try to obtain enough of the crude product so that you can carry out solubility tests with water and with hexane.

Pure samples of the chlorides of the six elements concerned are available and you should make a test-tube study of the behaviour of *small* quantities of *each* in water and hexane. In each case, decide whether a substance is insoluble, slightly soluble or soluble in the solvent concerned. From your observations and those of others, complete Table II.

Table 2 Anhydrous chloride properties

Element	Na	Mg	Al	Si	P	S
Formula of chloride						
Ease of reaction of chlorine with element						
Appearance of chloride						
Volatility of chloride						
Effect of water on chloride						
Effect of aqueous solution or suspension of chloride in H_2O on universal indicator						
Solubility of chloride in hexane						

17. Which of the six chlorides studied would be most difficult to prepare in a pure state by direct reaction of chlorine with the elements concerned? Suggest better methods for these.

18. Which of the elements concerned form chlorides and oxides which are both ionic?

19. Which of the elements concerned form chlorides and oxides which both *react* with water?

20. Which of the elements have chlorides and oxides which are intermediate in character between those mentioned in questions 18 and 19?

21. Both oxygen and chlorine are oxidizing agents. What general effect will they exert on the atoms of elements with which they combine?

22. What is the essential difference between the hydroxy compounds of metals and non-metals? Why are these compounds so different?

23. Can you explain the trend in the behaviour of the oxides and the chlorides of the elements Na–S with water? (Use your answers to questions 21 and 22 together with Graph (iv)).

Predict whether the heats of formation for these oxides and chlorides, per mole of oxygen and chlorine atoms respectively, increase or decrease from sodium to sulphur. Check your prediction by plotting these data against atomic number for these elements. (Graph (vi)).

Summarize the chemical evidence for periodicity as exemplified by the first twenty elements. To what extent does the chemistry of the hydrides of these elements conform to this pattern?

154

Notes 27

Standard: *

Time required: 1½ hours homework time; 1½ hours practical work

Reagents required:

Samples of the oxides and anhydrous chlorides of as many of the first twenty elements as possible—especially those of the elements Na, Mg, Al, Si, P and S (1g)

Hexane ($20cm^3$)

Chlorine cylinder or copious supplies of potassium permanganate and concentrated hydrochloric acid

Samples of the elements, Na, Mg, Al, Si, P and S (0.2g)

Apparatus required:

test-tubes

3 or 4 sets of apparatus for passing chlorine over heated elements

(See text below for details)

3 or 4 chlorine generators ($KMnO_4$-conc.HCl) if a chlorine cylinder is not available

Universal Indicator paper or solution

Since many students will have at least a nodding acquaintance with much of the subject material of this study before starting their Advanced Level courses, no attempt is made to present an heuristic introduction to chemical periodicity. Instead, attention is directed at the start to the key concepts of atomic number and ionization potential and the practical work is aimed at revising and extending knowledge of the simple properties of oxides and chlorides. The questions asked focus thought on structural considerations, but considerable freedom is left to the teacher concerning the extent to which he wishes to interpret matters in terms of the electronic theory of valency.

PRELIMINARY CONSIDERATIONS

1. Graph (iii) *suggests* a value of 8 elements from peak to peak or from minimum to minimum. Graphs (i) and (ii) are not inconsistent with this.

2. Comparison of Graphs (i) and (ii) for the elements: H, O, F, Cl shows that several elements occupy large 'atomic volumes' despite the fact that their covalent atomic radii are relatively small.

3. Substances which are gaseous at room temperature must exist as simple molecules (e.g. H_2, He, N_2, O_2, F_2, Ne, Cl_2, Ar). Other substances may also contain simple molecules or they may have polyatomic lattices (this term includes metals, ionic lattices and covalent lattices) and the simplest, but by no means infallible, way of differentiating between these two main types is to consider melting-points. Since forces between atoms in different molecules are usually far weaker than forces between adjacent atoms in a polyatomic lattice, it follows that a solid with a low melting-point is likely to have a molecular structure. In general, most substances melting below 400 K are molecular while those with melting points above 800 K almost certainly have polyatomic lattices. In between these temperatures there is considerable uncertainty.

155

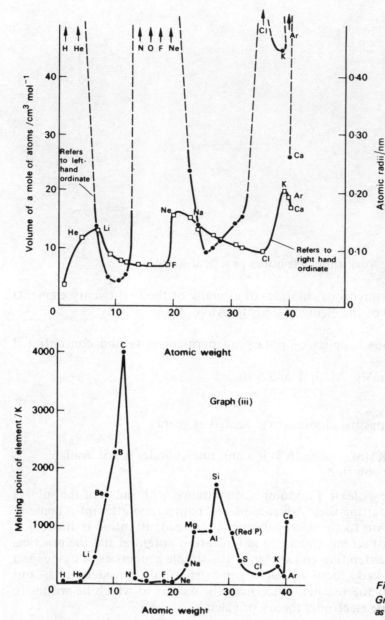

Fig 27.1

Graphs (i) and (ii): Volume of gram atoms and atomic radii respectively, plotted against atomic weight

Fig 27.2

Graph (iii): Melting point of the elements as a function of atomic weight

On this basis, Graph (iii) suggests

elements having simple molecular structures: H, He, N, O, F, Ne, Na (wrong), white P, S, Cl, K (wrong) and Ar

elements with polyatomic lattice structures: Be, B, C, Mg, Al, Si, red P and Ca

4. The metal - non metal character varies in a fairly regular fashion e.g. In Graph (iii), metals are found *only* on the left-hand side of the peaks and metal character dies out with increasing atomic number before the peak is reached.

5. Graphs (i) and (ii) both show that the position of potassium relative to argon and calcium is apparently anomalous when compared with the sequences: He, Li, Be and Ne, Na, Mg.

6. Atomic weights are dictated by the numbers of protons and neutrons in the nucleus of an atom. The number of neutrons in a nucleus has relatively little chemical effect (e.g. compare the isotopes of an element) and varies somewhat erratically from element to element. The atomic number, however, is equal to the number of electrons in a neutral atom and is unique for any given element.

156

7. If a potential difference of V is needed to remove an electron of charge e⁻ from a gaseous atom, then the energy of ionization is eV per atom or LeV (i.e. FV) per mole of gaseous atoms, where L is Avogadro's Number and F is the Faraday.

Strictly speaking, therefore, the first ionization potential of an element refers to both the energy needed to remove an electron from each of a mole of gaseous atoms (d) and to the energy needed to remove an electron from a single, gaseous atom (b). However, it is usual to employ the term in the first sense.

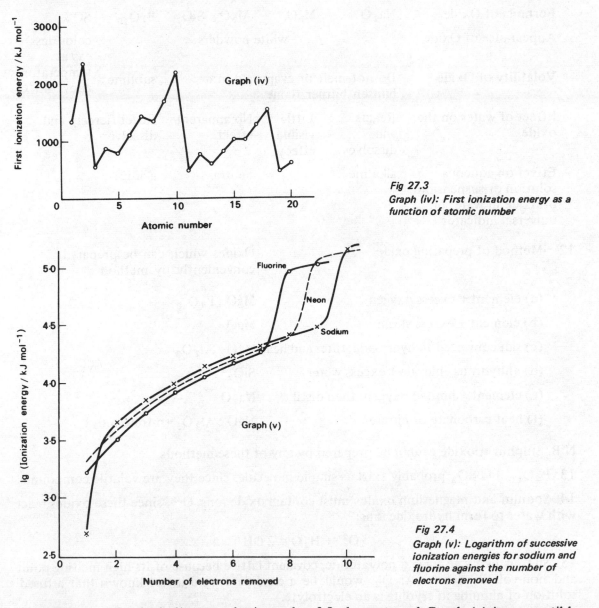

Fig 27.3

Graph (iv): First ionization energy as a function of atomic number

Fig 27.4

Graph (v): Logarithm of successive ionization energies for sodium and fluorine against the number of electrons removed

8. Graph (iv) clearly indicates a basic cycle of 8 elements and Graph (v) is compatible with this.

9. See Graph (v). The graph for neon should lie between those for fluorine and sodium because neon has an atomic number intermediate between the atomic numbers of the other two elements. As a result of this the nuclear attractive force for neon will be less than that of sodium but more than that of fluorine.

10. Electrode potentials refer to ionization in aqueous solution and will thus partly reflect the interaction between water and the ions formed. On the other hand, ionization potentials refer to the ionization of gaseous atoms and so must reflect *only* the degree of attraction between the electron and the nucleus.

11. Valencies bear a periodic relation to atomic number rather than to atomic weight.

The oxides: Sample data and notes on questions

Table 1: Oxide properties N.B. for P and S, phosphorus (V) oxide and sulphur trioxide only are considered. There is nothing against the inclusion of lower oxides, however, if desired. The same applies to Na_2O_2.

Element	Na	Mg	Al	Si	P	S
Formula of Oxide	Na_2O	MgO	Al_2O_3	SiO_2	P_4O_{10}	SO_3
Appearance of Oxide	white powders					colourless gas at temperatures above $45°C$
Volatility of Oxide	Do not melt or evaporate in a bunsen burner flame				sublimes	
Effect of water on the oxide	Reacts and dissolves	Little visible effect	No apparent effect		React fiercely and dissolve	
Effect on aqueous solution or suspension of oxide in water on universal indicator	alkaline		neutral		acidic	

12. Method of preparing oxide

Oxides which can be prepared conveniently by method

(a) element + excess oxygen MgO ; P_4O_{10}

(b) element + excess steam MgO

(c) salt converted to hydroxide; filter and heat MgO ; Al_2O_3

(d) anhydrous chloride + excess water SiO_2

(e) element + limited oxygen; then distil Na_2O

(f) heat carbonate or nitrate MgO ; Al_2O_3 (nitrate only)

N.B. Sulphur trioxide cannot be prepared by any of these methods

13. P_4O_{10} and SO_3 probably exist as simple molecules since they are volatile compounds.

14. Sodium and magnesium oxides must contain oxide ions, O^{2-}, since these oxides react with water to form hydroxide ions:

$$O^{2-} + H_2O = 2 OH^-$$

15. SiO_2 is likely to have a polyatomic, covalent lattice because of its high melting-point and non-volatile nature. Al_2O_3 would be a candidate were it not known that a fused solution of alumina in cryolite is an electrolyte.

16. P_4O_{10} and SO_3 are acidic oxides since they both produce acidic solutions in water. Strictly speaking, SiO_2 is also an acidic oxide, but it does not react with water.

The Anhydrous Chlorides

The chloride syntheses must be carried out in a fume cupboard. The apparatus shown on the next page has proved suitable.
It is vital that small quantities of elements are used and that heating is very gentle to start with. Unless care is taken, no product will be seen in the cases of phosphorus and sulphur.

158

In fact, it is possible to see a product in each case, though it is unlikely that enough will be collected to carry out tests on the sulphur and phosphorus compounds unless heating is strictly controlled.

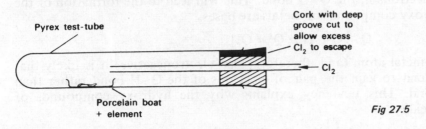

Fig 27.5

17. NaCl and $MgCl_2$ form readily, but being non-volatile, the metals will quickly become coated with a protective layer of chloride.
$MgCl_2$ could be made by dissolving the metal in dilute hydrochloric acid, followed by crystallization. The hydrated crystals would have to be dehydrated by heating in a stream of hydrogen chloride gas in order to prevent hydrolysis to magnesium oxide. NaCl could be made from the element by reaction of sodium with water, neutralizing the resultant solution with hydrochloric acid and evaporating to dryness.

18. Magnesium and sodium have chlorides and oxides which are both ionic.

19. Phosphorus and sulphur have chlorides and oxides which both react with water.

20. Aluminium and silicon have oxides and chlorides which are intermediate in character between those mentioned in questions 18 and 19.

21. Oxygen and chlorine are oxidizing agents because of their high electronegativity. i.e. high affinity for electrons. Thus, when they combine with most other elements they either remove electrons completely, forming ions, or they form covalent bonds in which the shared electrons spend more of their time nearer the oxygen and chlorine atoms. The general effect on an atom of combining with either oxygen or chlorine is that a net loss of electrons is experienced.

Table 2 Anhydrous chloride properties

Element	Na	Mg	Al	Si	P	S
Formula of chloride	NaCl	$MgCl_2$	Al_2Cl_6	$SiCl_4$	PCl_5	SCl_2
Ease of reaction of chlorine with element	violent reactions when heated				react readily at low temperature	
Appearance of chloride	white when powdered			colourless liquid	white powder	red-yellow liquid
Effect of water on chloride	chlorides dissolve		vigorous hydrolyze to give acidic solutions.		slow	
Effect of aqueous solution on suspension of chloride in H_2O on universal indicator	neutral		acidic solutions			
solubility of chloride in hexane	insoluble	sparingly soluble	miscible		sparingly soluble	

159

22. Consider a covalent molecule: Q–O–H. Graph (iv) shows that it is easier to remove an electron from a metal than from a non-metal atom. Thus, if Q is a metal (such as sodium), it is possible that the electronegative oxygen atom may be able to gain complete control of the pair of electrons in the Q–O bond. This will lead to the formation of the hydroxide ion. The hydroxy compounds of metals are bases.

$$Q \overset{\frown}{-} O - H \rightarrow Q^+ + OH^-$$

If, however, Q is a non-metal atom (and, therefore, also electronegative) it is likely that the oxygen atom will tend to gain the pair of electrons of the O–H bond rather than those of the Q–O bond. This tendency explains why the hydroxy compounds of non-metals are usually acidic.

$$Q - O \overset{\frown}{-} H \rightarrow Q - O^- + H^+$$

23. The properties of the chlorides of sodium and magnesium suggest ionic structures: (e.g. Na^+Cl^- and $Mg^{2+}(Cl^-)_2$) indicating that the chlorine atom is able to remove electrons completely from these metals.

The chlorides of phosphorus and sulphur, however, are not ionic, but it is to be expected that the inductive effect of the strongly electronegative chlorine will result in the formation of dipolar bonds, with small positive charges on the P and S atoms:

$$\overset{\diagdown}{\underset{\diagup}{>}} P^{\delta+} - Cl^{\delta-} \qquad\qquad - S^{\delta+} - Cl^{\delta-}$$

This will make the P and S atoms very susceptible to nucleophilic attack by the oxygen atom of the water molecule and will usually result in the hydrolysis of the non-metal chloride.

Thus, the usual pattern of metal chlorides dissolving in water while non-metal chlorides undergo hydrolysis can be understood in terms of the progressive increase in the difficulty of removing electrons from the elements in the sequence Na→S. A similar explanation can be given for the trends in oxide properties.

Heats of formation of oxides and chlorides

Two main factors need to be considered in predicting the trend in the heats of formation of the oxides and chlorides of the elements sodium to sulphur:

(i) The fact that it becomes increasingly difficult to remove electrons from atoms in this series.

(ii) The fact that the lattice energy of ionic substances is usually greater than that of molecular structures.

Both of these suggest that the heats of formation of the oxides and chlorides, per mole of oxygen or chlorine atoms, will become smaller as the period is crossed. This is illustrated by Graph (vi).

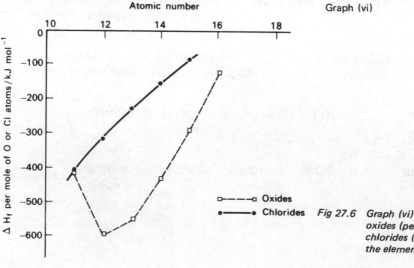

Fig 27.6 Graph (vi): Heat of formation of the oxides (per mole of O atoms) and of the chlorides (per mole of Cl atoms) for the elements Na–F

160

REFERENCES

1. *Chemistry To-Day—A Guide for Teachers*, (Chapter 3: 'An Experimental Approach to the Periodic System'), Bertil Englund. This book is published by the Organisation for Economic Co-Operation and Development (1963).
2. The Teachers' Guides for both the Nuffield Advanced Level Physical Science and the Nuffield Advanced Level Chemistry Projects contain many excellent suggestions for teaching 'Periodicity'.

Assignment 28

The Chemistry of the Halogens

(I) The Elements

(a) Make a comparison of the appearance of samples of chlorine, bromine and iodine. Record your results in the form of a table, adding any further data you wish.

(b) Discover the colour of solutions of chlorine, bromine and iodine in chloroform (or carbon tetrachloride). Use this information to establish what happens when chlorine water is added to an aqueous solution of (i) potassium iodide (ii) potassium bromide, with chloroform present in each case.

1. Why is it necessary to use chloroform to establish whether bromine or iodine is produced?

2. Which of these three elements is the strongest oxidizing agent?

3. Look up the electrode potentials. Do these confirm your results?

4. What would you expect to *see* if bromine water were added to an aqueous solution of (i) potassium chloride (ii) potassium iodide, with chloroform present in each case. Use the electrode potentials to arrive at your prediction.

(II) The Halogen Hydrides

(c) Add syrupy phosphoric acid to a small sample of each of the solid sodium or potassium halides and warm. Record your observations.

5. Does heating cause decomposition of any of the hydrogen halides? If so, which is most readily decomposed?

6. Does the syrupy phosphoric acid produce the halogen hydride because it is a stronger acid than the halogen hydride, or because it is less volatile?

7. What would you predict would happen if concentrated hydrochloric acid were added to anhydrous sodium phosphate (Na_3PO_4)?

(d) Add concentrated sulphuric acid to a small sample of each of the solid sodium or potassium halides. Note the appearance and (Caution!) the smell of the products. Suggest the identity of the products of these reactions.

8. Why does concentrated sulphuric acid produce a different reaction from that with phosphoric acid?

9. What does this suggest about the relative ease of oxidation of these halogen hydrides?

(III) The Silver Halides

(e) Place about $1cm^3$ of silver nitrate solution in each of four test-tubes and add an equal volume of potassium fluoride solution to one tube, potassium chloride to the next and potassium bromide and iodide to the third and fourth, respectively. Mix the contents of each tube and then add about $10cm^3$ of dilute ammonia solution to each.

162

10. Record your observations, and attempt to explain the solubility in the presence of ammonia solution, using the relative solubilities of the silver halides. Look up the solubilities in a data book, if the order of solubility is not obvious from your experiments.

(IV) Sodium Hypochlorite

(f) Investigate the effect on sodium hypochlorite solution of (i) dilute acid (ii) warming in the presence of a cobalt salt (iii) manganese hydroxide, prepared by adding alkali to a solution of a manganese (II) salt.

11. Record your observations, including identification of any gases evolved, and interpret the reactions.

(V) Hypochlorites, Chlorates and Perchlorates

(g) Compare the relative oxidizing power in aqueous solution of sodium hypochlorite, potassium chlorate and potassium perchlorate by investigating the reaction of each with (i) neutral potassium iodide solution (ii) acidified potassium iodide and (iii) acidified ammonium iron (II) sulphate (ferrous ammonium sulphate) solution.

Set out the results in the form of a table and draw up a list of the three substances in order of decreasing oxidizing power in aqueous solution.

12. The electrode potentials in acid solution are:

$$ClO_4^- + 8\,H^+ + 8e^- \rightleftharpoons Cl^- + 4\,H_2O \quad E = +1.38V$$

$$ClO_3^- + 6\,H^+ + 6e^- \rightleftharpoons Cl^- + 3\,H_2O \quad E = +1.45V$$

$$ClOH + H^+ + 2e^- \rightleftharpoons Cl^- + H_2O \quad E = +1.49V$$

$$Fe^{3+} + e^- \rightleftharpoons Fe^{2+} \qquad\qquad E = +0.77V$$

$$I_2 + 2e^- \rightleftharpoons 2I^- \qquad\qquad E = +0.54V$$

Do these values for the electrode potentials agree with the order of oxidizing power you have found?

13. Do all the reactions you would expect to occur, considering the electrode potentials, actually occur in practice? If not, what explanation can you give for this?

163

Notes 28

Standard: *
Time required: 1½ hours practical work plus 1 hour for questions
Reagents required:
  chlorine, bromine and iodine
  chloroform or carbon tetrachloride ($10cm^3$)
  (approx. molar) aqueous potassium bromide ($5cm^3$)
  (approx. molar) aqueous potassium iodide ($5cm^3$)
  (approx. molar) aqueous potassium chloride ($5cm^3$)
  (approx. molar) aqueous potassium fluoride ($5cm^3$)
  syrupy phosphoric acid ($10cm^3$)
  concentrated sulphuric acid ($10cm^3$)
  solid potassium (or sodium) chloride, bromide and iodide (1g)
  (approx. decimolar) silver nitrate solution ($5cm^3$)
  chlorine water ($10cm^3$)
  bromine water ($10cm^3$)
  (approx. molar) ammonia solution ($40cm^3$)
  sodium hypochlorite solution ($20cm^3$)
  potassium chlorate solution ($10cm^3$)
  1% potassium perchlorate solution ($10cm^3$)
  dilute hydrochloric and sulphuric acids ($10cm^3$)
  cobalt (II) chloride or nitrate solution ($2cm^3$)
  manganese (II) chloride or sulphate solution ($2cm^3$)
  dilute sodium hydroxide solution ($5cm^3$)
  ammonium iron (II) sulphate solution ($5cm^3$)
Apparatus required:
  test-tubes
  hard-glass test-tubes
  gas jar and cover glass
  chlorine cylinder or chlorine generator

Results of experiments and notes on questions
(a) Students should note the colour and physical state of each element, and may also include in the table melting points, boiling points, etc.

Element	Colour	State (room temp)	m.p./°C	b.p./°C
chlorine	green	gas	−102	−34
bromine	orange	liquid	−7	63
iodine	grey/black	solid	114	184

164

Chlorine forms a yellow/green colour
Bromine forms an orange colour $\Big\}$ in chloroform or carbon tetrachloride
Iodine forms a violet colour

When chlorine water is added to aqueous potassium iodide, the aqueous layer becomes brown; the chloroform layer becomes violet, thus showing that the iodide has been oxidized to iodine.

When chlorine water is added to aqueous potassium bromide, both the aqueous and chloroform layers become orange, showing that the bromide has been oxidized to bromine.

1. If chloroform is not used the colours of iodine and bromine in aqueous solution are so similar that one cannot say for certain whether bromine or iodine is present. The two elements do have different colours in solution in chloroform and thus the identity of the halogen present can be established.

2. Chlorine oxidizes both bromide and iodide ions to bromine and iodine, respectively and must therefore be the strongest oxidizing agent of the three halogens considered.

3. The electrode potentials of these three halogens are as follows:

$$Cl_2 + 2e^- \rightleftharpoons 2\,Cl^- \quad E = +1{\cdot}36V$$

$$Br_2 + 2e^- \rightleftharpoons 2\,Br^- \quad E = +1{\cdot}07V$$

$$I_2 + 2e^- \rightleftharpoons 2\,I^- \quad E = +0{\cdot}53V$$

Thus this confirms that chlorine is the strongest oxidizing agent of the three.

4. The electrode potentials indicate that bromine would be expected to oxidize iodide ions, but not chloride ions.
Thus adding bromine to aqueous potassium chloride in the present of chloroform would leave the free bromine unchanged and both layers would appear orange.
On adding bromine water to aqueous potassium iodide, one would predict that the orange coloured bromine would be reduced to colourless bromide ions as the iodide ions were oxidized to iodine, which would appear brown in the aqueous layer and violet in the chloroform layer.

(c) When syrupy phosphoric acid is added to solid potassium chloride, no change is apparent at room temperature, but on warming steamy fumes of hydrogen chloride are produced.
When potassium bromide is treated with the phosphoric acid, the observations are similar to those for the chloride, but if the fumes are passed into silver nitrate solution they can be shown to be hydrogen bromide.
When potassium iodide is treated with phosphoric acid at room temperature, a slight yellow colour can be observed, possibly due to oxidation of the hydrogen iodide by the air. On warming the brown colour of iodine is unmistakable, and starch paper is turned blue by the vapour, confirming that decomposition (or oxidation) of the hydrogen iodide is taking place. Since the colour appears in the test-tube, with vapour being evolved, it is likely that most of the free iodine results from thermal decomposition.

5. Hydrogen iodide is the only one of the three which appears to be decomposed by the heating and is thus the most readily decomposed.

6. The syrupy phosphoric acid produces the halogen hydride because the phosphoric acid is much less volatile than the halogen hydrides and thus, on heating, the equilibrium between the chloride ions and hydrogen chloride is disturbed, as hydrogen chloride is driven off. Hydrogen chloride is a stronger acid than phosphoric acid.

$$H_3PO_4 + Cl^- \rightleftharpoons H_2PO_4{}^- + HCl \uparrow$$

7. Since hydrochloric acid is a stronger acid than phosphoric acid, one would expect that on treatment of anhydrous sodium phosphate with hydrochloric acid, the phosphate ion would tend to accept protons from the hydrochloric acid and some phosphoric acid

165

would be produced. But if the mixture were heated, it would be the more volatile hydrogen chloride that would be evolved, not phosphoric acid

$$PO_4^{3-} + H^+Cl^- \rightleftharpoons HPO_4^{2-} + Cl^- ; HPO_4^{2-} + H^+Cl^- \rightleftharpoons H_2PO_4^- + Cl^- ;$$

$$H_2PO_4^- + H^+Cl^- \rightleftharpoons H_3PO_4 + Cl^-$$

(d) When concentrated sulphuric acid is added to a solid chloride, steamy white fumes of hydrogen chloride are evolved; there is no evidence of chlorine.

When concentrated sulphuric acid is added to a solid bromide, steamy fumes and an orange vapour are produced, suggesting that a mixture of hydrogen bromide and bromine is formed, there is no evidence of hydrogen sulphide.

On adding concentrated sulphuric acid to a solid iodide, the mixture becomes black, a violet vapour is sometimes seen and there is a smell of hydrogen sulphide and sulphur is also seen—these two products being reduction products of the sulphuric acid.

8. Concentrated sulphuric acid is quite a strong oxidizing agent, whereas phosphoric acid is not. The different reactions with sulphuric acid are due to it oxidizing the halogen hydride produced.

9. The halogen hydride most readily oxidized is obviously hydrogen iodide, followed by hydrogen bromide. Hydrogen chloride is not oxidized by sulphuric acid and is clearly the most difficult of the three to oxidize.

(e) On adding fluoride to silver nitrate solution, a cloudiness appears but no precipitate settles. The cloudiness disappears completely on the addition of ammonia solution.

Chloride ions produce a white precipitate with silver nitrate solution, which dissolve completely in ammonia solution.

Bromide ions produce a very pale yellow precipitate when added to silver nitrate solution. On addition of ammonia solution, some of the precipitate dissolves as is indicated by the clearing of the supernatant liquid.

Iodide ions produce a pale yellow precipitate when added to silver nitrate solution but very little of it dissolves in ammonia solution and the supernatant liquid remains cloudy. Both silver chloride and silver bromide darken on exposure to light; this is not noticeable in the case of silver iodide.

The solubility of the silver halides is:

Halide	Solubility/g at 20°C	Solubility Product/mol² dm⁻⁶
silver fluoride	170	
silver chloride	9×10^{-5}	2×10^{-10}
silver bromide	8×10^{-6}	5×10^{-13}
silver iodide	3×10^{-7}	8×10^{-17}

10. The solubility of silver halides in ammonia solution depends on the formation of the diammine silver (I) complex ion $[Ag(NH_3)_2]^+$.

$$Ag^+ + 2 NH_3 \rightleftharpoons [Ag(NH_3)_2]^+$$

The addition of ammonia to a saturated solution of a silver halide decreases the concentration of the free silver ion, Ag^+, and since the complex ion is a stable one, the concentration of the free silver ions can be decreased to such an extent that the product of the free silver ion concentration and the halide ion concentration, is below the value of the solubility product of the more soluble silver halides (AgF and Ag Cl). The less soluble the silver halide, the lower the concentration of free silver ions in the saturated solution, and the addition of ammonia cannot decrease the free silver ion concentration below this very low value.

(f) 11. Dilute acids cause rapid evolution of chlorine from sodium hypochlorite solution at room temperature. Hypochlorite solutions always contain chloride ions, so any dilute

166

acid will cause the reaction to occur as follows:

$$HOCl + H^+ + e^- \rightleftharpoons \tfrac{1}{2}Cl_2 + H_2O \qquad E = +1.63V$$

$$\tfrac{1}{2}Cl_2 + e^- \rightleftharpoons Cl^- \qquad\qquad\qquad E = +1.36V$$

Hence $HOCl + H^+ + Cl^- \rightleftharpoons Cl_2 + H_2O \qquad E = +0.27V$

On addition of a cobalt salt to the sodium hypochlorite solution, which is always alkaline, black cobalt oxide precipitates. This catalyses the decomposition of the hypochlorite giving oxygen and sodium chloride. Presumably the cobalt oxide acts as an intermediate-compound catalyst, being oxidized to a higher oxidation state, which releases oxygen on reverting to the original oxidation state.

$$2\,OCl^- \xrightarrow{\;Co_2O_3\;} O_2 + 2\,Cl^-$$

The white manganese (II) hydroxide, formed by adding alkali to manganese (III) ions, darkens in the presence of air which oxidizes it to manganese (III) oxide. But if sodium hypochlorite solution is added a black precipitate, manganese (IV) oxide is formed. The interpretation is as follows:

In alkaline solution $\quad ClO^- + H_2O + 2e^- \rightleftharpoons Cl^- + 2\,OH^- \qquad\qquad E = +0.89V$

$\qquad\qquad\qquad MnO_2 + 2\,H_2O + 2e^- \rightleftharpoons Mn(OH)_2 + 2\,OH^- \qquad E = -0.50V$

Hence $\qquad ClO^- + Mn(OH)_2 \rightleftharpoons MnO_2 + Cl^- + H_2O \qquad E = +1.39V$

(g) The results of experiments to investigate the relative oxidizing power of sodium hypochlorite, potassium chlorate and potassium perchlorate in aqueous solution are:

Substance	Neutral KI	Acidified KI	Acidified ammonium iron (II) sulphate
sodium hypochlorite	brown colour iodine	brown colour iodine	mixture gives deep red with KCNS
potassium chlorate	no change	yellow colour trace of iodine	mixture gives pale red with KCNS
potassium perchlorate	no change	no change	mixture gives just a trace of red with KCNS

Order of decreasing oxidizing power in aqueous solution:

sodium hypochlorite > potassium chlorate > potassium perchlorate

12. The electrode potentials suggest the same order as is given above *but* the values are very close together and one would not expect such a marked difference in oxidizing power based on the values of the electrode potentials.

13. Considering electrode potentials alone, one would predict that all three compounds should oxidize both iodide ions (in acid and alkaline solution) and iron (II) ions, in acid solution.

For example, $\quad ClO_4^- + 8\,H^+ + 8e^- = Cl^- + 4\,H_2O \qquad\qquad E = +1.38V$

$\qquad\qquad\qquad 8\,Fe^{3+} + 8e^- = 8\,Fe^{2+} \qquad\qquad\qquad\qquad E = +0.77V$

Hence $\qquad ClO_4^- + 8\,H^+ + 8\,Fe^{2+} = Cl^- + 4\,H_2O + 8\,Fe^{3+} \quad E = +0.61V$

The electrode potentials predict the tendency for one species to oxidize another, under standard conditions, in terms of energetics. Although the conditions are unlikely to be standard, that is not going to alter the potentials sufficiently to explain our apparent lack of reaction. A more likely explanation is, that the electrode potentials interpret the energetics of the reaction and *it should be remembered that they take no account of the kinetics of the reaction between the species.* In this case, the reaction between perchlorate ions and iron (II) ions in acid solution is presumably very slow.

Assignment 29
The Chemistry of Aluminium

(I) Reactions of the metal

(a) *With Dilute Hydrochloric Acid*
Place a few pieces of aluminium turnings in a test-tube and add about $5cm^3$ of dilute hydrochloric acid. Record your observations.

1. The standard electrode potentials for the relevant half-reactions are:

$$Al^{3+} + 3e^- \rightleftharpoons Al \qquad E = -1{\cdot}66V$$

$$2H^+ + 2e^- \rightleftharpoons H_2 \qquad E = 0{\cdot}00V$$

Thus, one would expect aluminium spontaneously to reduce hydrogen ions. What explanation can you suggest for the apparent reluctance of the aluminium to do this?
Place a few pieces of aluminium turnings in two further test-tubes. Add about $5cm^3$ of dilute hydrochloric acid to each and warm each tube over a bunsen burner. Leave one of the tubes in a rack; pour away the acid from the second tube, wash the aluminium with distilled water and then add about $5cm^3$ of dilute hydrochloric acid at room temperature. Record the results of these experiments, comparing the rate of evolution of gas.
Investigate the effect of dilute hydrochloric acid on aluminium turnings which have been immersed in mercuric chloride solution for about one minute.

2. What factors appear to affect the rate at which aluminium reacts with dilute hydrochloric acid?

(b) *With Dilute Sodium Hydroxide Solution*
Add a few aluminium turnings to about $5cm^3$ of sodium hydroxide solution in a test-tube and warm. Identify any gas evolved and record your observations.

(c) *With Oxygen*
Treat a piece of aluminium foil with mercuric chloride solution and then, using the fingers, hold the foil in the air.

3. What evidence is there of reaction?
The vigorous reaction between aluminium and oxygen can be used in the reduction of metal oxides by aluminium. Using the data given, calculate the heat of reaction between aluminium and iron (III) oxide. (Heats of formation: $Al_2O_3 = 1676kJ\ mol^{-1}$; $Fe_2O_3 = 825kJ\ mol^{-1}$)

(d) *With Chlorine*
Place a few pieces of aluminium turnings in a hard-glass test-tube fitted with a piece of hard-glass tubing and a cork, having a groove cut in it to allow unused gas to escape. Clamp the tube in a fume-cupboard and heat the aluminium, then pass chlorine over the heated aluminium, removing the bunsen burner once reaction has commenced, so that the vigour of the reaction may be observed. After the reaction, allow the apparatus to cool and retain the product for a later experiment.

(e) *With Sulphur*

N.B. This experiment must only be done under the direct supervision of your teacher.

Mix a teaspoonful of aluminium powder with about twice its bulk of flowers of sulphur on a piece of paper, place the mixture in a hard-glass test-tube and clamp it in a fume-cupboard. Heat the mixture carefully until reaction begins. (The mixture may be ejected from the tube, so make sure that it is pointing in a safe direction.)

After the apparatus has cooled, add a little water. Establish the identity of the gas evolved.

(II) Reactions of the hydroxide

Prepare a sample of aluminium hydroxide by placing about $5cm^3$ of aluminium chloride solution in a test-tube and adding dilute ammonia solution until no more precipitate is formed. The reaction may be represented by the following equation:

$$[Al(H_2O)_6]^{3+} + 3\ OH^- \rightleftharpoons Al(OH)_3(H_2O)_3 + 3\ H_2O$$

Separate the suspension into three portions. To the first portion add sodium hydroxide solution until no further change occurs. The reaction may be represented by the equation:

$$Al(OH)_3(H_2O)_3 + OH^- \rightleftharpoons [Al(OH)_4(H_2O)_2]^- + H_2O$$

To the second portion add dilute ammonia solution.

4. What explanation can you give for the different reaction with sodium hydroxide from that using ammonia solution?

5. Why do you think $[Al(OH)_4(H_2O)_2]^-$ is soluble in water whereas $Al(OH)_3(H_2O)_3$ is not?

To the third portion of the suspension of aluminium hydroxide, add dilute hydrochloric acid. Record your observation.

6. Explain this reaction, with the help of an equation, similar in form to those written above.

(III) Reactions of the chloride

Heat a sample of the anhydrous aluminium chloride, prepared in Experiment (d), in a dry hard-glass test-tube. Compare this with the behaviour of sodium chloride when heated.

7. Describe the action of heat on anhydrous aluminium chloride. What does this suggest about the bonding in anhydrous aluminium chloride?

Add a little water to a sample of the anhydrous aluminium chloride in a dry test-tube.

8. Interpret your observations. Does this confirm your prediction about the bonding in anhydrous aluminium chloride?

Dissolve a little *hydrated* aluminium chloride in distilled water and determine the pH of the solution.

Add a solution of sodium carbonate to your solution of hydrated aluminium chloride.

9. Interpret your observations and comment on the stability of aluminium carbonate.

10. Predict what would happen if crystals of hydrated aluminium chloride were heated in a dry hard-glass test-tube until no further change occurred.

Test your predictions.

(IV) Preparation of potash alum (Potassium aluminium sulphate)

Add an excess of aluminium turnings to about $10cm^3$ of approximately molar potassium hydroxide solution in a test-tube. Warm the mixture and leave until no more aluminium reacts. Decant the solution and add approximately molar sulphuric acid until the bulk of the precipitate formed, is re-dissolved.

11. Why does some of the precipitate not dissolve? What is this substance?

12. How could the formation of this substance be avoided?

Filter the mixture and evaporate to concentrate the solution before leaving it to crystallize.

When the solution is saturated, add a crystal of chrome alum and leave over night.

13. What do you observe on the crystal of chrome alum?

14. What conditions must be fulfilled before this phenomenon occurs?

15. What is meant by the term 'an alum'? What is the general formula of an alum?

Notes 29

Standard: **

Time required: 1½ hours practical time plus about 1 hour answering questions.

Reagents required:

aluminium turnings

(approx. molar) dilute hydrochloric acid (30cm^3)

(approx. molar) sodium hydroxide solution (20cm^3)

(approx. molar) mercuric chloride solution (10cm^3)

aluminium foil (2g)

flowers of sulphur (1g)

(approx. molar) dilute ammonia solution (20cm^3)

sodium chloride crystals (1g)

hydrated aluminium chloride crystals (1g)

(approx. molar) sodium carbonate solution (5cm^3)

(approx. molar) potassium hydroxide solution (10cm^3)

crystals of chrome alum (1g)

(approx. molar) aluminium chloride solution (5cm^3)

Apparatus required:

test-tubes

100cm^3 beaker

4 hard-glass test-tubes

filtration apparatus

evaporating basin

crystallizing dish

pH meter (or Universal Indicator papers)

chlorine generator (or chlorine cylinder)

hard-glass test-tube, fitted with grooved cork and hard-glass tube

bunsen-burner, tripod and gauze

Results of experiments and notes on questions

(I) Reactions of the metal

(a) When aluminium turnings are treated with dilute hydrochloric acid at room temperature very little reaction occurs at first. After about ten or twenty minutes the reaction speeds up and hydrogen is readily evolved.

1. The standard electrode potentials predict what would tend to happen under standard conditions, but they do not predict the speed at which the reaction will take place and other factors, such as condition of the surface of the aluminium, may slow the reaction initially—as is the case in this example.

Warming the aluminium in the dilute hydrochloric acid causes reaction to occur rapidly and, being exothermic, the rate increases still further.

Aluminium which has been warmed in the acid, to initiate the reaction, will react readily with hydrochloric acid at room temperature.

171

Likewise aluminium, which has been treated with mercuric chloride solution, reacts readily with hydrochloric acid at room temperature.

2. It therefore appears that apart from the obvious effect of temperature, the state of the surface of the aluminium affects the rate at which it reacts. If a fresh surface is prepared, or the original surface layer rendered pervious, then aluminium reacts quite readily.

(b) When aluminium turnings are treated with dilute sodium hydroxide solution, reaction is slow at first but, on warming, reaction proceeds rapidly and as a result of the exothermic nature of the reaction the rate continues to increase until the solution boils. Hydrogen is liberated.

(c) 3. A white powder 'grows' on the treated surface of the aluminium and much heat is evolved. In many cases the aluminium becomes too hot to hold!

As an illustration of the vigour of the reaction between aluminium and oxygen, it can be shown that the heat of reaction between aluminium and iron (III) oxide is

$$2\,Al + Fe_2O_3 = 2\,Fe + Al_2O_3 \; ; \Delta H = -851\,kJ\,mol^{-1}$$

It would be a good idea to demonstrate the Thermit reaction at this stage. The details are as follows:

Dry some aluminium powder and iron (III) oxide in an oven at about 120°C the day before use. Mix about 36g of iron (III) oxide and 12g of aluminium powder and place it in the fire-clay crucible. (If a hole about an eighth of an inch in diameter is drilled in the bottom of the crucible, and covered with paper, the molten iron produced can be allowed to drop into water in a can, adding to the spectacle.) Make a depression in the mixture, add a little magnesium powder and insert a piece of magnesium ribbon about 1½ inches long. Set up in a fume-cupboard and light the magnesium.

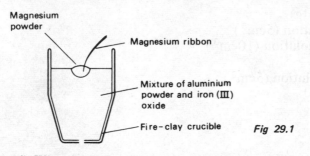

Magnesium powder

Magnesium ribbon

Mixture of aluminium powder and iron (III) oxide

Fire-clay crucible   *Fig 29.1*

(d) When chlorine is passed over heated aluminium, it is possible to maintain the reaction without heating, if the supply of chlorine is sufficiently rapid. The aluminium then reacts producing a bluish flame, as evidence of the exothermic nature of the reaction. The reaction need not be continued until all the aluminium has reacted, but sufficient anhydrous aluminium chloride must be prepared for the two experiments to be performed with it.

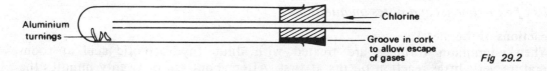

Aluminium turnings

Chlorine

Groove in cork to allow escape of gases   *Fig 29.2*

(e) The reaction between aluminium and sulphur can be performed satisfactorily with very fine aluminium powder. Teachers should ensure that students do not use more of the reagents than is recommended, and that they do not grind the mixture in a mortar—mixing with a spoon, or spatula, on a piece of paper is sufficient. Treatment of the product with a little water produces hydrogen sulphide, the presence of which can be confirmed by the darkening of a moist lead acetate paper.

This series of experiments should establish the fact that aluminium is a reactive metal, particularly if it is not protected by the impervious layer of oxide.

172

(II) Reactions of the hydroxide

4. Aluminium hydroxide reacts with sodium hydroxide solution to produce the soluble aluminate ion, the high concentration of hydroxide ions removing protons from the aluminium hydroxide to do so. There is much lower concentration of hydroxide ions in ammonia solution than in sodium hydroxide solution, and it should also be noted that aluminium ions are not readily complexed with ammonia molecules, so that this mechanism does not cause the aluminium hydroxide to dissolve.

5. The fact that the $[Al(OH)_4(H_2O)_2]^-$ ion is charged gives it greater polarity than the neutral aluminium hydroxide and may be the explanation of its solubility.

6. Aluminium hydroxide also 'dissolves' in dilute hydrochloric acid, because the basic character of the aluminium hydroxide causes it to accept protons and become the hydrated aluminium ion.

$$Al(OH)_3(H_2O)_3 + 3 H^+ \rightleftharpoons [Al(H_2O)_6]^{3+}$$

(III) Reactions of the chloride

No change occurs on heating sodium chloride crystals in a hard-glass test-tube; they do not melt or sublime—this is typical of an ionic compound.

7. Anhydrous aluminium chloride sublimes on heating—this suggests it is a covalent compound.

8. Anhydrous aluminium chloride is vigorously hydrolyzed, with the evolution of steamy fumes of hydrogen chloride—this is typical of the behaviour of covalent chlorides.
A solution of hydrated aluminium chloride in distilled water has a pH of about 4·5. On addition of sodium carbonate solution, a precipitate occurs and carbon dioxide is evolved. The precipitate (probably aluminium hydroxide) may or may not subsequently dissolve, depending on the proportions.

9. The relatively high concentration of hydrogen ions in the aqueous aluminium chloride causes the formation of carbonic acid, which decomposes liberating carbon dioxide. Aluminium carbonate will therefore not exist in the presence of any moisture.

10. Since the hydrated aluminium ion releases protons, one might predict that, on heating the hydrated crystals, some volatile hydrogen chloride might be driven off leaving aluminium hydroxide and ultimately aluminium oxide, with water being evolved.
Heating hydrated aluminium chloride crystals does liberate water vapour and steamy fumes of hydrogen chloride and a residue insoluble in water and dilute hydrochloric acid—presumably aluminium oxide is left.

(IV) Preparation of Potash Alum

11. If glass apparatus is used in this reaction, some silica from the glass reacts to form silicate ions, which on acidification form silica again. This silica does not react with acids and so, unlike aluminium hydroxide, does not re-dissolve.

12. The formation of this silica could be avoided by using nickel, or even aluminium apparatus when the strong alkali is being used.

13. Potash alum crystallizes around the chrome alum crystal, producing a transparent, colourless overgrowth.

14. Overgrowths form as a saturated solution evaporates, if the two substances crystallize in the same crystalline form. This is the case for alums, which all have the same general formula.

15. Alums are double salts; they are sulphates of a monovalent metal (or the ammonium radical) and a trivalent metal. The general formula may be written as

$$M^I M^{III}(SO_4)_2 . 12H_2O \text{ or } M^I_2 SO_4 . M^{III}_2(SO_4)_3 . 24H_2O$$

Assignment 30
The Chemistry of Nitrites and Nitrates

INTRODUCTION

This series of experiments is designed to survey the chemistry of nitrites in relation to nitrates and other simple nitrogen compounds. In order to interpret the behaviour of the reagents used, it will be necessary to ascertain whether a reaction has occurred and, if so, what products have been formed. Thus, very careful observations must be made, and additional tests may be required.

The half-equations given below are listed in order of decreasing standard reduction potential and, when you have established the identity of the products of a reaction, these tables will be of help in interpreting the reaction and writing an overall equation for it.

Table 1

	Oxidizing agent						Reducing agent			
	(i) MnO_4^-	$+ 8H^+$	$+ 5e^-$	$\rightleftharpoons Mn^{2+}$	$+ 4H_2O$					
Strength	(ii) $2NO_2^-$	$+ 8H^+$	$+$	$\rightleftharpoons N_2$	$+ 4H_2O$		Strength			
of	(iii) Br_2		$+$	$\rightleftharpoons 2Br^-$			of			
Oxidizing	(iv) HNO_2	$+ H^+$	$+$	$\rightleftharpoons NO$	$+ H_2O$		reducing			
agent	(v) NO_3^-	$+ 3H^+$	$+ e^-$	$\rightleftharpoons HNO_2$	$+ H_2O$		agent			
decreases	(vi) Fe^{3+}		$+$	$\rightleftharpoons Fe^{2+}$			increases			
	(vii) I_2		$+$	$\rightleftharpoons 2I^-$						
	(viii) N_2	$+ 8H^+$	$+$	$\rightleftharpoons 2NH_4^+$						
	(ix) NO_3^-	$+ 6H_2O +$		$\rightleftharpoons NH_3$	$+ 9OH^-$					
	(x) NO_2^-	$+ 5H_2O +$		$\rightleftharpoons NH_3$	$+ 7OH^-$					
	(xi) $[Al(OH)_4]^-$		$+$	$\rightleftharpoons Al$	$+ 4OH^-$					

Example

If permanganate ions react with iron (II) ions, in acid solution, it can be shown that manganese (II) ions and iron (III) ions are formed. Thus it would seem that half-equations (i) and (vi) are involved. Combining these half-equations gives the overall equation:

$$MnO_4^- + 8H^+ + 5Fe^{2+} \rightleftharpoons Mn^{2+} + 4H_2O + 5Fe^{3+}$$

1. Complete the other half-equations, by inserting the number of electrons involved in each case.

2. Assign each of the nitrogen-containing species to a position in Table 2 showing the oxidation number of the nitrogen in the species.

174

Table 2

Oxidation Number. Ion or molecule

```
+V   ┼
+IV  ┼
+III ┼
+II  ┼
+I   ┼
 O   ┼
-I   ┼
-II  ┼
-III ┼
```

N.B. Under standard conditions, no oxidizing agent can react with a reducing agent above it in the table of reduction potentials.

Conversely, an oxidizing agent will react with a reducing agent below it in the table, but the reaction may be so slow as to be of no practical significance.

Strictly, these reduction potentials only apply under standard conditions.

3. What are 'standard' conditions in this context?

4. Predict whether iron (III) ions would oxidize (a) bromide ions (b) iodide ions, under standard conditions.

EXPERIMENT WORK

(a) Test for nitrite and nitrate ions

Add about five drops of a fresh solution of iron (II) sulphate, acidified with dilute sulphuric acid, to approximately 2cm³ of dilute sodium nitrite solution.

Note the colour change, produced in the presence of *dilute* sulphuric acid. The reaction, performed under these conditons, is used as a test for nitrite ions.

Add about five drops of a fresh solution of iron (II) sulphate, acidified with dilute sulphuric acid, to approximately 2cm³ of dilute potassium nitrate solution. Note the different reaction from that using a nitrite, and carefully run concentrated sulphuric acid down the side of the tube to form a separate layer. Note the appearance of this mixture. This reaction is used as a test for the presence of nitrate ions.

(b) Add dilute hydrochloric acid to about 2cm³ of aqueous sodium nitrite solution in a test-tube. Note any changes in appearance of the solution, and the colour of the gas near the surface of the liquid and at the mouth of the tube. Warm the solution until the reaction is complete. Test the remaining solution for the presence of (i) nitrite (ii) nitrate ions.

Nitrous acid is a weak acid and will thus be the initial product of acidification of a solution of nitrite ions.

5. Is there any evidence for the formation of nitrogen (II) oxide (nitric oxide) as one of the products of the decomposition of nitrous acid?

6. Using the appropriate half-equations, construct an overall equation to account for the products you have identified, starting from nitrous acid only.

7. In the light of the table of reduction potentials, explain the behaviour of nitrous acid in this reaction.

(c) Add sodium nitrite solution dropwise to about 2cm³ of bromine water, acidified with dilute sulphuric acid, until no further colour change occurs.

8. Was there any evidence of a gas being released before the colour of the free bromine disappeared?

9. Construct an overall equation for the reaction, using the appropriate half-equations.

(d) Add sodium nitrite solution dropwise to about 2cm³ of potassium permanganate solution acidified with dilute sulphuric acid.

10. Was there any evidence of release of a gas before the permanganate was decolourized?

11. Construct an overall equation for the reaction from the appropriate half-equations.

(e) Add sodium nitrite solution dropwise to about 2cm³ of potassium iodide solution, acidified with dilute sulphuric acid.

12. Describe your observations and explain how the nature of the products of the reaction may be deduced from them. Write an overall equation for the reaction.

(f) Repeat the reaction used in experiment (a) with a solution of nitrite ions and iron (II) ions but boil the solution to decompose the brown complex and the excess nitrous acid. Establish the oxidation state of the iron in the resulting solution.

13. Write an overall equation for the reaction if the mixture is boiled.

(g) Make about 2cm³ of sodium nitrite solution alkaline by the addition of sodium hydroxide solution, add some aluminium turnings (or Devarda's alloy) and warm the mixture. Identify the nitrogen-containing gas released.

14. Write an overall equation for the reaction.

15. Explain why the reaction is carried out in alkaline conditions, and why aluminium is used. What other metal do you think would perform this reaction with nitrites?

(h) Boil about 2cm³ of sodium nitrite solution with excess ammonium chloride until no gas, other than steam, is evolved. (This may be achieved by boiling the mixture until gas is no longer evolved, and then adding more solid ammonium chloride and repeating until the addition of further ammonium chloride does not produce more gas.) Attempt to establish the identity of the gas evolved, and test the remaining solution for the presence of nitrite ions.

16. Write an equation for the reaction of ammonion ions and nitrite ions.
Repeat experiments (b) to (h) substituting potassium nitrate solution for sodium nitrite and warming the solution if little or no reaction occurs at room temperature. Record your observations and write equations where possible.

17. What procedure would you adopt to test for nitrate ions in the presence of nitrite ions?

18. Give examples of reactions in which nitrous acid, or the nitrite ion, behaves as a reducing agent.

19. Give examples of reactions in which nitrous acid, or the nitrite ion, behaves as an oxidizing agent.

20. In some experiments nitrous acid, or the nitrite ion, behaved as a reducing agent. What results were obtained on repeating these experiments using nitric acid, or the nitrate ion? What does this suggest about the ability of nitric acid, or nitrates, to act as reducing agents?

21. Quoting experimental evidence, compare the efficiency as an oxidizing agent of nitrous acid, or the nitrite ion, with that of nitric acid, or the nitrate ion.

22. Is this comparison in agreement with the order indicated, for standard conditions, by the table of reduction potentials?

23. Nitrous acid can oxidize iodide ions to iodine, but is itself oxidized by bromine. Comment on this with reference to the position of the relevant half-equations in the table of reduction potentials.

176

Notes 30

Standard: **

Time required: 1½ hours practical time plus about 1 hour answering questions

Reagents required:
    iron (II) sulphate (1g)
    dilute sulphuric acid (20cm^3)
    sodium nitrite solution (20cm^3)
    potassium nitrate solution (20cm^3)
    concentrated sulphuric acid (2cm^3)
    dilute hydrochloric acid (5cm^3)
    bromine water (5cm^3)
    potassium permanganate solution (5cm^3)
    potassium iodide solution (5cm^3)
    sodium hydroxide solution (10cm^3)
    potassium hexacyanoferrate (II) solution (1cm^3)
    potassium hexacyanoferrate (III) solution (1cm^3)
    aluminium turnings (or Devarda's alloy) (1g)
    ammonium chloride solution (10cm^3)
    ammonium chloride crystals (1g)
    litmus papers

Apparatus required:
    test-tubes
    teat pipettes
    bunsen burner
    100cm^3 beaker

Notes on questions and results of experiments

1. The completed half-equations are:

(ii) $2 NO_2^- + 8 H^+ + 6e^- \rightleftharpoons N_2 + 4 H_2O$

(iii) $Br_2 + 2e^- \rightleftharpoons 2 Br^-$

(iv) $HNO_2 + H^+ + e^- \rightleftharpoons NO + H_2O$

(v) $NO_3^- + 3 H^+ + 2e^- \rightleftharpoons HNO_2 + H_2O$

(vii) $I_2 + 2e^- \rightleftharpoons 2I^-$

(viii) $N_2 + 8 H^+ + 6e^- \rightleftharpoons 2 NH_4^+$

(ix) $NO_3^- + 6 H_2O + 8e^- \rightleftharpoons NH_3 + 9 OH^-$

(x) $NO_2^- + 5 H_2O + 6e^- \rightleftharpoons NH_3 + 7 OH^-$

(xi) $Al(OH)_4^- + 3e^- \rightleftharpoons Al + 4 OH^-$

2. The oxidation number of the nitrogen-containing species can be represented as follows:

Oxidation Number   Ion or molecule

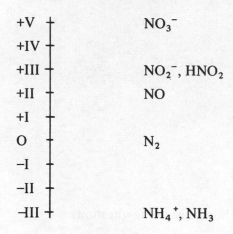

Oxidation Number	Ion or molecule
+V	NO_3^-
+IV	
+III	NO_2^-, HNO_2
+II	NO
+I	
O	N_2
–I	
–II	
–III	NH_4^+, NH_3

3. Standard conditions are a temperature of 25°C and pressure of one atmosphere, with dissolved substances in a solution of molar concentration. (For more advanced work the concentration of the dissolved substances should be such that the relevant species have an activity of one.)

4. Since the table shows that iron (III) ions are stronger oxidizing agents than iodine, but weaker than bromine, one would predict that iron (III) ions would oxidize iodide ions under standard conditions, but would not oxidize bromide ions.
(a) On adding acidified iron (II) sulphate solution to sodium nitrite solution, a brown colour is formed throughout the solution.
On adding acidified iron (II) sulphate solution to potassium nitrate solution, no colour change occurs until the concentrated sulphuric acid is run down the side of tube to form a layer at the bottom of the tube. A brown colour forms at the junction of the two layers.
(b) On adding dilute hydrochloric acid to sodium nitrite solution, the solution becomes pale blue and bubbles of gas are evolved. The gas released from the surface of the liquid is colourless, but it turns brown on coming into contact with the air at the mouth of the tube. On warming, the blue colour disappears and the evolution of gas increases until the reaction is complete; during warming bubbles of brown gas appear to be released at the surface of the solution.
After cooling, the solution obtained when no further evolution of gas occurs, gives a yellow colour with iron (II) sulphate, acidified with dilute sulphuric acid, but forms a brown ring when concentrated sulphuric acid is added.
This suggests that very few nitrite ions are present, but that there is quite a high concentration of nitrate ions.

5. The fact that the gas evolved, on acidification of sodium nitrite solution, is colourless at the surface of the liquid, but turns brown on contact with air, suggests that nitrogen (II) oxide (nitric oxide) is produced.

6. The half-equations (iv) and (v) suggest that, in acid solution, one molecule of nitrous acid can oxidize another molecule of nitrous acid (i.e. disproportionation occurs). The half-equations can be combined as follows:

$$Eq(iv)\ HNO_2 + H^+ + e^- = NO + H_2O\quad E = +1 \cdot 00V$$

$$Eq(v)\ NO_3^- + 3H^+ + 2e^- = HNO_2 + H_2O\quad E = +0 \cdot 94V$$

Multiplying equation (iv) by two, and reversing equation (v) gives, on addition

$$3\ HNO_2 = 2\ NO + H_2O + NO_3^- + H^+\quad E = +0 \cdot 06V$$

7. The reduction potential for the reaction represented by equation (iv) is greater than that for the reaction represented by equation (v), so one would expect that the oxidizing agent (HNO_2) in equation (iv) would oxidize the reducing agent (HNO_2) in equation (v) i.e. one would predict disproportionation.

The nitrogen (IV) oxide (nitrogen dioxide) released on warming is probably due to some thermal decomposition of the nitrous acid.
(c) On addition of nitrous acid to bromine water, the orange colour of the bromine is removed and no gas is evolved until excess nitrous acid is present.

8. There was no evidence of gas being evolved before the colour of the bromine was removed.

9. The fact that no gas was evolved, as the nitrous acid reacted with the bromine, suggests that the nitrous acid was oxidized producing nitrate ions. The two relevant half-equations are (iii) and (v)

$$Eq(iii) \qquad Br_2 + 2e^- = 2Br^- \qquad\qquad E = +1 \cdot 07V$$

$$Eq(v) \quad NO_3^- + 3H^+ + 2e^- = HNO_2 + H_2O \quad E = +0 \cdot 94V$$

Reversing equation (v) and adding gives

$$Br_2 + HNO_2 + H_2O = 2\, Br^- + NO_3^- + 3\, H^+ \; E = +0 \cdot 13V$$

10. (d) On addition of nitrous acid to acidified potassium permanganate solution, the permanganate is decolourized and no gas is evolved until excess nitrous acid has been added.

11. The relevant half-equations are (i) and (v)

$$Eq(i) \quad MnO_4^- + 8\, H^+ + 5e^- = Mn^{2+} + 4\, H_2O \; E = +1 \cdot 51V$$

$$Eq(v) \; NO_3^- + 3\, H^+ + 2e^- = HNO_2 + H_2O \qquad E = +0 \cdot 94V$$

Multiplying equation (i) by two, and multiplying equation (v) by five, reversing it and adding, gives

$$2\, MnO_4^- + 5\, HNO_2 + H^+ = 2\, Mn^{2+} + 5\, NO_3^- + 3H_2O \; E = +0 \cdot 57V$$

12. (e) On addition of nitrous acid to acidified potassium iodide solution, iodine is liberated, shown by the brown colour of the solution, and a colourless gas is evolved which turns brown at the mouth of the tube. This is in keeping with a reduction of the nitrous acid, producing nitrogen (II) oxide (nitric oxide).
The relevant half-equations are (iv) and (vii)

$$Eq(iv) \; HNO_2 + H^+ + \; e^- = NO + H_2O \; E = +1 \cdot 00V$$

$$Eq(vii) \qquad\qquad I_2 + 2e^- = 2\, I^- \qquad\qquad E = +0 \cdot 54V$$

Multiplying equation (iv) by two, and reversing equation (vii) gives, on addition

$$2\, HNO_2 + 2\, H^+ + 2\, I^- = 2NO + 2H_2O + I_2 \; E = +0 \cdot 46V$$

(f) Boiling a solution of sodium nitrite with acidified iron (II) sulphate solution causes decomposition of the brown complex formed at room temperature. Brown fumes are formed at the mouth of the tube and a yellow-brown solution remains, when no further gas is evolved.
The resulting solution gave an intense blue colour with potassium hexacyanoferrate (II) but only a slight blue colour with potassium hexacyanoferrate (III) suggesting that the predominant oxidation state of the resulting iron compound was three.

13. The relevant half-equations are (iv) and (vi)

$$Eq(iv) \; HNO_2 + H^+ + e^- = NO + H_2O \; E = +1 \cdot 00V$$

$$Eq(vi) \qquad\qquad Fe^{3+} + e^- = Fe^{2+} \qquad\qquad E = +0 \cdot 77V$$

179

Reversing equation (vi) and adding gives

$$HNO_2 + H^+ + Fe^{2+} = NO + H_2O + Fe^{3+} \quad E = +0.23V$$

(g) Warming an alkaline solution of sodium nitrite with aluminium turnings liberates ammonia, as indicated by the fact that moist red litmus paper held in the gas turns blue.

14. The relevant equations are (x) and (xi)

$$Eq(ix) \quad NO_2^- + 5H_2O + 6e^- = NH_3 + 7OH^- \quad E = -0.16V$$

$$Eq(xi) \quad [Al(OH)_4]^- + 3e^- = Al + 4OH^- \quad E = -2.35V$$

Multiplying equation (xi) by two, reversing it and adding, gives

$$NO_2^- + 5H_2O + 2Al + OH^- = NH_3 + 2[Al(OH)_4]^- \quad E = +2.19V$$

15. Alkaline conditions are used so that ammonia gas is evolved, rather than ammonium ions formed in solution. Aluminium is used because it acts as a strong reducing agent in alkaline solution—other metals with amphoteric hydroxides could be used instead of aluminium e.g. zinc.

(h) Boiling sodium nitrite solution with excess ammonium chloride releases a colourless gas which is neutral to litmus, and has no smell—presumably nitrogen. The remaining solution does not give the results obtained above, using sodium nitrite solution e.g. no iodine is liberated from acidified potassium iodide solution.

16. The relevant equations are (ii) and (viii)

$$Eq(ii) \quad 2NO_2^- + 8H^+ + 6e^- \rightleftharpoons N_2 + 4H_2O$$

$$Eq(viii) \quad N_2 + 8H^+ + 6e^- \rightleftharpoons 2NH_4^+$$

Reversing Eq(viii) and adding gives

$$2NH_4^+ + 2NO_2^- \rightleftharpoons 2N_2 + 4H_2O$$

which simplifies to

$$NH_4^+ + NO_2^- \rightleftharpoons N_2 + 2H_2O$$

17. To test for nitrate ions in the presence of nitrite ions, one could boil the solution with excess ammonium chloride until no more gas was evolved and then perform the brown ring test.

Experiments (b) to (h) repeated using potassium nitrate instead of sodium nitrite.

(b) No apparent reaction occurs on acidification of the potassium nitrate and boiling the solution does not remove nitrate ions.

(c) The bromine water is not decolourized; there is apparently no reaction.

(d) The potassium permanganate solution is not decolourized; there is apparently no reaction.

(e) Potassium nitrate solution reacts only slowly with potassium iodide acidified with dilute hydrochloric acid. Surprisingly the addition of concentrated hydrochloric acid does not bring about much oxidation of the iodide ions.

(f) Boiling iron (II) sulphate solution, acidified with dilute sulphuric acid, with potassium nitrate solution causes little reaction. Testing the mixture after boiling gives a deep blue colour with potassium hexacyanoferrate (III) and little blue colour with potassium hexacyanoferrate (II), showing that the iron is predominantly in the oxidation state of II.

(g) Boiling an alkaline solution of potassium nitrate with aluminium turnings, produces a gas which is alkaline to litmus and smells like ammonia.

The relevant equations are (ix) and (xi)

$$Eq(ix) \quad NO_3^- + 6H_2O + 8e^- = NH_3 + 9OH^-$$

$$Eq(xi) \quad [Al(OH)_4]^- + 3e^- = Al + 4OH^-$$

Multiplying equation (ix) by three, and equation (xi) by eight and reversing it gives, on addition

$$3\,NO_3^- + 8\,Al + 5\,OH^- + 18\,H_2O = 3\,NH_3 + 8\,[Al(OH)_4]^-$$

(h) There is no apparent evolution of gas (other than steam) on boiling potassium nitrate solution with excess ammonium chloride. On cooling the solution, the presence of nitrate ions can be established by the brown ring test. The fact that nitrate ions do not react with ammonium ions below 100°C is important in detecting a nitrate in the presence of a nitrite. (See question 17)

18. Nitrous acid behaved as a reducing agent in the reactions with bromine water, and with potassium permanganate.

19. Nitrous acid behaves as an oxidizing agent in the reactions with iron (II) sulphate, acidified potassium iodide, aluminium turnings in alkaline solution and ammonium ions.

20. Although nitrous acid and nitrites can behave as reducing agents, nitric acid and nitrates rarely do so. There was no reaction between nitric acid and bromine water or potassium permanganate.

21. Nitrous acid, or the nitrite ion, is usually a stronger oxidizing agent than nitric acid, or the nitrate ion, as is illustrated by the fact that nitrous acid readily oxidizes acidified potassium iodide and acidified iron (II) sulphate, whereas nitric acid causes no appreciable reaction with the same reagents.

22. For the reactions quoted in the table of reduction potentials, there is agreement between the reduction potentials and the experimental evidence obtained, where comparison is possible. In the case where the reduction potentials suggest that nitrate ions would be stronger oxidizing agents than nitrite ions (half-equations (ix) and (x)), there is no experimental evidence to enable a comparison.

23. The reduction potential for the half-reaction in which nitrous acid is reduced to nitrogen (II) oxide (nitric oxide) is greater than the reduction potential for the conversion of iodine to iodide ions, so nitrous acid can oxidize iodide ions.
The reduction potential for the reaction in which bromine is converted to bromide ions is greater than the electrode potential for the reaction in which nitrate ions are reduced to nitrous acid, so bromine can oxidize nitrous acid to nitrate ions.

REFERENCE

Mahan, *College Chemistry* Addison Wesley (1966).

Assignment 31
The Properties of Hydrogen Peroxide

INTRODUCTION

Hydrogen peroxide, H_2O_2, has the structure:

$$\begin{array}{c} H \\ \quad \diagdown \\ \qquad O-O \\ \qquad\qquad \diagdown \\ \qquad\qquad\quad H \end{array}$$

The two H–O bonds are not coplanar and the structure is best visualized as a half open book.

In this practical you will carry out several experiments designed to illustrate the diverse chemical character of this compound. Throughout it will be vital to make careful observations and to record these in detail. Whenever possible try to summarize your conclusions by writing equations to illustrate what you think has occurred. You will find that it is helpful to consider the following equation and half-equations:

(1) $H_2O_2 \rightleftharpoons H^+ + HO_2^-$

(2) $H_2O_2 + 2\,e^- \rightleftharpoons 2\,OH^-$

(3) $H_2O_2 \rightleftharpoons 2\,H^+ + O_2 + 2\,e^-$

1. Which of the terms: *acid, base, alkali, oxidizing agent, reducing agent* is most applicable to hydrogen peroxide if it reacts:
(a) according to Equation (1)? (b) according to Equation (2)? (c) according to Equation (3)?

EXPERIMENT (i)

Acidify a small portion of potassium iodide solution with a little dilute sulphuric acid and then add a few drops of the H_2O_2 solution provided.

2. What is the coloured product and which of the following reagents, if added to the mixture, is likely to be useful in confirming its identity?

anhydrous copper sulphate; barium chloride; silver nitrate; starch

3. How has H_2O_2 behaved in its reaction with iodide ions?

EXPERIMENT (ii)

Acidify a little H_2O_2 solution with dilute sulphuric acid. To this mixture add a few drops of potassium permanganate solution.

4. What is the gas which was evolved?

5. What does the formation of this gas suggest about the manner in which the H_2O_2 has behaved in this reaction?

6. Why was sulphuric acid used in preference to hydrochloric acid in this experiment?

182

EXPERIMENT (iii)

Place about 3cm^3 of the H_2O_2 solution in a test tube and add a small amount of manganese (IV) oxide (manganese dioxide). You may assume that the manganese oxide is acting as a catalyst for this reaction. Identify the gas evolved.

7. How is the equation for this reaction related to half-equations (2) and (3), given on the previous page?

8. How is the hydrogen peroxide behaving in this reaction?

EXPERIMENT (iv)

Try the effect of the hydrogen peroxide solution on (a) blue litmus paper (b) red litmus paper (c) solid sodium bicarbonate.

9. Attempt to place the following compounds in order of increasing acidity:

water; carbonic acid; hydrogen peroxide.

Give reasons for your answer.

EXPERIMENTS (v)–(ix)

Devise experiments   eroxide reacts with:

(v) lead sul
(vi) sulph
(vii) silver   ions)
(viii) hydrog
(ix) iron (II)
Make a table   eh aves as an oxidizing agent and
those in which i

EXPERIMENT (x)

Place about 3cm^3 a test-tube and add to it
approximately equal   r (care: ether is extremely
inflammable). Add a d   e the colour of the ether
layer.

10. Ether is a covalent c   th coloured product
from the fact that it is notic
By diluting the hydrogen pe   ow sensitive a test
this is for hydrogen peroxide.

183

Notes 31

Standard: *

Time required: 1½ hours practical work plus 1 hour answering questions

Reagents required:

Solids:	manganese (IV) oxide [manganese dioxide]	(0·5g)
	sodium hydrogen carbonate [sodium bicarbonate]	(0·5g)
Solutions:	hydrogen peroxide [20 vols]	(30cm³)
	potassium iodide	(2cm³)
	dilute sulphuric acid	(15cm³)
	starch	(1cm³)
	potassium permanganate	(1cm³)
	lead acetate	(1cm³)
	hydrogen sulphide	(5cm³)
	silver nitrate	(2cm³)
	sodium hydroxide	(5cm³)
	iron (II) sulphate	(3cm³)
	potassium dichromate	(3cm³)
	ether	(3cm³)

Apparatus required:

Test-tubes and a dropper or teat pipette for each student

Notes on experiment work and questions

1. (a) In the first equation hydrogen ions are being formed i.e. the hydrogen peroxide is acting as an acid.

(b) In this case the hydrogen peroxide is removing electrons from elsewhere i.e. it is behaving as an oxidizing agent.

(c) In the third equation the hydrogen peroxide is acting as an electron donor i.e. it is a reducing agent.

2. The brown colour formed in the first experiment is caused by the liberation of I_2 (or more strictly I_3^-). This can be confirmed by adding starch solution; the latter turns dark blue in the presence of free iodine.

$$H_2O_2 + 2e^- \rightarrow 2\,OH^-$$

$$2\,OH^- + 2\,H^+ \rightarrow 2\,H_2O$$

$$\underline{2\,I^- \rightarrow \quad I_2 + 2e^-}$$

$$H_2O_2 + 2\,H^+ + 2\,I^- = 2\,H_2O + I_2$$

3. The above equation shows that H_2O_2 has behaved as an oxidizing agent in Experiment (i).

4. With care the gas which is evolved can be identified as oxygen by means of the glowing splint test.

184

5. Equation (3) shows that the liberation of oxygen should be indicative of hydrogen peroxide behaving as a reducing agent. The decolouration of the permanganate solution confirms this, showing that the hydrogen peroxide has been oxidized.

$$5\,H_2O_2 \rightarrow 10\,H^+ + 5\,O_2 + 10e^-$$
$$\frac{2\,MnO_4^- + 16\,H^+ + 10e^- \rightarrow 2\,Mn^{2+} + 8\,H_2O}{2\,MnO_4^- + 5\,H_2O_2 + 6\,H^+ = 2\,Mn^{2+} + 5\,O_2 + 8\,H_2O}$$

6. Hydrochloric acid is not used because the MnO_4^- ion can oxidize Cl^- ions to Cl_2.

Experiment (iii)
The appearance of oxygen again suggests that hydrogen peroxide is acting as a reducing agent. However, since oxidation and reduction are always complementary, if we assume that MnO_2 is only acting as a catalyst, it would appear that some of the H_2O_2 must be acting as an oxidizing agent.

7. Adding Equations (2) and (3) with the equation: $H^+ + OH^- = H_2O$, the overall equation is seen to be the familiar:

$$2\,H_2O_2 = 2\,H_2O + O_2$$

8. The hydrogen peroxide is both oxidized and reduced by itself, i.e. it disproportionates.

Experiment (iv)
(a) the blue litmus turns red (b) the red litmus is unaffected (c) solid sodium hydrogen carbonate with cold hydrogen peroxide solution reacts to yield a colourless gas. However, tests show that this is oxygen (produced by catalytic decomposition of H_2O_2 induced by the ionic salt) rather than carbon dioxide.

9. Thus, the sequence of increasing acid strength is: H_2O H_2O_2 H_2CO_3
This is confirmed by the pK_a values

$$H_2O\ 15{\cdot}7 \quad H_2O_2\ 11{\cdot}8 \quad HCO_3^-\ 10{\cdot}3 \quad H_2O + CO_2\ 6{\cdot}4$$

N.B. The result of Experiment (iv) really only allows the conclusion that H_2O_2 is a weaker acid than the HCO_3^- ion. Carbonic acid is mentioned on the pupils' sheets because many students may not have encountered step-wise dissociation of acids at this stage in their Advanced Level course.
It is worthwhile asking students to predict the relative acidities of H_2O_2 and H_2O, reasoning in terms of electronegativity and the numbers of oxygen atoms.

Experiment (v)
A good procedure is to take a damp piece of filter paper which has been dipped in lead acetate solution before being exposed briefly to hydrogen sulphide, and to place the paper in a test-tube containing a little hydrogen peroxide. The black lead sulphide is rapidly *oxidized* to white lead sulphate:

$$PbS + 4\,H_2O_2 = PbSO_4 + 4\,H_2O$$

Experiment (vi)
Since laboratory solutions of sulphurous acid or sodium sulphite will almost certainly have been in part oxidized to sulphate ions by the air, it is vital to do a control experiment.

$$SO_3^{2-} + H_2O_2 = SO_4^{2-} + H_2O$$

The formation of sulphate ions is demonstrated by adding dilute hydrochloric acid and barium chloride solution.

Experiment (vii)
On adding the hydrogen peroxide the brown silver oxide, Ag_2O, is almost immediately blackened, indicating that it has been *reduced* to metallic silver:

$$Ag_2O + H_2O_2 = H_2O + O_2 + 2\,Ag$$

185

The finely divided silver then acts as a very efficient catalyst for the decomposition of hydrogen peroxide and so much oxygen is also evolved.

Experiment (viii)

A milky precipitate of sulphur forms indicating that the hydrogen peroxide has *oxidized* the hydrogen sulphide to sulphur:

$$H_2S + H_2O_2 = S + 2H_2O$$

Experiment (ix)

Partial oxidation of most iron (II) sulphate solutions by the air demands that a control experiment must be performed. The fact that hydrogen peroxide oxidizes Fe^{2+} ions to Fe^{3+} ions is shown by testing for the latter with either potassium thiocyanate (gives blood red colour) or with hexacyanoferrate (II) ions (ferrocyanide ions). The latter give prussian blue in the presence of Fe^{3+} ions.

$$H_2O_2 + 2Fe^{2+} + 2H^+ = 2H_2O + 2Fe^{3+}$$

Experiment (x)

A deep blue colouration, thought to be due to CrO_5 (which contains Cr (VI) is seen in the ether layer. In the aqueous layer it rapidly decomposes to give a green solution, but it is much more stable in the ether layer.

10. The fact that the compound is quite soluble in ether suggests that it is not a complex ion but a neutral molecule.

Rough experiments show that even when the 10 'vol' hydrogen peroxide solution is diluted by about a hundred-fold it can still be easily detected by means of this test.

186

Assignment 32

Determination of the Oxidation State of Iron in some of its Compounds by Titration

Weigh accurately between 1·0 and 1·2g of iron powder into a 250cm³ conical flask, fitted with a Bunsen valve.

Add 50·0cm³ of 1·00M sulphuric acid and heat the flask gently until all the iron has dissolved. Cool and pour the contents of the flask into a 200cm³ graduated glask, adding the washings and making up to 20cm³ with distilled water. Shake the flask until the solution is homogeneous.

1. Explain the action of a Bunsen valve. Why is it used in this experiment?

(I) Determination of the oxidation state of iron in this solution

Pipette 20·0cm³ portions of this solution into a 250cm³ titration flask and titrate against 0·50M sodium hydroxide solution using screened methyl orange as indicator.

Repeat the titration until two concordant readings are obtained.

Set out results as shown:

Weight of flask + iron =   g

Weight of flask alone =   g

Weight of iron =   g

    Final burette reading/cm³

    Initial burette reading/cm³

    Result/cm³

2. How many moles of iron were added initially?

3. Write the equation for the reaction of the excess sulphuric acid with sodium hydroxide.

4. How many moles of sulphuric acid were added initially?

5. How many moles of sulphuric acid remained in 200cm³ of the diluted solution?

6. How many moles of sulphuric acid reacted with the iron?

7. How many moles of hydrogen ions (H⁺) does one mole of iron react with?

8. How many electrons does one iron atom lose to the hydrogen ions?

9. What is the oxidation state of iron in the salt which could be obtained by crystallization of the solution made by dissolving iron in dilute sulphuric acid?

10. The salt which could be crystallized from this solution is thus called?

(II) Determination of the oxidation state of iron in the compound formed by oxidation of the compound identified in Part (I), by potassium permanganate

Pipette 20·0cm³ of the diluted solution, (as in part (I)), into a 250cm³ titration flask and titrate against 0·020M potassium permanganate solution. Repeat the titration until two concordant readings are obtained. Set out results as shown:

Final burette reading/cm³

Initial burette reading/cm³ _____ _____ _____

Result/cm³ _____ _____ _____

11. Is this titration being performed in acid solution? Write the half-equation for the reduction of permanganate ions (MnO_4^-) under these conditions.

12. How many moles of iron were weighed out and dissolved (see part (I))?

13. How many moles of iron (. . .) ions were there in 200cm³ of the diluted solution?

14. How many moles of permanganate ions would be required to oxidize this number of iron (. . .) ions?

15. How many moles of permanganate ions would be required to oxidize one mole of iron (. . .) ions?

16. How many electrons does one permanganate ion accept on reduction?

17. How many electrons does one iron (. . .) ion lose in this reaction?

18. What was the iron (. . .) ion oxidized to in this reaction?

Notes 32

Standard: *

Time required: 1½ hours

Reagents required:
   1·00M sulphuric acid (70cm³)
   iron (metal) powder [reduced by hydrogen] (1·5g)
   N.B. If coarser iron is used it greatly prolongs the time taken to dissolve.
   distilled water (250cm³)
   0·50M sodium hydroxide solution (100cm³)
   0·020M potassium permanganate solution (100cm³)
   screened methyl orange solution (12 drops)

Apparatus required:
   1 x 250cm³ conical flask, fitted with bung and Bunsen valve
   Bunsen burner, tripod and gauze
   1 x 200cm³ graduated flask
   1 x 50·0cm³ pipette [1 x 25·0cm³ pipette could be used]
   1 x 20·0cm³ pipette
   1 x 250cm³ titration flask
   1 burette
   2 x 150cm³ beakers

Typical results and notes on questions

1. A Bunsen valve can be constructed from a piece of rubber tubing by making a narrow slit with a razor blade and fitting one end to the glass tubing leading through the bung and sealing the other end of the rubber tubing with a piece of glass rod. Alternatively a rubber 'policeman' can be slit with a razor blade and fitted to the end of the glass tubing which leads through the bung.

The valve allows steam, and other gases, to escape yet prevents air entering the flask. In this experiment it is important to prevent air entering the flask as it could oxidize the iron compound produced by the reaction of the iron with the acid.

Results:

Weight of iron powder = 1·00g

(I) 20·0cm³ of the diluted solution required 12·6cm³ of 0·50M NaOH to neutralize the excess acid.

2. The number of moles of iron added initially = $\frac{1·00}{56}$ = 0·0179 moles

3. The equation for the reaction between sulphuric acid and sodium hydroxide is:

$$H_2SO_4 + 2NaOH = Na_2SO_4 + 2H_2O$$

4. The number of moles of sulphuric acid added initially = $\frac{50·0}{1000}$ x 1·00 = 0·05 moles

5. The number of moles of sulphuric acid remaining in 200cm³ of the diluted solution =

$$\frac{12 \cdot 6}{1000} \times 0 \cdot 50 \times \frac{1}{2} = 0 \cdot 0315 \text{ moles}$$

6. Hence $0 \cdot 05 - 0 \cdot 0315 = 0 \cdot 0185$ moles of sulphuric acid reacted with the iron.

7. Hence one mole of iron reacts with $0 \cdot 0185 \times 2 \times \frac{56}{1 \cdot 00}$ moles of hydrogen ions = $2 \cdot 07$ moles.

8. Thus one iron atom loses $2 \cdot 07 \simeq 2$ electrons to the hydrogen ions

9. The iron is thus present in solution in the oxidation state of +2.

10. The salt which could be crystallized from solution is thus called iron (II) sulphate.

(II) $20 \cdot 0 \text{cm}^3$ of the diluted solution required $18 \cdot 2 \text{cm}^3$ of $0 \cdot 02 \text{M}$ $KMnO_4$ for oxidation. 11. The titration is being performed in acid solution as a large excess of sulphuric acid was added initially. The half-equation for the reduction of permanganate ions in acid solution is:

$$5e^- + 8H^+ + MnO_4^- = Mn^{2+} + 4H_2O$$

12. The number of moles of iron weighed out initially = $0 \cdot 0179$ moles.

13. There were $0 \cdot 0179$ moles of iron (II) ions in 200cm^3 of diluted solution, since one mole of iron (Fe) produces one mole of iron (II) ions (Fe^{2+}).

14. The number of moles of permanganate ions needed to oxidize this number of iron (II) ions = $\frac{18 \cdot 2}{1000} \times 0 \cdot 020 \times 10 = 0 \cdot 00364$ moles.

15. Thus the number of moles of permanganate ions needed to oxidize one mole of iron (II) ions = $0 \cdot 00364 \times \frac{56}{1 \cdot 00} = 0 \cdot 204$ moles.

16. On reduction, one permanganate ion accepts five electrons.

17. Hence one iron (II) ion loses $5 \times 0 \cdot 204 \simeq 1$ electron in this reaction.

18. The iron (II) ion was oxidized to the iron (III) ion in this reaction.

Assignment 33

An Investigation of the Simple Chemistry of Iron as an Illustration of the Typical Properties of a Transition Element

THE PROPERTIES OF IRON (II) AND IRON (III) COMPOUNDS

(I) Reactions of the 'simple' hydrated ions

Prepare a fresh solution of iron (II) sulphate by dissolving a few iron (II) sulphate crystals in distilled water. Similarly, prepare a solution of iron (III) chloride. Note the colours of these two solutions and use them to carry out the following:

(a) Take about $1 cm^3$ of each solution in separate test-tubes and add to each an equal volume of potassium thiocyanate solution. Record your observations

(b) Treat about $1 cm^3$ of each of the two iron solutions with equal volumes of potassium hexacyanoferrate (III) (i.e. $K_3 Fe(CN)_6$) solution.

(c) Repeat test (b) but this time use potassium hexacyanoferrate (II) solution ($K_4 Fe(CN)_6$)

(d) Repeat test (b) this time using KOH or NaOH solutions instead of the $K_3 Fe(CN)_6$)

In each of tests (b), (c) and (d) it will be necessary to record the colours of any precipitates which are formed and to note whether their appearance changes on standing.

1. Basing your answers on the above reactions, suggest how you would test to show:
(a) the presence of a simple iron (II) compound (b) the presence of a simple iron (III) compound (c) the absence of simple iron (II) and (d) the absence of simple iron (III) compounds
(e) Try out your methods of detection and investigate methods of converting iron (II) to iron (III) and vice-versa, using the following procedures:
(i) Take about $2 cm^3$ of your aqueous solution of iron (III) chloride and add about $4 cm^3$ of sulphurous acid. Boil the mixture for about a minute and carry out a test to establish whether reduction has occurred.
(ii) Take about $2 cm^3$ of fresh aqueous iron (II) sulphate solution and add about $4 cm^3$ of 20vol hydrogen peroxide solution. Boil the mixture with care for about five minutes before testing to establish whether oxidation has taken place.

2. Why is it necessary to boil for a few minutes in this last case?

(II) Reactions of the hexacyanoferrate (III) and hexacyanoferrate (II) ions

(a) Take about $1 cm^3$ of a solution of each of the potassium salts containing the above ions and treat each with about $1 cm^3$ of an aqueous solution of sodium hydroxide. What do you observe?

3. Try to explain why your observations are different from those you noted in 1(d).
(b) Mix $1 cm^3$ portions of solutions of potassium hexacyanoferrate (III) and potassium hexacyanoferrate (II). What do you observe?

4. Does this last observation confirm your explanation of question 3?

(III) The effect of iron (III) compounds on the decomposition of hydrogen peroxide

Place about $5 cm^3$ of 20 volume hydrogen peroxide solution in each of two test-tubes and add 5cm³ of an aqueous solution of sodium hydroxide to each. To one of the tubes add 3 drops of an aqueous solution of iron (III) chloride. Compare the rates of evolution of gas in the two tubes. Repeat the test in the absence of the alkali.

5. What iron (III) compound appears to affect the rate of decomposition of hydrogen peroxide?

6. What explanation can you suggest?

(IV) The action of heat on iron (II) oxalate

7. What are the formulae of oxalic acid and iron (II) oxalate?

Heat about 2g of iron (II) oxalate in a hard-glass test-tube until evolution of gas appears to cease. Allow the remaining solid to cool before tipping it onto a tile. Then repeat the above test, this time tipping out the residue while it is still hot. Compare the appearances of the two residues noting down your observations. Dissolve a small sample of each residue in dilute hydrochloric acid and carry out tests to establish the oxidation state of the iron compounds formed.

8. How do you account for your observations?

9. Why do you think that iron (II) oxalate was chosen as the iron (II) salt for this experiment?

10. What is the equation for the thermal decomposition of iron (II) oxalate?

(V) The magnetic properties of the hydrated iron (III) ion

Describe what you observe when a strong aqueous solution of iron (III) chloride contained in a U−tube is placed so that the meniscus in one arm of the U-tube is just below the centre of the pole pieces of a strong electromagnet. (If a permanent magnet is used it is easier to clamp the U-tube and move the magnet horizontally into position). Repeat the experiment using zinc chloride instead of the iron (III) chloride.

11. What are the electronic configurations of the hydrated iron (III) and zinc ions?

12. What term is applied to an ion which behaves in a similar fashion to the hydrated iron (III) ion when it is placed in a magnetic field?

13. How do these configurations account for the difference in the magnetic behaviours of these two ions?

The following factors:
Variable Oxidation States
Catalytic Activity
Coloured Ions
Complex Ion Formation
Paramagnetic Properties
are all deemed to be typical of the chemistry of transition metals. Bearing in mind the results which you have obtained from these series of experiments, write a short paragraph giving specific reasons why iron is classified as a transition element.

Notes 33

Standard: **

Time required: 1½ hours practical work plus 1 hour answering questions

Reagents required:

iron (II) sulphate	(1g)
iron (III) chloride	(1g)
potassium thiocyanate solution	(5 cm³)
potassium hexacyanoferrate (III) solution	(15 cm³)
potassium hexacyanoferrate (II) solution	(15 cm³)
sodium hydroxide solution	(20 cm³)
sulphurous acid	(5 cm³)
20 volume hydrogen peroxide solution	(5 cm³)
iron (II) oxalate	(4g)
iron (III) chloride solution [very concentrated]	(15 cm³)
zinc chloride solution [very concentrated]	(15 cm³)
dilute hydrochloric acid	(10 cm³)

Apparatus required:

test-tubes
bunsen burner
hard-glass test tube
porcelain tile
U-tube (made by bending glass tubing of approximately 3mm internal diameter)
strong electromagnet (preferably with movable pole pieces)
clamp and stand

Notes on experimental work and questions

(I) Iron (II) sulphate solution is pale green; iron (III) chloride is yellow or brown.

(a) On adding potassium thiocyanate solution the blood-red complex ion is formed with the iron (III) chloride solution; a pale red solution results from treatment of iron (II) sulphate because of some oxidation of iron (II) ions to iron (III) ions.

(b) Potassium hexacyanoferrate (III) forms prussian blue with the solution containing iron (II) ions; a brown solution (no prussian blue) is formed with the iron (III) ions.

(c) Potassium hexacyanoferrate (II) forms prussian blue with the solution containing iron (III) ions; it forms a light blue precipitate with the solution of iron (II) ions, because oxidation will have produced iron (III) ions and a small amount of prussian blue will result.

(d) On addition of hydroxide ions to iron (II) ions a gelatinous light green precipitate is formed, which darkens and becomes rust-coloured on standing in contact with air. The addition of hydroxide ions to iron (III) ions forms a rust coloured precipitate of iron (III) hydroxide. It is this which is formed as a result of oxidation, by the air, that causes the darkening of the precipitate formed from iron (II) ions.

1. (a) The presence of a simple iron (II) compound could be established by addition of a solution of potassium hexacyanoferrate (III), which would produce prussian blue.

193

(b) The presence of a simple iron (III) compound could be established by addition of a solution of potassium hexacyanoferrate (II), which would produce prussian blue, or potassium thiocyanate solution which would form the blood-red colouration.

(c) The absence of any simple iron (II) compound could be established by the addition of potassium hexacyanoferrate (III), which would form no prussian blue.

(d) The absence of any simple iron (III) compound could be established by the addition of potassium thiocyanate solution, which would give an almost colourless solution (i.e. no red colouration)

(e) (i) On addition of sulphurous acid to iron (III) chloride solution a red complex is formed, but this decomposes on boiling, leaving a pale green solution. Reduction is shown to have occurred by adding potassium thiocyanate, which gives an almost colourless solution.

(ii) Addition of hydrogen peroxide to iron (II) sulphate causes the colour to change from pale green to yellow on boiling. Potassium thiocyanate gives a blood-red colour indicating that oxidation has occurred. It is also possible to show that no iron (II) ions remain by adding potassium hexacyanoferrate (III) which forms no prussian blue.

2. The prolonged boiling is necessary to decompose the excess hydrogen peroxide, which could interfere with some of the tests to establish oxidation of the iron (II) ions.

(II) (a) On addition of sodium hydroxide solution, in turn, to hexacyanoferrate (II) and hexacyanoferrate (III) ions, no precipitate of the iron hydroxides occurs.

3. The lack of any iron hydroxide precipitate means that there must be very few simple iron (II) or iron (III) ions in the solution. In other words, the hexacyanoferrate complex ions are very stable indeed.

(b) On mixing solutions of hexacyanoferrate (II) and hexacyanoferrate (III) ions, no colour change, or precipitate is observed (i.e. no prussian blue is formed.)

4. This implies that there are no free iron (II) or iron (III) ions, and is consistent with the explanation of question 3.

(III) The addition of iron (III) chloride to hydrogen peroxide increases the rate of evolution of gas only if alkali is present.

5. It thus appears that iron (III) hydroxide is the catalyst.

6. The catalyst may be a surface catalyst and/or may be oxidized by the hydrogen peroxide and subsequently revert to the lower oxidation state, with the evolution of oxygen.

(IV) 7. The formula of oxalic acid is $\begin{matrix} COOH \\ | \\ COOH \end{matrix}$, and the formula of iron (II) oxalate is $\begin{matrix} COO \\ | \\ COO \end{matrix} Fe$

Iron (II) oxalate is a yellow powder, and on heating in a hard-glass test tube it evolves a mixture of carbon monoxide and carbon dioxide and leaves a black residue. If this residue is tipped on to a tile whilst still hot it glows as it is spontaneously oxidized by the air and turns a rusty-brown colour. If the residue is cooled before exposing to the air little change is observed.

Dissolving the residues in hydrochloric acid and testing with potassium hexacyanoferrate (II) shows that the residue which was exposed to the air whilst still hot is largely an iron (III) compound, whereas the other residue is largely an iron (II) compound.

8. The residue in the test-tube (i.e. out of contact with the air) is iron (II) oxide, which is spontaneously oxidized by the air if hot, but only slowly oxidized if cool.

9. Iron (II) oxalate is chosen for this experiment because on decomposition the gases produced are non-oxidizing, since carbon monoxide is present.

10. The equation for the thermal decomposition of iron (II) oxalate is:

in the test tube, $\begin{matrix} COO \\ | \\ COO \end{matrix} Fe = FeO + CO + CO_2$ on exposure to air $4FeO + O_2 = 2Fe_2O_3$

194

(V) For this experiment a very concentrated solution of iron (III) chloride is needed. This can be made by putting about $10cm^3$ of water in a beaker and adding lumps of iron (III) chloride until the solution is fairly viscous. If this solution is placed in a U-tube, with the meniscus in one arm of the tube just below the pole-pieces of a strong electromagnet, the liquid will move up the tube and thus move into the magnetic field. On switching off the electromagnet the solution can be seen to drop out of the field. (The effect is most noticeable if moveable, pointed pole-pieces are used, as these can be placed close to the U-tube and provide the strongest magnetic field where it is required.)

If a strong solution of zinc chloride is used, the meniscus will either not move, or if the field is sufficiently intense, the meniscus will move away from the field.

11. The electronic configurations of the relevant ions are:

hydrated iron (III) ion $[Fe(H_2O)_6]^{3+}$

hydrated zinc ion $[Zn(H_2O)_6]^{2+}$

	3d	4s	4p	4d
$[Fe(H_2O)_6]^{3+}$	↑ ↑ ↑ ↑ ↑	↑↓	↑↓ ↑↓ ↑↓	↑↓ ↑↓
$[Zn(H_2O)_6]^{2+}$	↑↓ ↑↓ ↑↓ ↑↓ ↑↓	↑↓	↑↓ ↑↓ ↑↓	↑↓ ↑↓

12. A solution which moves into the magnetic field, as the iron (III) chloride solution does, is said to be paramagnetic.

13. The paramagnetic effect of certain ions is dependent upon the number of unpaired electrons in the ion (the more unpaired electrons in an ion, the greater its paramagnetic effect). Ions with no unpaired electrons, e.g. the hydrated zinc ion, do not exhibit paramagnetism.

SUMMARY

Variable oxidation state is illustrated by the iron (II) and iron (III) compounds used in the majority of these experiments. The oxidation states are determined in Assignment Number 32.

Catalytic activity is illustrated by experiment (III) above.

Coloured ions are observed in experiment (I) above. The pale green hydrated iron (II) ion, and the yellow hydrated iron (III) ion are examples.

Complex ion formation is illustrated by the preparation of the iron (III)/thiocyanate complex in experiment I(a). Complex ions containing iron are also used in experiments I(b) and (c), and (II).

Paramagnetism of the hydrated iron (III) ion is illustrated in experiment (V).

Transition elements may be defined as those elements which can use electrons from the penultimate shell, for compound formation. The different number of valency electrons which a transition element may use gives rise to variable oxidation state, and this in turn may explain some of the catalytic activity of transition metals and their compounds. The small differences in energy levels occupied by electrons in transition metal ions means that transitions between various energy levels may be accompanied by the absorption, or emission of radiation in the visible part of the spectrum. Complex ion formation depends on the availability of orbitals able to receive electron pairs from the ligand molecules or ions and iron has the $4s$, $4p$ and $4d$ orbitals available and, in some cases, the $3d$ orbitals may be used as well. The unpaired electrons in many iron-containing ions are responsible for the paramagnetism, as explained above.

Thus iron may be classified as a transition element, because it may use electrons from the penultimate shell, for compound formation, and because it exhibits the characteristic properties normally associated with transition metals.

Assignment 34
The Chemistry of Chromium

The most important compounds of chromium are probably potassium chromate and dichromate, K_2CrO_4 and $K_2Cr_2O_7$ respectively.

1. What are the colours and appearances of these two salts?

2. Would you expect these salts to be soluble in water?

3. What are the names and formulae of the ions you would expect to be present in their aqueous solutions?

The relationship between the chromate and dichromate ions:

Make separate solutions of the two salts by dissolving about 0·5 g of each in $10cm^3$ portions of distilled water. Roughly divide each solution into two so that you have two tubes each containing about $5cm^3$ of potassium dichromate solution and two each containing a like volume of potassium chromate solution. Set aside one tube of each salt solution for reference purposes. To the remaining K_2CrO_4 solution add a few *drops* of dilute H_2SO_4. Compare the colour of the resulting solution with those of the reference solutions. Examine the effect of neutralising the dilute H_2SO_4 with a few drops of dilute NaOH. Investigate the effects of a few drops of NaOH solution on the untreated $K_2Cr_2O_7$ solution followed by a few drops of dilute H_2SO_4. Record your observations.

4. What do you conclude about the relationship between the chromate and dichromate ions?

5. What are the oxidation states of Cr in each ion?

6. What is the ground-state electron configuration for a Cr *atom*?

7. Can you suggest why Cr does not form stable compounds in which it has an oxidation state in excess of that which it exhibits in the chromate and dichromate ions?

8. Complete and balance the following ionic equations:

$$Cr\,O_4^{2-}{}_{aq} + H^+{}_{aq} = \qquad\qquad and \; Cr_2\,O_7^{2-}{}_{aq} + OH^-{}_{aq} =$$

9. Do the above equations represent acid-base or redox equilibria?

10. What is the structure of the dichromate ion?

Chromyl chloride

Mix about 0·1 g of solid $K_2Cr_2O_7$ with a similar mass of solid NaCl. Carefully add about $2cm^3$ of concentrated H_2SO_4 and warm gently. The coloured volatile product is called chromyl chloride and has the formula CrO_2Cl_2.

11. What colour is chromyl chloride and what element might it be confused with?

12. What is the oxidation state of Cr in chromyl chloride?

13. Bearing in mind your answer to question 12 and your observations in the first experiment, what would you expect to be formed when chromyl chloride is dissolved in alkaline solution?

Allow a little chromyl chloride vapour to sink into a tube containing a few drops of bench NaOH solution. Shake to dissolve the chromyl chloride and note the colour of the solution. Carry out a test to confirm your guess concerning the identity of the chromium species in this solution.

14. How would you distinguish between CrO_2Cl_2 and the element alluded to in question 11?

The redox behaviour of the dichromate ion

EXPERIMENT A

Heap about 2-3g of dry ammonium dichromate in the centre of a small sheet of asbestos. Using a wooden splint, ignite the top of the pile. Describe your observations being particularly careful to note any sign which suggests that a colourless gas is evolved.

15. If the gas mentioned above is nitrogen, have the ammonium ions been reduced in this reaction? (Give an electronic half-equation to illustrate your answer.)

16. By considering the initial and final oxidation states of nitrogen in this reaction together with the formula of ammonium dichromate, make a guess as to the oxidation state of the chromium in the solid green residue.

17. Assuming that the green residue is an oxide of chromium with the oxidation state you have guessed, suggest a balanced chemical equation for the thermal decomposition of ammonium dichromate, indicating which ion is being oxidized and which reduced.

EXPERIMENT B

The above experiment suggests that the dichromate ion can behave as an oxidizing agent, being itself reduced in the process. The oxidation state of chromium in the reduced product can be confirmed by the following titration:

Weigh out accurately $0.45-0.50$g of solid $K_2Cr_2O_7$ in a small beaker. Transfer the weighed sample into a 250 cm^3 conical flask taking care to wash the last traces of the solid into the flask with distilled water. Add about 50cm^3 of distilled water and about 15cm^3 of concentrated hydrochloric acid. Swirl the flask until the $K_2Cr_2O_7$ has all dissolved and then add about 5g of solid KI. When some 5 minutes or so has elapsed, titrate the liberated iodine to a starch end-point with 0.5M sodium thiosulphate solution.
N.B. (i) The starch should not be added until near the end-point of the titration.
(ii) At the end-point the solution is green—not colourless as in most thiosulphate titrations.

18. How many moles of the $S_2O_3^{2-}$ ion did you use per titration?

19. What is the ionic equation for the reaction between iodine and thiosulphate ions?

20. How many moles of I_2 must have been formed by the dichromate?

21. How many moles of potassium dichromate were present initially?

22. How many moles of I_2 were formed per mole of potassium dichromate?

Assuming that the chromium is reduced to a simple, hydrated chromium ion of unspecified charge, complete the equation:

$$Cr_2O_7^{2-} \quad + \quad H^+ \quad + \quad I^- \quad = \qquad + \quad I_2 \quad + \quad H_2O$$

23. What is the oxidation state of chromium in the compound formed when it is reduced by iodide ions?

24. Why was it necessary to wait for a short while after adding the KI before titrating?

25. In this titration great accuracy was not required since we were merely seeking to

establish an oxidation state which we assumed was an integer. However, if you wished to conduct this titration very accurately, what improvements might you make to the procedure?

EXPERIMENT C

The preparation of a chromium (III) compound

Dissolve about 6g of potassium dichromate in $40cm^3$ of distilled water and cool the mixture. Add about $5cm^3$ of concentrated sulphuric acid and stir with a thermometer until the temperature is below $25°C$. Now add $4cm^3$ of ethanol in a *dropwise fashion keeping the temperature below 50°C throughout*. Set the resulting solution aside to crystallise overnight.

26. What are the functions of the ethanol and the sulphuric acid?

27. What shape are your crystals? What family of compounds has crystals of this shape?

28. What is the identity of the crystals you have obtained?

29. Give a balanced chemical equation for the reaction involved in the previous experiment.

30. What is a double salt?

EXPERIMENT D

The Lowest Valency State of Chromium

Place about 2g of solid potassium dichromate and some 10g of zinc turnings together with $15cm^3$ of distilled water in a small conical flask. Add enough petroleum ether (60-80) to cover the water with a layer about a centimetre thick. Finally add about $15cm^3$ of concentrated hydrochloric acid and close the flask with a bung equipped with a bunsen valve. Set the flask aside and note the colour of the aqueous layer from time to time. *N.B. Petroleum ether is very inflammable*. When the aqueous layer has assumed a blue colour proceed as follows:

(i) Using a dropper remove a little of the aqueous solution and squirt it into a test-tube.

31. The blue solution is a solution of chromium (II) chloride and contains simple Cr^{2+} (chromous) ions. What happens to chromous ions on exposure to air?

It is clearly essential to protect the chromous solution from the air. This can be done by removing some of the petroleum ether in the dropper along with a sample of the chromous solution. Using this technique carry out the following two tests:

(ii) Add a little chromous solution to a tube containing a few grains of lead sulphate beneath about a centimetre of petroleum ether. Shake for a moment or so. What has happened to the lead sulphate?

32. What is the predominant chemical characteristic of chromium (II) ions?

(iii) Prepare about $5cm^3$ of a saturated solution of sodium acetate in water and cover this with a layer of petroleum ether. Using a dropper as before, add a few cm^3 of the chromium (II) solution to the sodium acetate. The red precipitate that should be obtained is chromium (II) acetate. This can be viewed as an uncharged complex of chromium (II). Examine the effect of complexing on the stability of chromium (II) with respect to air.

EXPERIMENT E

A chromium (III) complex sulphate

Make a solution of some 2g of 'chrome alum' in about $20cm^3$ of distilled water. N.B. *Do not warm in preparing the solution*. Put $5cm^3$ aliquots of this solution in each of two test-tubes. Gently warm one of the tubes in a bunsen flame for about a minute. At the end of this time cool the warm tube and add $10cm^3$ of bench barium chloride solution to both tubes. Centrifuge both tubes.

33. Which tube contains the most barium sulphate precipitate?

34. What colour change occurs on warming an aqueous solution of potassium chromium (III) sulphate?

35. How do you account for the change in colour on warming and for the difference in the amounts of barium sulphate?

Notes 34

Standard: **

Time Required: This practical is planned to occupy two 1½ hour laboratory sessions with the pupils working in pairs. This time can be decreased, however, by teacher demonstration of certain experiments, e.g. A, D and E.

Reagents required:

potassium chromate (1g)	starch (1cm³)
potassium dichromate (15g)	ethanol (5cm³)
dilute sulphuric acid (5cm³)	zinc turnings (10g)
dilute sodium hydroxide solution (5cm³)	lead sulphate (1g)
sodium chloride (1g)	sodium acetate (10g)
concentrated sulphuric acid (10cm³)	chrome alum (2g)
concentrated hydrochloric acid (30cm³)	dilute barium chloride solution (20cm³)
potassium iodide (5g)	petroleum ether [preferably
0·5M sodium thiosulphate solution (50cm³)	100–120°C range] (20cm³)
	distilled water (200cm³)

Apparatus required:
  test-tubes
  2 droppers
  splints
  250cm³ conical flask
  100cm³ conical flask equipped with a bunsen valve
  beakers
  thermometer (110°C to −10°C)
  centrifuge

Notes on experimental work and questions

1. Potassium chromate is yellow; potassium dichromate is orange. Both are crystalline powders.

2. Yes. Most potassium salts are reasonably soluble in water.

3. K^+, $CrO_4{}^{2-}$, $Cr_2O_7{}^{2-}$; the potassium, chromate and dichromate ions respectively.

The Relationship between the chromate and dichromate ions
A white tile or a piece of paper to act as a uniform, light background usually helps.

4. The easy interconversion of the two ions on adding acid and alkali suggests that the chromate and dichromate ions are in acid-base equilibrium with each other.

5. Assigning an oxidation state of −II to oxygen in these ions, it can be seen that the chromium atoms in each ion must have an oxidation state of VI in each case in order to account for a net charge of −2 on each ion.

6. $1s^2\ 2s^2\ 2p^6\ 3s^2\ 3p^6\ 3d^5\ 4s^1$

7. Only the six 4s and 3d electrons can be lost in the reactions of chromium.

8. $2CrO_4^{2-}(aq) + 2H^+(aq) = Cr_2O_7^{2-}(aq) + H_2O(l)$

$Cr_2O_7^{2-}(aq) + 2OH^-(aq) = 2CrO_4^{2-}(aq) + H_2O(l)$

9. Acid-base equilibria; no change in oxidation numbers.

10. $^-O - \overset{\displaystyle O}{\underset{\displaystyle O}{Cr}} {\diagdown} O {\diagup} \overset{\displaystyle O}{\underset{\displaystyle O}{Cr}} - O^-$

Chromyl Chloride

11. Chromyl chloride appears as a deep red, oily liquid or vapour. It could be confused with bromine.

12. If each oxygen has an oxidation number of $-II$ and each chlorine $-I$, then the oxidation number of the chromium atom must be $+VI$ to account for the absence of ionic charges.

13. We would expect CrO_2Cl_2 in alkaline solution to form the chromate ion since they are both Cr(VI) species. This can be confirmed by adding drops of acid and alkali to the suspected chromate solution.

14. Bromine dissolved in an alkaline solution is colourless whereas chromyl chloride gives a yellow solution.

The redox behaviour of the dichromate ion
Experiment A
15. The oxidation numbers of nitrogen in NH_4^+ and N_2 are $-III$ and O respectively. Thus, we can see that the ammonium ion is oxidized as it is converted to the nitrogen molecule:

$$2NH_4^+ \rightarrow N_2 + 8H^+ + 6e^-$$

16. If two nitrogen atoms are each oxidized by 3 units, we can guess that the two chromium atoms in a molecule of ammonium dichromate are probably each reduced by 3 units. i.e. Chromium ends up as a Cr(III) compound. N.B. This is no more than a guess—for one thing, we have no real right to assume that there is only one chromium product!

17. $\underset{\text{is oxidized}}{2NH_4^+} + \underset{\text{is reduced}}{Cr_2O_7^{2-}} \rightarrow N_2 + 4H_2O + Cr_2O_3$

Experiment B
If 0.50g of solid potassium dichromate are used the theoretical volume of 0.5M sodium thiosulphate solution needed is 20.4cm^3. In practice, we have found that titres are usually about 1–2% less than this.
Let $t$cm^3 be the actual titre when m grams of potassium dichromate are used

18. $0.5\ t/1000$ moles of $S_2O_3^{2-}$

19. $2S_2O_3^{2-}(aq) + I_2(aq) = S_4O_6^{2-}(aq) + 2I^-(aq)$

20. $0.25\ t/1000$ moles of I_2

21. $m/294$ moles of $Cr_2O_7^{2-}$ (N.B. Molecular Weight of $K_2Cr_2O_7$ is 294)

22. $294 \times 0.25\ t/1000m$ moles of I_2 per mole of $Cr_2O_7^{2-}$, which *should* prove to be approximately equal to 3!

$$\text{Hence } Cr_2O_7^{2-}(aq) + 14H^+(aq) + 6I^-(aq) \rightleftharpoons 2Cr^{3+}(aq) + 3I_2(aq) + 7H_2O(l)$$

23. $+III$

24. Because the reaction between $Cr_2O_7^{2-}$ and I^- takes a finite time to reach near completion.

25. The most obvious improvement would be to make a standard solution of potassium dichromate instead of relying on a single weighing of a small sample.

Experiment C

26. The ethanol acts as a reducing agent, being itself oxidized to acetaldehyde. Although the reaction may not involve direct electron transfer, it can be formally considered as:

$$CH_3CH_2OH \rightarrow CH_3CHO + 2H^+ + 2e^- \text{ accompanied by}$$

$$6e^- + Cr_2O_7^{2-} + 14H^+ \rightarrow 2Cr^{3+} + 7H_2O$$

The sulphuric acid provides the acid medium necessary for the reduction of the dichromate ion (see second half-equation)

27. The crystals are octahedral. The alums, general formula $M_2^I SO_4 . M_2^{III}(SO_4)_3 . 24H_2O$, have crystals of this shape.

28. 'chrome alum'. $K_2SO_4 . Cr_2SO_4 . 24H_2O$

29. $3CH_3.CH_2OH_{(l)} + Cr_2O_7^{2-}{}_{(aq)} + 8H^+_{(aq)} \rightleftharpoons 2Cr^{3+}_{(aq)} + 7H_2O_{(l)} + 3CH_3.CHO_{(aq)}$

30. A double salt consists of crystals of a substance composed of two salts in simple stoichiometric ratio, but which in solution shows all the reactions of the constituent single salts.

Experiment D(i)

31. The blue solution quickly becomes green on exposure to air, suggesting that Cr^{2+} is readily oxidized to Cr^{3+} ions by air.

Experiment D(ii)

As more and more chromous solution is added, the white $PbSO_4$ becomes greyer and greyer. Increasing amounts of metallic lead are being formed.

32. The predominant chemical characteristic of a Cr(II) ion is that it is a very strong reducing agent.

Experiment D(iii)

A red precipitate will only be obtained if the sodium acetate solution is a saturated one. The appearance of chromous acetate does not change on exposure to air for a few minutes.

N.B. An additional interesting experiment can be done with anhydrous chromic chloride, $CrCl_3$. This *appears* to be insoluble in water, but on adding a little Cr(II) solution it dissolves relatively easily. This 'catalytic' power of Cr(II) is thought to be due to electron exchange at the surface of the solid chromium (III) chloride:

$$Cr^{3+}_{(s)} + Cr^{2+}_{(aq)} \rightleftharpoons Cr^{2+}_{(aq)} + Cr^{3+}_{(aq)}$$

Experiment E

33. The unheated tube should contain the most barium sulphate precipitate.

34. On warming above 60°C the violet solution of potassium chromium (III) sulphate becomes green.

35. Some of the sulphate ions are becoming complexed on heating, i.e. A complex salt is being formed

$$\text{e.g. } Cr(H_2O)_6^{3+} + SO_4^{2-}{}_{aq} \rightleftharpoons CrSO_4(H_2O)_5^+ + H_2O$$

The sulphato complex ion formed would not be expected to show the reactions of the simple sulphate ion. Accordingly, there would be a reduction in the free sulphate ion concentration and a decrease in the amount of $BaSO_4$ formed.

FURTHER PROJECT

Prepare samples of the hydrate isomers: chloropentaquochromium (III) chloride and hexaquochromium (III) chloride. (See Reference 2)

REFERENCES

1. *Inorganic and Theoretical Chemistry* F. Sherwood Taylor. Chap XXI (Tenth Edition) Heinemann (1961)
2. *Practical Inorganic Chemistry,* G. Pass and H. Sutcliffe; Chapman and Hall (1968)

Assignment 35

A Survey of the Common Oxidation States of Manganese

One of the commonest and most useful of all manganese compounds is potassium permanganate, $KMnO_4$. This crystalline salt dissolves in water to give a deep purple solution which owes its colour to the presence of the permanganate ion, MnO_4^-.

1. What is the oxidation state of manganese in the permanganate ion?

2. Manganese does not form compounds in which its oxidation state is greater than that in MnO_4^-. Which of the following is most likely to be the outer electron configuration for a neutral manganese atom:

(a) $3d^2 4s^2$? (b) $3d^3 4s^2$? (c) $3d^2 4s^5$? (d) $3d^9 4s^2$? (e) $3d^5 4s^2$

3. In view of the oxidation state of manganese in the MnO_4^- ion, which of the following statements is most likely to be true of the MnO_4^- ion:
(a) it will probably be a strong reducing agent?
(b) it could be a strong acid?
(c) it can be expected to undergo oxidation readily?
(d) it could well be an oxidizing agent?
(e) its reactions are likely to be very slow?
This survey consists of four titration experiments. Each titration should be done in duplicate and all burette readings should be recorded. Note should also be taken of any colour changes or precipitates seen.

EXPERIMENT 1 The reaction of potassium permanganate in acid solutions

Pipette $10.0cm^3$ of a 0.05 M solution of oxalic acid, $H_2C_2O_4$, into a conical flask and add about $10cm^3$ of dilute sulphuric acid. Warm the mixture until it is just too hot to hold against your hand and then titrate it rapidly with 0.02 M potassium permanganate solution. The end-point is when the mixture is just tinted pink by a drop of excess permanganate solution.

4. In the light of *observations* which you made during the titration try to decide which of the following is most likely to be the half-equation for the reaction undergone by the oxalic acid:

(a) $2 e^- + H_2C_2O_4 \rightleftharpoons 2 H^+ + 2 CO_2$

(b) $H_2C_2O_4 \rightleftharpoons OH^- + HCO_3^- + C$

(c) $H_2C_2O_4 \rightleftharpoons 2 H^+ + 2 CO_2 + 2 e^-$

(d) $2 e^- + H_2C_2O_4 \rightleftharpoons OH^- + HCO_3^- + C$

5. How many moles of MnO_4^- ion were used in each titration of Experiment 1?

6. How many moles of oxalic acid were used in each titration?

7. Assuming your answers to questions 4–6, how many moles of electrons were provided by the oxalic acid per mole of MnO_4^- ion?

204

8. What is the oxidation state of manganese at the end of the titration?

9. Assuming that the manganese product is a simple hydrated ion, Mn^{x+}, where the value of x is dictated by your answer to question 8, complete and balance the following equation:

$$MnO_4^- \ + \ H_2C_2O_4 \ + \ H^+ \ \rightarrow \ + \ H_2O \ +$$

10. Complete the following half-equation for the reduction of the MnO_4^- ion to Mn^{x+}

$$MnO_4^- \ + \ H^+ \ + \ e^- \ \rightleftharpoons \ H_2O$$

EXPERIMENT 2 The reduction of potassium permanganate in neutral or slightly alkaline solution

Run $10.0cm^3$ of 0.02 M potassium permanganate solution from a burette into a conical flask and warm it gently. Mix about $5cm^3$ of '20 volume' hydrogen peroxide solution with a few drops of bench sodium hydroxide solution. Add drops of this alkaline solution of hydrogen peroxide to the warm potassium permanganate, swirling as you do so. Continue adding drops and warming until the solid which forms (an oxide of manganese with oxidation state P) has coagulated and you can be sure that the remaining solution does not contain any permanganate ion. (It should not be necessary to add more than about $2cm^3$ of alkaline hydrogen peroxide solution) Boil the mixture gently for about 5 minutes in order to destroy any excess hydrogen peroxide. Then add about $20cm^3$ of dilute sulphuric acid and pipette $10.0cm^3$ of 0.05 M oxalic acid solution into the mixture. Warm until the manganese oxide has all disappeared and then titrate the hot solution with 0.02 M potassium permanganate solution.

11. Bearing in mind your conclusions to Experiment 1, what is likely to happen to manganese (P) oxide when it is treated with excess oxalic acid in acid conditions?

12. What volume of oxalic acid solution must have been used in reacting with the manganese (P) oxide per titration?

13. How many moles of electrons were provided by the oxalic acid per titration in reacting with the manganese (P) oxide?

14. Assuming that 1 mole of MnO_4^- ions gives 1 mole of manganese in oxidation state P on treatment with alkaline hydrogen peroxide solution, how many moles of $Mn(P)$ were formed per titration?

15. What must be the value of P? What is the probable formula for manganese (P) oxide?

16. Why is it customary to carry out permanganate titrations in acid solution?

17. What are the half-equations for: (i) MnO_4^- forming manganese (P) oxide in neutral or alkaline solution? (ii) manganese (P) oxide being reduced in acid solution?

18. What are the equations for the reaction of (i) MnO_4^- with H_2O_2 in neutral solution? (ii) manganese (P) oxide reacting with oxalic acid in acidic solution?

EXPERIMENT 3: The reaction of the permanganate ion with manganese (II) sulphate

Place about $20cm^3$ of distilled water and about $10cm^3$ of approximately 1.5×10^{-2} M $Mn(II)SO_4$ solution in a conical flask. Run in $4.0cm^3$ of 0.02 M potassium permanganate solution and swirl well until there is no sign of any unreacted MnO_4^- ion. What do you think is formed at this stage? Add approximately $20cm^3$ of dilute sulphuric acid and pipette in $10.0cm^3$ of 0.05 M oxalic acid solution. Warm the mixture until a clear solution is obtained and titrate the latter while it is still hot with 0.02 M potassium permanganate solution.

19. Of the $10cm^3$ of oxalic acid added, what volume was oxidized by the product of the reaction between the $4.0cm^3$ of potassium permanganate and the $10cm^3$ of $Mn(II)SO_4$ solution?

20. How does this compare with the volume of 0·05 M oxalic acid that would have been needed to react with the 4cm³ of the potassium permanganate alone under acidic conditions?

21. How can you account for the relation between the answers to 20 and 19?

22. Suggest an equation for the reaction between MnO_4^- ions and Mn^{2+} ions in alkaline solution.

23. Why are both the exact volume and concentration of the $Mn(II)SO_4$ solution unimportant?

EXPERIMENT 4: The behaviour of permanganate ions in concentrated solutions of alkalies

Pipette 10·0cm³ of 0·02 M potassium permanganate solution into a flask containing about 50 pellets (4—5g) of solid potassium hydroxide. Simmer the mixture on a low bunsen flame for about 5 minutes and note any changes of colour. At the end of this time, add approximately 50cm³ of dilute sulphuric acid. Again, be alert for colour changes. When you have made certain that the mixture is now acidic, pipette 10·0cm³ of 0·05 M oxalic acid solution into it and warm the mixture until it is colourless. Then titrate the excess oxalic acid with 0·02 M potassium permanganate solution, as in the previous three experiments.

24. Of the 10·0cm³ of oxalic acid solution added, what volume must have been needed to reduce the acidified product of the reaction of 10·0cm³ of 0·02 M $KMnO_4$ with excess alkali?

25. What volume of the oxalic acid solution would have been needed to react with 10·0cm³ of the $KMnO_4$ solution if the latter had not been first treated with excess alkali?

26. What fraction of the oxidizing capacity of 10cm³ of 0·02 M $KMnO_4$ solution is lost by first boiling it with excess alkali?

27. What is the oxidation state of the manganese in the ion produced by boiling the MnO_4^- ion with excess alkali?

28. Assuming that the ion formed has the general formula MnO_4^{y-}, what is the value of y?

29. Balance and complete the following half-equation to show the effect of concentrated alkalies on the permanganate ion:

$$MnO_4^- + e^- \rightleftharpoons MnO_4^{y-}$$

30. The relevant half-equation for the oxidation of the hydroxide ion is

$$4\,OH^- \rightleftharpoons 2\,H_2O + O_2 + 4\,e^-$$

What is the balanced ionic equation for the reaction between permanganate ions and hydroxide ions in strongly alkaline solution?

31. Bearing in mind your observations, what do you think happens to the MnO_4^{y-} ion when it is acidified?

FURTHER WORK

1. Draw a diagram showing the oxidation states of the most important manganese compounds, together with the conditions under which they can be interconverted.
2. In the light of Experiments 1—4, contrast the chemistry of manganese with that of the metals of Groups I and II of the periodic table.

Notes 35

Standard: **

Time required: 2½ hours practical work; 1½ hours homework afterwards

Reagents required:

0·05M oxalic acid solution [6·30g of $H_2C_2O_4.2H_2O$ per dm^3]	($120cm^3$)
dilute sulphuric acid	($200cm^3$)
dilute sodium hydroxide solution	($1cm^3$)
0·020M potassium permanganate solution [3·16g of $KMnO_4$ per dm^3]	($120cm^3$)
'20' volume hydrogen peroxide solution	($5cm^3$)
approx. 1·5 x 10^{-2} M manganese (II) sulphate solution	($30cm^3$)
[3·3g of $MnSO_4.4H_2O$ per dm^3]	
potassium hydroxide pellets	(10g)
distilled water	($100cm^3$)

Apparatus required

burette
10·0cm³ pipette
2 conical flasks
measuring cylinders: 1 x 10cm³ and 1 x 50cm³ (or 100cm³)
tripod and gauze
bunsen burner
teat pipette

Introduction

In addition to being a general introduction to manganese chemistry, this study aims to illustrate the versatility of the titration technique.

N.B. The systematic name for potassium permanganate is potassium manganate (VII). The trivial name still enjoys universal usage, however, and so it has been retained for the students' sheets.

Notes on questions and sample data

1. Assuming an oxidation state of −II for each oxygen atom, the manganese must have an oxidation state of +VII in MnO_4^- in order to account for the overall single negative charge on the ion.

2. If the maximum oxidation state of manganese is +VII it is likely that there are 7 electrons in the outer two subshells. Thus, alternative (e), $3d^5 4s^2$, is the most likely configuration. ($3d^2 4s^5$ is impossible because there can never be more than two electrons in any given s subshell)

3. In view of the high oxidation state of manganese in the MnO_4^- ion, alternative (d) (the MnO_4^- ion could well be an oxidizing agent) is the most likely statement to be correct.

Experiment 1: Sample Data:

10·0cm³ of 0·05 M oxalic acid solution needed 10·0cm³ of 0·02 M potassium permanganate solution.

4. Half-equations (b) and (d) suggest the part conversion of oxalic acid to carbon. No black precipitate is seen.

Half-equation (a) does not balance for charge.

Half-equation (c) is supported by the fact that a colourless, odourless gas is seen to be evolved as the permanganate solution is run into the hot oxalic acid solution. Presumably, this gas is carbon dioxide.

5. Number of moles of MnO_4^- ion used per titration $= \dfrac{10}{1000} \times 0.02 = 2 \times 10^{-4}$ moles

6. Number of moles of oxalic acid used per titration $= \dfrac{10}{1000} \times 0.05 = 5 \times 10^{-4}$ moles

7. Assuming half-equation (c) of question 4:

Number of moles of electrons provided by 5×10^{-4} moles of oxalic acid $= 10 \times 10^{-4}$

Thus, number of moles of electrons provided for each mole of MnO_4^- ion $=$

$$\frac{10 \times 10^{-4}}{2 \times 10^{-4}} = 5$$

8. This suggests that the manganese is reduced to a species where its oxidation state is 5 units lower than that in the MnO_4^- ion, i.e. Mn(II)

9. If Mn^{x+} has the manganese in the +II oxidation state, the ion must be Mn^{2+}. Knowing this, together with the fact that 5×10^{-4} moles of $H_2C_2O_4$ react with 2×10^{-4} moles of the MnO_4^- ion, it is easy to show that the balanced equation for the reaction involved in Experiment 1 is:

$$2\,MnO_4^- + 5\,H_2C_2O_4 + 6\,H^+ \rightarrow 2\,Mn^{2+} + 8\,H_2O + 10\,CO_2$$

10. It follows that the half-equation for the reduction of the MnO_4^- ion to the Mn^{2+} ion is:

$$MnO_4^- + 8\,H^+ + 5\,e^- \rightleftharpoons Mn^{2+} + 4\,H_2O$$

Experiment 2: Sample Data:

$6.4 cm^3$ of 0.02 M $KMnO_4$ solution needed to turn solution permanently pink.

It is important not to add a large excess of hydrogen peroxide. Even though the great majority of the excess is rapidly destroyed in the presence of the manganese (IV) oxide which forms, if a large excess is added it is possible for enough to remain to affect the titration readings.

11. Experiment 1 shows that in acid solution the oxalic acid is capable of reducing MnO_4^- ions to Mn^{2+} ions. Thus it is likely that the manganese (P) oxide is also reduced to Mn^{2+} ions in the presence of excess acid.

12. $6.4 cm^3$ of 0.02 M $KMnO_4$ solution react with $6.4 cm^3$ of 0.05 M $H_2C_2O_4$ solution under acid conditions (See Experiment 1). Thus, $3.6 cm^3$ of 0.05 M $H_2C_2O_4$ must have been used per titration in reducing the manganese (P) oxide to Mn^{2+} ions.

13. Each oxalic acid molecule provides 2 electrons. Thus, $\dfrac{2 \times 3.6}{1000} \times 0.05 = 3.6 \times 10^{-4}$ moles of electrons are provided by the oxalic acid per titration in reducing the manganese (P) oxide.

14. Number of moles of $Mn(P)$ per titration $= \dfrac{10}{1000} \times 0.02 = 2 \times 10^{-4}$ moles

15. From the answers to questions 13 and 14, the number of moles of electrons provided per mole of $Mn(P) =$

$$\frac{3.6 \times 10^{-4}}{2 \times 10^{-4}} = 1.8 \approx 2$$

This suggests that $Mn(P)$ is 2 oxidation units above Mn^{2+}, i.e. The precipitate is manganese (IV) oxide, MnO_2.

16. In acid solution the permanganate ion is reduced to the almost colourless Mn^{2+} ion and so the colour of the MnO_4^- ion serves to act as its own indicator. This is not true in the case of neutral or alkaline conditions where the permanganate ion is reduced to a brown, murky precipitate of MnO_2.

17. (i) Under neutral or alkaline conditions, reduction is from Mn(VII) to Mn(IV). Thus, 3 electrons are added per mole of MnO_4^- ion and the half-equation can be written as

$$MnO_4^- + 2\,H_2O + 3\,e^- \rightleftharpoons 4\,OH^- + MnO_2$$

(ii) Assuming that the reduction in acid solution is Mn(IV) to Mn(II), 2 electrons are involved per mole of MnO_2. Thus, the half-equation can be written as

$$MnO_2 + 4\,H^+ + 2\,e^- \rightleftharpoons Mn^{2+} + 2\,H_2O$$

18. (i) The half-equation for the oxidation of H_2O_2 in alkaline solution is

$$H_2O_2 + 2\,OH^- \rightleftharpoons 2\,H_2O + O_2 + 2\,e^-$$

Combining this with the half-equation given in the answer to question 17(i), we get:

$$2\,MnO_4^- \;+\; 4\,H_2O \;+\; 6\,e^- \rightleftharpoons 8\,OH^- + 2\,MnO_2$$
$$\underline{\; 3\,H_2O_2 \;+\; 6\,OH^- \;\rightleftharpoons 6\,H_2O + 3\,O_2 + 6\,e^-}$$
$$2\,MnO_4^- \;+\; 3\,H_2O_2 \rightarrow 2\,OH^- + 2\,H_2O + 3\,O_2 + 2\,MnO_2$$

(ii) Similarly, for the reduction of manganese (IV) oxide by oxalic acid

$$MnO_2 + 4\,H^+ \quad + 2\,e^- \rightleftharpoons Mn^{2+} + 2\,H_2O$$
$$\underline{H_2C_2O_4 \rightleftharpoons \quad 2\,H^+ + 2\,CO_2 + 2\,e^-}$$

and adding gives $\quad MnO_2 + H_2C_2O_4 + 2\,H^+ \rightarrow Mn^{2+} + 2\,H_2O + 2\,CO_2$

Experiment 3: Sample Data
$6.0\,cm^3$ of 0.02 M $KMnO_4$ solution needed to turn the final mixture pink.
A large excess of manganese (II) sulphate is to be avoided since it enhances the chance of forming some Mn (III) species rather than the more stable manganese (IV) oxide.

19. The titration data shows that there must have been $6.0\,cm^3$ of unreacted oxalic acid before the final titration. Thus, $4.0\,cm^3$ of the original oxalic acid solution must have been oxidized by the product of the reaction of $4.0\,cm^3$ of potassium permanganate solution with the excess manganese (II) sulphate.

20. $4.0\,cm^3$ of 0.02 M $KMnO_4$ would need $4.0\,cm^3$ of 0.05 M oxalic acid solution to reduce it under acid conditions.

21. The previous two answers show that treatment with excess manganese (II) sulphate seems to have no effect on the oxidizing capacity of the $4.0\,cm^3$ of permanganate solution.
This can be explained in two ways:
(a) The reaction between MnO_4^- and Mn^{2+} ions does not result in reduction of the permanganate ion.
(b) The reaction between the two ions results in the reduction of the permanganate ion and the oxidation of the manganese (II) ions to some common species with the manganese oxidation state between +VII and +II. This would not affect the total oxidizing capacity of the system.
The latter is supported by the fact that the reaction between the MnO_4^- and Mn^{2+} ions results in a brown precipitate resembling the manganese (IV) oxide, whose identity was established in Experiment 2.

22. The correct equation can be guessed as follows

$$3\,Mn^{2+} \quad + 12\,OH^- \rightleftharpoons 3\,MnO_2 \quad + \quad 6\,H_2O + 6\,e^-$$

$$2\,MnO_4^- + 4\,H_2O + 6\,e^- \rightleftharpoons 8\,OH^- + 2\,MnO_2$$

and adding gives

$$2\,MnO_4^- + 3\,Mn^{2+} + 4\,OH^- \rightarrow 5\,MnO_2 + 2\,H_2O$$

N.B. The experiment does not enable us to discount explanations of the type:

$$4\,Mn(VII) + Mn(II) \rightarrow 5\,Mn(VI)$$
$$\text{or}\quad 3\,Mn(VII) + 2\,Mn(II) \rightarrow 5\,Mn(V)\quad \text{etc.}$$

23. The exact volume and concentration of the manganese (II) sulphate solution used are relatively unimportant, providing that there is enough Mn^{2+} to react with all the MnO_4^-. (But see note at the beginning of Experiment 3, above)

Experiment 4: Sample Data:
$1 \cdot 9\,cm^3$ of $0 \cdot 02$ M potassium permanganate solution needed for the final titration.
Boiling with a large excess of hydroxide ions converts the purple MnO_4^- ions into a dark green solution. When the latter is acidified it is rapidly destroyed and replaced by a brown precipitate suspended in a purple solution.

24. The sample data show that $8 \cdot 1\,cm^3$ of the oxalic acid solution must have been needed to reduce the acidified product of the reaction of $10 \cdot 0\,cm^3$ of $0 \cdot 02$ M potassium permanganate solution with excess alkali.

25. $10 \cdot 0\,cm^3$ of the oxalic acid solution under acid conditions can reduce $10 \cdot 0\,cm^3$ of the potassium permanganate solution (See Experiment 1)

26. Thus, boiling with excess alkali results in a fractional loss of $\dfrac{1 \cdot 9}{10}$ of the oxidizing capacity of the permanganate solution.
(Assume, as was suggested by Experiment 3, that adding acid to the green solution will not affect the oxidizing capacity of the system)

27. Reduction of permanganate ions under acid conditions results in the oxidation state of manganese being lowered by 5 units.
Treatment of potassium permanganate solution with excess alkali lowers the oxidizing capacity of the MnO_4^- ion by

$$\frac{1 \cdot 9}{10} \approx \frac{1}{5}$$

Thus, we can deduce that boiling with excess alkali converts the MnO_4^- ion into a species containing Mn(VI).

28. If MnO_4^{y-} is a Mn(VI) species and each oxygen has an oxidation state of $-II$, then

$$y = |+6 - (4 \times 2)| = 2$$

29. Thus, the half-equation must be

$$MnO_4^- + e^- \rightleftharpoons MnO_4^{\,2-}$$

30. Multiplying the above half-equation by 4 and adding it to that given on the students' sheets for the oxidation of the hydroxide ion we get

$$4\,MnO_4^- + 4\,OH^- \rightarrow 2\,H_2O + O_2 + 4\,MnO_4^{2-}$$

31. The brown precipitate and the purple solution obtained on acidifying the green manganate (VI) ion solution, suggest that MnO_2 and MnO_4^- ions are formed on adding acid to the MnO_4^{2-} ion:

$$3\,MnO_4^{2-} + 4\,H^+ \rightarrow 2\,MnO_4^- + MnO_2 + 2\,H_2O$$

FURTHER WORK

1. The following diagram is a possible way of representing the relationships existing between the common oxidation states of manganese:

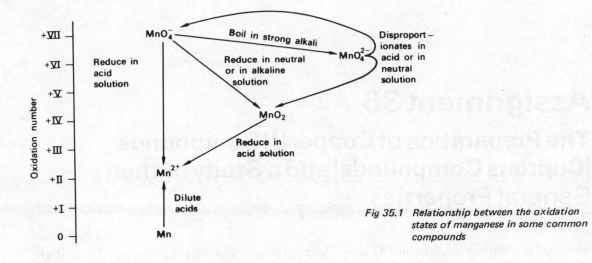

Fig 35.1 *Relationship between the oxidation states of manganese in some common compounds*

2. Experiments 1–4 illustrate several of the characteristic transition metal features of the chemistry of manganese:

e.g. (1) coloured compounds:
        manganese (IV) oxide — brown/black
        manganate (VI) ion — green
        manganate (VII) ion — purple

(2) catalysis:
        effect of manganese (IV) oxide on decomposition of excess hydrogen peroxide

(3) variable oxidation states: +II, +IV, +VI, +VII

FURTHER PROJECTS

1. The preparation of a manganese (III) compound. e.g. manganese (III) phosphate. (See Reference 1) or Tris-(acetylacetonato) manganese (III). (See Reference 2)
2. The preparation of solid potassium manganate (VI) (See Reference 1)
3. The oxidation of MnO_2 to potassium manganate (VII) (See Reference 1)

REFERENCES

1. *Practical Inorganic Chemistry* G PASS and H. SUTCLIFFE; Chapman and Hall (1968).
2. *Experimental Chemistry: A Laboratory Manual* G.P. RENDLE *et al.* Edward Arnold (1967).

Assignment 36

The Preparation of Copper (I) Compounds (Cuprous Compounds) and a Study of their General Properties

INTRODUCTION

Most of the copper compounds that are met early in a chemical career are those of the element in the +II oxidation state. You can probably answer the following questions already:

1. What is the colour of the oxide made by heating copper metal in excess air or oxygen? What is its formula?

2. What is the formula of the blue crystals of hydrated copper sulphate?

3. What do you *see* when a few drops of a solution of sodium hydroxide in water are added to an aqueous solution of copper (II) sulphate? What are the name and formula of the precipitate?

4. What do you *see* when excess of an aqueous solution of ammonia (ammonium hydroxide) is added to some of this precipitate? What are the name and formula of the copper ion that has been formed?

The preparation of copper (I) oxide

This compound is best made by reducing a solution of a copper (II) compound under alkaline conditions.

Put about 5cm³ of a strong aqueous solution of copper (II) sulphate (Fehling's Solution 'A' will do) in a boiling tube and add *just* enough of a solution of potassium sodium tartrate and sodium hydroxide (Fehling's Solution 'B') to cause the precipitate which forms initially to redissolve.

To this solution add about 1–2g of glucose and warm for a few moments. A red precipitate should separate out. Centrifuge or allow this precipitate to settle out. Decant the supernatant liquor and finally wash the precipitate with about 10cm³ of distilled water.

5. Why must the solution be alkaline?

6. What is the function of the tartrate ion in Fehling's 'B' Solution? (*cf.* question 4).

7. Why is glucose used rather than some stronger reducing agent?

8. For what purpose is Fehling's Solution normally used in the laboratory?

9. Assuming that the solid you have prepared is a copper oxide, how do you know that it cannot be copper (II) oxide?

Using small portions of your freshly prepared copper (I) oxide and a commercial sample of copper (II) oxide, compare the behaviour of the two oxides with dilute solutions of the three mineral acids on your bench. Add the acids *dropwise* to very small portions (not more than 0·1g) of the oxides until there is excess acid and then warm for a moment or two. Briefly record your observations in the form of a table and try to answer the following questions:

212

10. What is the solid left after boiling the copper (I) oxide with excess dilute sulphuric acid? Has any copper (II) sulphate been formed?

11. Why is there no solid left after boiling the copper (I) oxide with excess dilute nitric acid?

12. What is the oxidation state of copper in the compound formed by adding excess dilute hydrochloric acid to copper (I) oxide? (Check by adding *drops* of dilute sodium hydroxide solution carefully)
You should now try to write equations for all the reactions involved in the above tests.

13. Which of the two half equations given here must have the most positive standard reduction potential (i.e. have the greatest tendency to proceed to the right)?

$$Cu^+_{(aq)} + e^- \rightleftharpoons Cu_{(s)} \qquad Cu^{2+}_{(aq)} + e^- \rightleftharpoons Cu^+_{(aq)}$$

14. What is meant by the term 'disproportionation'?

15. The reaction of copper (I) oxide with dilute sulphuric acid *suggests that simple copper (I) salts* (i.e. those giving rise to the Cu^+ ion) *will always be unstable in aqueous solution.* Suggest why the $Cu^{2+}_{(aq)}$ ion might be more stable than the simple hydrated copper (I) ion.

The stability of copper (II) halides (cupric halides)

Using a gentle flame, heat small portions of anhydrous copper (II) bromide and copper (II) chloride, side by side, in ignition tubes. Be alert for evidence of thermal decomposition. Note down the appearance of the residues.

16. What are the residues remaining in the tubes?

17. What do you think happens when a sample of copper (II) oxide is heated strongly?

18. Are solid copper (I) compounds stable at room temperature?

19. Which of the two compounds used in this test decomposed most readily?

20. Predict whether copper (II) iodide will decompose readily or with reluctance when it is heated. Write an equation to indicate what you think will be formed when it does decompose and indicate the oxidizing and reducing agents.

The preparation of copper (I) iodide (cuprous iodide)

Add approximately 5cm³ of potassium iodide solution to a like volume of copper (II) sulphate solution. Centrifuge or allow the precipitate to settle. Decant the supernatant liquor and wash the precipitate with about 10cm³ of distilled water. Describe the appearance of the precipitate (copper (I) iodide) and treat small portions of it with solutions of ammonia and sodium thiosulphate. Record your observations.

21. Try to decide what the oxidation state of the copper is in each of the compounds formed in the above tests.

The preparation of copper (I) chloride (cuprous chloride)

Dissolve sufficient copper (II) oxide to cover the bottom of a boiling-tube (about 0·5g) in approximately 10cm³ of concentrated hydrochloric acid. Add about 1g of copper turnings and boil the mixture gently for about 2–3 minutes. Then pour off the liquid into about 200cm³ of distilled water. Allow the precipitate of copper (I) chloride to settle and wash it well with distilled water either by decanting or by means of a centrifuge. Record the appearance of the clean precipitate.

22. What is formed when copper metal is heated with copper (II) chloride in the presence of excess chloride ions?

23. Explain why copper (I) chloride is precipitated when the solution is added to excess distilled water.

Investigate the effects of (i) ammonia solution (ii) sodium thiosulphate and (iii) concentrated hydrochloric acid on portions of the washed precipitate of copper (I) chloride. Record your observations and suggest what compounds are formed in these tests.

24. The reactions of copper (I) chloride resemble those of what other metal halide?

25. Copper (I) oxide, iodide and chloride are all very insoluble in water, but stable in the presence of water. Under what conditions are copper (I) compounds stable in aqueous *solution*?

Does complexing always favour the formation of copper (I) compounds?

To 2–3cm³ of aqueous copper (II) sulphate solution add excess ammonia solution. Finally, add about 5cm³ of an aqueous solution of potassium iodide. Compare your observations with those you made during the preparation of copper (I) iodide.

26. What observations suggest that a redox reaction has not occurred?

27. Why is no copper (I) iodide formed in the presence of ammonia?

28. Why does copper (I) oxide react with dilute sulphuric acid to produce copper metal and a copper (II) compound whereas in the preparation of copper (I) chloride the reverse process occurs?

29. Basing your comments on your experimental results, briefly discuss the evidence for classifying copper as a transition metal.

214

Notes 36

Standard: ***

Time: About 2 hours of practical work is involved. This is best done in two sessions.

Reagents required:

dilute sulphuric acid	($10 cm^3$)	Fehling's Solution 'A'	($10 cm^3$)
dilute nitric acid	($10 cm^3$)	Fehling's Solution 'B' or	
dilute hydrochloric acid	($10 cm^3$)	sodium potassium tartrate	
potassium iodide solution	($10 cm^3$)	i.e. Rochelle Salt	($10 cm^3$)
copper (II) sulphate solution	($15 cm^3$)	glucose	(2g)
ammonia solution	($20 cm^3$)	anhydrous copper (II)	
sodium thiosulphate solution	($20 cm^3$)	chloride	(1g)
concentrated hydrochloric acid	($20 cm^3$)	anhydrous copper (II)	
copper (II) oxide	(1g)	bromide	(1g)
copper turnings	(1g)		
distilled water	($250 cm^3$)		

Apparatus required:

Test-tubes and rack, 2 boiling tubes, 2 ignition tubes and a $250 cm^3$ beaker

Notes on experiments and questions

1. Black; CuO

2. $CuSO_4 . 5H_2O$

3. Pale blue, gelatinous precipitate of copper (II) hydroxide

4. Pale blue, precipitate dissolving to give a deep blue solution containing the tetrammino copper (II) ion

5. Oxides and hydroxides are usually precipitated in alkaline solutions (cf question 3)

6. The tartrate ion, $^-O_2C.CH(OH).CH(OH).CO_2^-$, complexes the Cu_{aq}^{2+} ion, thus preventing the precipitation of $Cu(OH)_2$ by the alkali. Precipitation of the latter is undesirable since it might contaminate the copper (I) oxide.
N.B. Ammonium hydroxide can be used instead of the tartrate for this preparation, but it is slightly less reliable.

7. Stronger reducing agents will produce copper metal.
N.B. By using ammonium hydroxide (avoid a large excess) instead of the tartrate and hydrazine sulphate instead of glucose it is *possible* to produce highly attractive copper mirrors on the inside of a boiling tube. However, do not be disappointed if you get a precipitate of copper rather than a mirror!

8. Fehling's solution, a very weak oxidizing agent, is reduced by aldehydes, of which glucose is an example, to copper (I) oxide.

9. The colour is wrong.

	copper (I) oxide	copper (II) oxide
dilute H_2SO_4	Blue solution of $CuSO_4$ and a red precipitate of Cu metal	Blue solution of $CuSO_4$
dilute HNO_3	Blue solution and a red precipitate which dissolves on warming giving a blue-green solution	Blue-green solution of $Cu(NO_3)_2$
dilute HCl	White precipitate which dissolves in excess acid to give a colourless solution	Green solution of copper (II) chloride, complexed mainly as $CuCl_3^-$ etc

10. Metallic copper; copper (II) sulphate has been formed

$$Cu_2O_{(s)} + 2H^+_{(aq)} \rightleftharpoons Cu_{(s)} + Cu^{2+}_{(aq)} + H_2O_{(l)}$$

11. Dilute nitric acid can oxidize metallic copper

12. +I : $CuCl_{(s)} + Cl^-_{(aq)} \rightleftharpoons CuCl_2^-_{(aq)}$

13. The left-hand half-equation has the most positive redox potential. In the reaction of copper (I) oxide, with dilute sulphuric acid, the left hand half-equation can be considered to drive the right-hand half-equation backwards.

14. A reaction in which a single species acts on itself to produce oxidized and reduced products is known as a disproportionation reaction.

15. Presumably, the extra hydration energy of a small, dipositive ion compared with that of a larger, monopositive ion outweighs the second ionization potential of copper. (Ionic radii: Cu^+ 0·096 nm; Cu^{2+} 0·069 nm)

It is not possible to justify this by a superficial glance at the data, but it is easy to show that the energy needed *per electron removed* from a copper atom is less for forming an hydrated copper (II) ion than for an hydrated copper (I) ion:

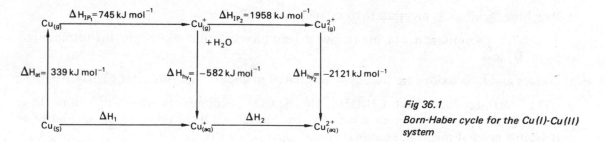

Fig 36.1
Born-Haber cycle for the Cu (I)-Cu (II) system

Simple arithmetic shows that ΔH_1 is +502 kJ mol^{-1} for $Cu^+_{(aq)}$ while ΔH_2 is +419 kJ mol^{-1}.

The Stability of Copper (II) halides

Copper (II) bromide decomposes very rapidly and bromine can be seen distilling up the tube, but copper (II) chloride must be subjected to quite strong heating before chlorine can be detected.

16. Copper (I) halides

17. Copper (I) oxide will be formed; it may be worth pointing out that thermal decomposition, producing a gas, will result in an increase in entropy for the system. Reactions involving an entropy increase are favoured at high temperatures.

216

18. Copper (I) oxide and halides are all stable at room temperature. Copper (I) sulphate can be made under non-aqueous conditions and there are many complex salts of copper (I) which are very stable as solids.

19. Copper (II) bromide

20. Copper (II) iodide decomposes spontaneously at room temperature

$$2Cu^{2+}_{(aq)} + 4I^-_{(aq)} \rightarrow 2CuI_{(s)} + I_2{(aq)}$$

$$\underset{\text{Oxidizing agent}}{\phantom{2Cu^{2+}_{(aq)}}} \quad \underset{\text{Reducing agent}}{\phantom{4I^-_{(aq)}}}$$

The preparation of copper (I) iodide

The precipitate, when washed free of the brown I_3^- ions, is white.
(i) On addition of a few drops of ammonium hydroxide the copper (I) iodide dissolves to give a pale blue solution which rapidly darkens, thus suggesting that the complex ion $[Cu(NH_3)_2]^+$, mentioned in many books, is oxidized to some extent to $[Cu(NH_3)_4]^{2+}$.
(ii) Copper (I) iodide dissolves in sodium thiosulphate solution to give a colourless solution of a complex ion.

21. Students can only guess; in the case of ammonia the colour *suggests* the +II oxidation state (unfilled d subshell configuration, $3d^9$), whereas, the absence of colour in the thiosulphate complex suggests a copper (I) compound.

The preparation of copper (I) chloride

The precipitate is white. It is important to wash it well in order to free it from acid before attempting to test the effect of the thiosulphate ion on it.

22. A complex copper (I) chloride ion,

$$Cu^{2+}_{(aq)} + Cu_{(s)} + 2Cl^-_{(aq)} \rightarrow 2CuCl_{(s)}$$

followed by $$CuCl_{(s)} + Cl^-_{(aq)} \rightarrow CuCl_2^-{(aq)}$$

23. An equilibrium constant can be written

$$K = \frac{[CuCl_2^-]}{[CuCl][Cl^-]}$$

CuCl is rather insoluble in water, but, because of the high chloride ion concentration, the undiluted solution is probably unsaturated with respect to CuCl. However, at the instant of dilution the concentration of each species is reduced about twenty-fold. Thus, the concentration product in the denominator is reduced by a factor of 400 on dilution and this means that a constant value of K can only be maintained if much of the $CuCl_2^-$ species dissociates into the relatively insoluble CuCl and Cl^- ions.
N.B. We admit that the above argument is a teaching rationalization rather than an explanation. However, we prefer it to the often quoted le Chatelier reasoning: on dilution the chloride ion concentration falls and so, in order to minimize this effect, some $CuCl_2^-$ dissociates.

(i) and (ii)
Reactions of copper (I) chloride with ammonium hydroxide and sodium thiosulphate are identical with those described for copper (I) iodide.
(iii)
With concentrated hydrochloric acid copper (I) chloride forms a dark green solution. This is probably a mixture of both copper (I) and copper (II) complex chlorides.

24. The reactions of copper (I) chloride resemble those of silver chloride.

25. Copper (I) complex ions are usually stable in aqueous solution e.g. $CuCl_2^-$ and $Cu(CN)_4^{3-}$. However, some copper (II) complex ions, notably *bis*-ethylenediamine copper (II), are more stable than their copper (I) counterparts.

Does complexing always favour the formation of copper (I) compounds?

No, there are exceptions, one of which has just been quoted.

26. There is no trace of the brown I_3^- ion which we would expect to be formed if the copper (II) species had been reduced.

27. No precipitate of CuI would be expected in the presence of ammonia but, in fact there is no evidence for the formation of any copper (I) species. This suggests that $Cu(NH_3)_4^{2+}{}_{(aq)}$ is a weaker oxidizing agent than $Cu^{2+}{}_{(aq)}$.

28. The simple 'answer' is that just as ammonia impairs the oxidizing power of copper (II), the presence of chloride ions enhances it to such an extent that it can oxidize copper metal.

However, teachers may well be interested in a more detailed consideration of the situation.

Complexing always affects redox behaviour and although many copper (I) complexes enjoy a greater stability than their copper (II) counterparts, the general effect of adding a complexing ligand is to stabilize higher oxidation states. i.e. decrease their oxidizing power.

e.g. uncomplexed cobalt (III) ions will oxidize water, but in the presence of ammonia, cobalt (II) ammines are readily oxidized to cobalt (III) ammines.

Similarly, simple hydrated iron (III) ions, Fe^{3+}, will oxidize iodide ions to iodine but hexacyanoferrate (III) ions will not do so.

Standard electrode potentials indicate these facts very clearly:

$$Co^{3+}_{(aq)} \quad + \quad e^- \rightleftharpoons Co^{2+}_{(aq)} \quad E_0 = +1\cdot30V$$
$$Fe^{3+}_{(aq)} \quad + \quad e^- \rightleftharpoons Fe^{2+}_{(aq)} \quad \quad +0\cdot77V$$
$$I_3^-{}_{(aq)} \quad + \quad 2e^- \rightleftharpoons 3I^-_{(aq)} \quad \quad +0\cdot54V$$
$$Fe(CN)_6^{3-} \quad + \quad e^- \rightleftharpoons Fe(CN)_6^{4-} \quad \quad +0\cdot36V$$
$$Co(NH_3)_6^{3+} + \quad e^- \rightleftharpoons Co(NH_3)_6^{2+} \quad +0\cdot10V$$

The redox behaviour of copper in the absence and presence of chloride ions is summarized by the following redox potentials:

$$Cu^+_{(aq)} + e^- \rightleftharpoons Cu_{(s)} \quad E_0 = +0\cdot52V \quad CuCl_{(s)} + e^- \rightleftharpoons Cu_{(s)} + Cl^-_{(aq)} \quad E_0 = +0\cdot14V$$
$$Cu^{2+}_{(aq)} + e^- \rightleftharpoons Cu^+_{(aq)} \quad \quad\quad +0\cdot15V \quad Cu^{2+}_{(aq)} + Cl^-_{(aq)} + e^- \rightleftharpoons CuCl_{(s)} \quad\quad +0\cdot54V$$

$$\overline{2Cu^+_{(aq)} \quad \rightleftharpoons Cu_{(s)} + Cu^{2+}_{(aq)} \; +0\cdot37V \quad Cu^{2+}_{(aq)} + Cu_{(s)} + 2Cl^-_{(aq)} \rightleftharpoons 2CuCl_{(s)} \; +0\cdot40V}$$

Thus, disproportionation is to be expected if water is the only complexing ligand present (i.e. water stabilizes copper (II)), but not in the presence of chloride ions. Both ammonia and iodide ions also prevent disproportionation of copper (I). The situation is shown clearly in the following diagram:

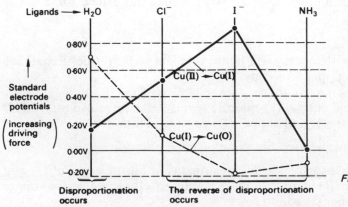

Fig 36.2 Effect of various ligands on the disproportionation of Cu(I) in aqueous solution

218

N.B. (i) It is interesting to note that $Cu^{2+}_{(aq)}$ ions would not be able to oxidize iodide ions to triiodide ions if copper (I) did not interact with iodide ions.

(ii) It is a useful exercise to calculate the standard redox potential for

$$Cu(NH_3)_4^{2+} + I^-_{(aq)} + e^- \rightleftharpoons CuI_{(s)} + 4\,NH_3\,{(aq)}$$

from data to be found in the literature.

e.g. Assuming

$$1 \quad Cu(NH_3)_4^{2+} + 2e^- \rightleftharpoons Cu_{(s)} + 4NH_3\,{(aq)} \quad E_0 = -0.065V$$
$$2 \quad Cu^{2+}_{(aq)} + I^-_{(aq)} + e^- \rightleftharpoons CuI_{(s)} \qquad\qquad +0.86V$$
$$3 \quad Cu^{2+}_{(aq)} + 2e^- \rightleftharpoons Cu_{(s)} \qquad\qquad\qquad +0.34V$$

The desired half-equation is got by reversing (3) and adding it to (1) and (2). Thus, the standard electrode potential for:

$$Cu(NH_3)_4^{2+} + I^-_{(aq)} + e^- \rightleftharpoons CuI_{(s)} + 4\,NH_3\,{(aq)}$$

is

$$\frac{-(2 \times 0.065) + (1 \times 0.86) - (2 \times 0.34)\,V}{1}$$

$$-0.13 + 0.86 - 0.68 = +0.05V$$

This is much less than the potential needed to oxidize iodide ions to triiodide ions.

FURTHER PROJECT

Dissolve 2g of thiourea in about $10cm^3$ of hot distilled water. Add about 0.5g of copper turnings followed by $2-3cm^3$ of concentrated hydrochloric acid. Warm gently and identify the gas evolved.

Hydrogen is liberated and it is a useful exercise for bright pupils to consider why this is so. In giving an answer it is useful to refer to the Nernst equation as the relation which dictates the variation of redox potentials under non-standard conditions. Thus, if the thiourea complexes copper (I) so effectively that the free $Cu^+_{(aq)}$ concentration remains vanishingly small, it is possible to conceive that the electrode potential for

$$Cu^+_{(aq)} + e^- \rightleftharpoons Cu_{(s)}$$

may, under the experimental conditions, fall below 0.0V, thus allowing hydrogen to be liberated.

Solid *tris*-thioureacopper (1) chloride can be isolated from the remaining solution. (See Reference 1)

REFERENCES

1. Palmer *Experimental Inorganic Chemistry*, Cambridge University Press (1954)
2. *Some Thermodynamic Aspects of Inorganic Chemistry,* D.A. Johnson, Cambridge University Press (1968).
(This last reference contains a very helpful discussion of the factors influencing the relative stability of different oxidation states)

Assignment 37

The Preparation of an Oxoacid of Iodine - A Redox Potential Enigma?

INTRODUCTION

Potassium chlorate has the formula $KClO_3$

1. What are the name and formula of the acid from which this salt is derived?

2. What ought the name of HIO_3 to be?

3. What is the oxidation number of iodine in (a) free iodine (b) HIO_3?

4. If we wish to make HIO_3 starting from free iodine, what type of reagent must the latter be treated with?

5. Balance the following half reactions (You may assume that all formulae are correct)

$$2\,IO_3^-{}_{(aq)} + 12\,H^+_{(aq)} + \quad e^- \rightleftharpoons I_2{}_{(s)} + \quad 6\,H_2O_{(l)} \quad E_0 = 1{\cdot}20V$$

$$NO_3^-{}_{(aq)} + \quad H^+_{(aq)} + \quad e^- \rightleftharpoons NO_2{}_{(s)} + \quad H_2O_{(l)} \quad E_0 = 0{\cdot}81V$$

6. Assuming that the above standard redox potentials are correct, would you expect nitric acid to be able to convert I_2 to IO_3^-?

EXPERIMENTAL WORK

Weigh out about 2g of finely powdered iodine into an evaporating basin and, *in a fume cupboard*, add about $25cm^3$ of fuming nitric acid (density $1{\cdot}50$ g cm^{-3}). Simmer the mixture gently until there is no sign of any iodine remaining and then allow the basin and its contents to cool.

7. What gas is evolved during the simmering?
In order to simplify the subsequent discussion, you may assume that this gas is produced by the reaction of nitric acid with iodine although it is probable that a considerable proportion of it results from thermal decomposition of some of the nitric acid.

8. How would you set about trying to establish that the gas was not produced solely by thermal decomposition of the nitric acid?
When the basin has cooled, decant the liquor from the crystals (X) and very *gently* warm the crystals for a few moments in order to evaporate residual nitric acid. Stop warming as soon as X appears to be dry or shows any signs of darkening.

Test X as follows in an attempt to identify it
(i) Warm a few crystals of X in a hard-glass test-tube, keeping the temperature below about $200°C$ if possible. Record your observations.
(ii) Heat a few crystals of X a little more strongly and identify the gases evolved.
(iii) Dissolve a few crystals of X in $2-3cm^3$ of distilled water and add a few drops of barium chloride solution.
(iv) Dissolve a few crystals of X in about $5cm^3$ of distilled water and add potassium iodide solution dropwise until the latter is in excess. Note all visible changes very carefully.

220

9. What substances do you think were formed in tests (i) and (ii)?

10. What was precipitated in test (iii)? (Look up solubility products of suitable barium-iodine compounds)

11. Suggest equations for all chemical changes involved in test (iv). One of these is a redox reaction; indicate the reducing agent and the oxidizing agent.
(v) Dissolve about 1g of X in about 100cm^3 of water (Solution Y).
Saturate about 25cm^3 of distilled water with sulphur dioxide and dilute the solution to a volume of about 1000cm^3 (Solution Z).
Mix about 10cm^3 of Solution Y with about 50cm^3 of distilled water in a conical flask and add a squirt of starch solution.
Add about 10cm^3 of Solution Z to about 50cm^3 of distilled water in another conical flask and mix the contents of the two flasks rapidly. What do you see?

12. Has a redox reaction occurred?

13. What is a solution of sulphur dioxide in water called?

14. With the help of redox potential tables in data books, attempt to explain what reactions take place in test (v).

15. Assuming that by now you are prepared to accept that X is HIO_3, how do you account for the fact that nitric acid is capable of oxidizing iodine to HIO_3? Derive a balanced chemical equation to represent the oxidation.

Notes 37

Standard: ***

Time required: 2 hours. The preparation of iodic acid usually takes about 45 minutes and a similar period is needed to conduct the tests on the product.

Reagents required:
  Iodine (2g)
  fuming nitric acid [i.e. density 1·50 g cm^{-3} or 94% by weight] (25cm^3)
  sulphur dioxide cylinder
  starch solution (1cm^3)
  potassium iodide $\Big\}$ bench reagent solutions (1cm^3)
  barium chloride
  distilled water (25cm^3)   A further 1200cm^3 of distilled water is needed for test (v).

Apparatus required:
  test-tubes
  evaporating basin
  3 x 250cm^3 conical flasks (or beakers)
  1 x 1 litre beaker
  a stirring rod
  a 50cm^3 measuring cylinder

Introduction

A thorough discussion of the principles underlying the preparation of iodic acid by this method would constitute a useful undergraduate exercise. However, the experiment has much to offer the Advanced Level student, and, while there may be teachers who consider that the treatment outlined below is so facile as to be misleading, experience has shown that it can be of considerable value in an Advanced Level course.

The main aim of the student sheet is to illustrate that it is unwise to rely solely on standard redox potentials in considering whether or not a particular redox reaction will take place.

Notes on questions and experimental work

1. Potassium chlorate is derived from the acid $HClO_3$, chloric acid

2. Since $HClO_3$ is called chloric acid, then HIO_3 can be called iodic acid

3. The oxidation number of iodine (a) in free iodine is 0 (by definition)
   (b) in HIO_3 is +5

4. The change in oxidation number from 0 to 5 shows that free iodine must be treated with an oxidizing agent in order to convert it to iodic acid.

5. The balanced half equations are

$$2\,IO_3^-{}_{(aq)} + 12\,H^+_{(aq)} + 10\,e^- \rightleftharpoons I_{2\,(s)} + 6\,H_2O_{(l)}$$

$$NO_3^-{}_{(aq)} + 2\,H^+_{(aq)} + e^- \rightleftharpoons NO_{2\,(g)} + H_2O_{(l)}$$

222

6. The standard redox potentials quoted on the student sheet do not suggest that nitric acid should be able to convert iodine into iodic acid; rather, they indicate that under *standard* conditions iodic acid is capable of oxidizing nitrogen dioxide to nitric acid.

7. When cold fuming nitric acid is added to iodine no violent reaction occurs. However, close examination of the surface of the iodine reveals the slow formation of a white solid. On simmering, the reaction becomes quite vigorous and clouds of nitrogen dioxide are evolved.

8. This is included as an open-ended question. An obvious 'control' experiment is to heat some of the fuming nitric acid on its own. When this is done, rather less nitrogen dioxide seems to be evolved than when iodine is present. However, this is inconclusive as the iodine could be a catalyst for the thermal decomposition of fuming nitric acid.
After about 15–20 minutes heating, the clouds of nitrogen dioxide die down and no free iodine can be seen. Once the contents of the basin have been allowed to cool, it is easy to pour off the great majority of the nitric acid from the crystals of iodic acid. Evaporation of the last drop or two of nitric acid without decomposing the iodic acid is very difficult. With extreme care it is possible to do it by heating the basin directly, but it is advisable to use a sand or oil bath. The pure crystals of iodic acid are white, but the usual product is a pale yellow because of the presence of some iodine pentoxide.
Tests (i) On heating the powder becomes yellower as more I_2O_5 is formed. Most students succeed in effecting further decomposition into iodine and oxygen (test ii).

$$2 HIO_3 = I_2O_5 + H_2O$$

(ii) When the crystals are heated more strongly, complete thermal decomposition takes place. Clouds of violet iodine vapour are seen and a glowing splint relights when placed in the tube

$$2 I_2O_5 = 2 I_2 + 5 O_2$$

(iii) A white precipitate of barium iodate forms when an aqueous solution of iodic acid is treated with a solution of barium chloride.

(iv) A grey precipitate of I_2 is formed at first (relatively insoluble in water)

$$6 H^+_{(aq)} + IO_3^-_{(aq)} + 5 I^-_{(aq)} = 3 I_{2 (s)} + 3 H_2O_{(l)}$$

On addition of excess potassium iodide, the free iodine is converted into the complex tri-iodide ion and dissolves to give a clear, brown solution

$$I^-_{(aq)} + I_{2 (s)} = I_3^-_{(aq)}$$

9. Answered above

10. The solubility product of barium iodate is 6×10^{-10} mol^3 dm^{-9} at 298 K. Barium iodide is very soluble in water.

11. Equations for the chemical change taking place during test (iv) are given above. The first of these is a redox reaction in which the iodate ion is the oxidizing agent and the iodide ion is the reducing agent.

Test (v) It is suggested that one student makes up the solutions for the class. This is the well-known 'iodine clock' reaction. Within 5–10 seconds after mixing the colourless mixture suddenly turns dark blue as excess iodine is formed and reacts with the starch to give a blue complex.

12. Assuming that the students recognise the blue starch-iodine colour, they ought to deduce that a redox process has taken place.

13. A solution of sulphur dioxide in water is usually called sulphurous acid.

14. Much guidance will probably be needed in order to deduce the reactions which take place during test (v). The relevant redox potentials are

(a) IO_3^-(aq) $+ 6 H^+$(aq) $+ 5 e^- \rightleftharpoons \frac{1}{2} I_2$(s) $+ 3 H_2O$(l) $E_0 = +1·19V$

(b) $\frac{1}{2} I_2$(s) $+ e^- \rightleftharpoons I^-$(aq) $E_0 = +0·62V$

(c) $4 H^+$(aq) $+ SO_4^{2-}$(aq) $+ 2 e^- \rightleftharpoons H_2SO_3$(aq) $+ H_2O$(l) $E_0 = +0·17V$

Combining (a) and (b) gives

(d) IO_3^-(aq) $+ 6 H^+$(aq) $+ 6 e^- \rightleftharpoons I^-$(aq) $+ 3 H_2O$(l) $E_0 = +1·09V$

Thus, iodate ions can be reduced by sulphurous acid to iodide ions and as long as there is any H_2SO_3 present in the mixture no free iodine can be formed because it would be immediately reduced to iodide ions. However, as soon as the H_2SO_3 has all been oxidized to H_2SO_4 iodine can persist:

$$IO_3^-\text{(aq)} + 6 H^+\text{(aq)} + 5 I^-\text{(aq)} = 3 I_2\text{(s)} + 3 H_2O\text{(l)}$$

The appearance of the blue starch-iodine colour therefore heralds the oxidation of the last trace of sulphurous acid.

15. There is considerable scope for debate concerning the reason why 94% nitric acid can oxidize iodine to iodic acid. (e.g. Is HNO_3 the real oxidizing species?) No claim is made that the suggestions outlined below represent the whole truth. In fact, it may very well be that the attempt to apply redox potentials to such a system represents little more than a futile exercise. However, the following reasoning does provide an explanation in terms of principles the student will probably have met already and, at worst, it should offer a useful target for the sceptical class to shoot at.

The conditions of the experiment are far from standard (i.e. unit activities for all species and a temperature of 298 K).

The Nernst Equation predicts that the relevant non-standard redox potentials at 400 K are given by the expressions:

$$E_{HNO_3} = 0·81 + \frac{0·08}{10} \lg \frac{[NO_3^-]^{10}\,[H^+]^{20}}{[NO_2^-]^{10}\,[H_2O]^{10}} = 0·81 + 0·08 \lg \frac{[NO_3^-]\,[H^+]^2}{[NO_2^-]\,[H_2O]}$$

and $$E_{HIO_3} = 1·20 + \frac{0·08}{10} \lg \frac{[IO_3^-]^2\,[H^+]^{12}}{[I_2]\,[H_2O]^6}$$

Since we know that reaction does occur, we must assume that the effective redox potentials under the conditions of the experiment, E_{HNO_3} and E_{HIO_3}, are such that $E_{HNO_3} > E_{HIO_3}$, despite the fact that the reverse is true for the standard redox potentials.

For this to be true, the expression $\dfrac{[NO_3^-]^{10}}{[NO_2^-]^{10}}\dfrac{[H^+]^{20}}{[H_2O]^{10}}$ must be much greater than $\dfrac{[IO_3^-]^2\,[H^+]^{12}}{[I_2]\,[H_2O]^6}$

In view of the fact that the acid is so concentrated, any attempt to guess at the activities of the species involved would be futile, but it does seem reasonable that the two expressions are of the desired magnitudes at the beginning of the experiment. Presumably, the activity of the nitrate ion remains very high throughout the experiment, while the continuous loss of nitrogen dioxide ensures that the activity of nitrogen dioxide in solution remains very small. This being so, it is not unreasonable that

$$\frac{[NO_3^-]^{10}\,[H^+]^{20}}{[NO_2^-]^{10}\,[H_2O]^{10}} \gg \frac{[IO_3^-]^2\,[H^+]^{12}}{[I_2]\,[H_2O]^6}$$

and remains so until effectively all of the iodine has been converted into iodic acid.

N.B. The importance of the loss of nitrogen dioxide in maintaining a high value for E_{HNO_3} can be reconciled with the dictum that loss of a volatile product results in the displacement of a chemical equilibrium in the direction which leads to the formation of more of that product (i.e. An application of Le Chatelier's principle).

Combining the two half-equations, an overall equation for the reaction can be obtained

$$10\ NO_{3\ (aq)}^- + 20\ H_{(aq)}^+ + 10\ e^- \rightleftharpoons 10\ NO_{2\ (g)} + 10\ H_2O_{(l)}$$
$$I_{2\ (s)} + 6\ H_2O_{(l)} \rightleftharpoons 2\ IO_{3\ (aq)}^- + 12\ H_{(aq)}^+ + 10\ e^-$$
$$\overline{8\ H_{(aq)}^+ + 10\ NO_{3\ (aq)}^- + I_{2\ (s)} \rightleftharpoons 10\ NO_{2\ (g)} + 2\ IO_{3\ (aq)}^- + 4\ H_2O_{(l)}}$$

or alternatively $\quad 10\ HNO_{3\ (aq)} + I_{2\ (s)} \rightleftharpoons 10\ NO_{2\ (g)} + 2\ HIO_{3\ (aq)} + 4\ H_2O_{(l)}$

FURTHER PROJECTS

1. Assuming the values quoted on the student sheet for $E^0_{HIO_3}$ and for $E^0_{HNO_3}$, calculate a value for the overall equilibrium constant

$$K = \frac{[NO_2]^{10}\ [IO_3^-]^2\ [H_2O]^4}{[H^+]^8\ [NO_3^-]^{10}\ [I_2]}$$

2. Investigate the effects of using different volumes of solutions Y and Z in test (v). Check whether it is necessary to have an excess of iodic acid or an excess of sulphurous acid.

HOMEWORK ASSIGNMENTS

1. Make a list of the name and formulae of the halogen oxides.
2. List the common halogen oxoacids. How are they made? What uses have they? What molecular structures do they have?
3. How do the acid strengths of the oxoacids of any given halogen vary with the oxidation number of the halogen? How do you account for this trend?
4. Make notes on the application of iodine pentoxide to the analysis of organic compounds.

Assignment 38
Reactions of Alcohols

INTRODUCTION

1. Give the structural formulae of butane, dimethyl ether, chloroethane and ethanol, together with their respective molecular weights. Tabulate their important physical properties (e.g. boiling point, solubility in water). Bearing their structures in mind, suggest reasons for the unusual properties of alcohols. Predict where bond cleavage is likely to occur in chloroethane and ethanol. The relevant electro-negativities are

$$C = 2.5 \; ; H = 2.1 \; ; Cl = 3.0 \; ; O = 3.5$$

EXPERIMENTAL WORK

(a) *Reaction with sodium*
To 10 drops of methanol add a small, clean piece of sodium. (Cut off the surface layer if the sodium has been oxidized.) When the sodium has completely dissolved, pour the residual solution on to a piece of dry, red litmus paper. Then add a drop of distilled water.

2. Record your observations and explain the action of the water. Try to explain the relative reactivity of water and methanol with sodium in terms of the electron-releasing effect of the methyl group.

(b) *Reaction with phosphorus halides*
To 10 drops of ethanol add a little phosphorus pentachloride. Collect some of the fumes evolved, by drawing them into a syringe or teat pipette, and identify them by bubbling them into silver nitrate solution acidified with dilute nitric acid.

3. Compare this reaction with the hydrolysis of non-metal chlorides. Write equations for the reaction you performed and for the reaction between phosphorus pentachloride and methanol.

(c) *Esterification reactions*
(i) Methyl and ethyl acetates
Add 5 drops of glacial acetic acid to 5 drops of methanol in a test tube. Carefully add 3 drops of concentrated sulphuric acid and, after mixing, warm the mixture for a few minutes. Pour the contents of the test tube into about 30cm³ of water in a beaker. Repeat the experiment substituting ethanol for methanol, and compare the smell of the two esters formed.

4. Why is the sulphuric acid used?

5. What is the reason for warming the mixture?

6. Would this be a useful test for distinguishing between methanol and ethanol?

(ii) Methyl and ethyl salicylates
Prepare these esters using the same procedure, but substituting salicylic acid for the glacial acetic acid.

7. Compare the smell of these two esters. Would this reaction be a useful test for distinguishing between methanol and ethanol?

(d) *Tests to distinguish between methanol and ethanol*
(i) The iodoform test
To 5 drops of each alcohol, in turn, add about $1\,cm^3$ of a solution of iodine in potassium iodide and dilute sodium hydroxide solution dropwise until the colour due to the iodine just disappears. Warm, if necessary, and note the appearance and smell of the contents of each test tube.

8. Which alcohol produces iodoform?

9. Which functional group must be present for iodoform to be produced?

10. Do you think propan-2-ol will give a positive result to this test? Try it.

(ii) Oxidation by alkaline potassium permanganate
To a small quantity of solid potassium permanganate in a test tube add 10 drops of dilute sodium hydroxide solution followed by 5 drops of methanol.

11. Note the changes of appearance over a period of about a minute. What is the identity of each of the reduction products of the permanganate you have noticed?

Add about $1\,cm^3$ of distilled water to extract the soluble salts from the products of the reaction and filter.
Add 1 drop of concentrated hydrochloric acid to the filtrate and test for the evolution of carbon dioxide by using a syringe (or teat pipette) and lime water.
Repeat this procedure substituting ethanol for methanol.

12. Explain the chemistry of this test.

(e) *Oxidation by acidified potassium dichromate*
To 5 drops of each alcohol, (methanol, ethanol and propan-2-ol) in turn, add 10 drops of dilute sulphuric acid and 5 drops of potassium dichromate solution. Warm each mixture and note the colour and smell of the products.

13. What are the oxidation products of these three alcohols?

14. Briefly suggest practical details for the preparation of (a) acetaldehyde (b) acetic acid from ethanol.

(f) *Catalytic oxidation of methanol*
Warm 10 drops of methanol in a test tube and introduce a red-hot copper spiral into the vapour.

15. Observe the reaction carefully and suggest a possible mechanism for the catalysis. Explain the changes in colour which occur on the surface of the copper. Try to repeat the experiment holding the hot portion of the copper at different points in the test tube.

Notes 38

Standard: *
Time required: 2 hours
Reagents required:

methanol	(10cm³)
ethanol	(10cm³)
propan-2-ol	(5cm³)
sodium	(0·5g)
phosphorus pentachloride	(1g)
glacial acetic acid	(1cm³)
approx. molar solution of iodine in potassium iodide	(5cm³)
solid potassium permanganate	(1g)
copper spiral	
salicylic acid	(1g)
conc. sulphuric acid	(1cm³)
conc. hydrochloric acid	(1cm³)
potassium dichromate solution	(5cm³)
dilute nitric acid	(5cm³)
dilute sulphuric acid	(10cm³)
lime water	(5cm³)
dilute sodium hydroxide solution	(10cm³)
dilute silver nitrate solution	(5cm³)

Apparatus required:
  test tubes
  2 beakers
  syringe or teat pipettes
  filtration apparatus
  bunsen burner

Typical results and answers to questions

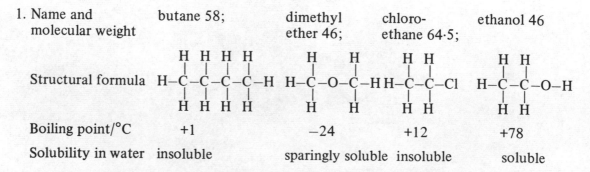

1. Name and molecular weight	butane 58;	dimethyl ether 46;	chloro-ethane 64·5;	ethanol 46
Boiling point/°C	+1	−24	+12	+78
Solubility in water	insoluble	sparingly soluble	insoluble	soluble

The presence of the hydroxyl group in ethanol causes polarity in the molecule, giving rise to higher boiling point and greater solubility in water than is the case for the other

228

ydrogen bonding in ethanol will increase the 'effective' molecular weight of the compound.

In polar conditions, bond breakage is likely to occur between atoms which have the greatest difference in electronegativity. Thus one might predict that under these conditions, bond breakage in chloroethane would be likely to occur between the carbon and the chlorine, and in ethanol the break would be expected to occur between the oxygen and hydrogen atoms (as is the case in the reaction with sodium).

2. Sodium reacts less vigorously with methanol than with water as a result of the electron-releasing effect of the methyl group which decreases the extent to which the oxygen atom attracts the electrons of the O—H bond. Methanol thus has a smaller tendency to produce hydrogen ions than does water. The organic product of the reaction is the methoxide ion and in the presence of water it will readily accept a proton producing the hydroxide ion since it is a stronger base than the hydroxide ion. Thus the red litmus paper is turned blue.

3. Hydrolysis of non-metal chlorides usually produces hydrogen chloride; the hydroxyl group of the water being substituted by a chlorine atom. In this case the hydroxyl group of the alcohols is likewise substituted by a chlorine atom and hydrogen chloride can be detected in the gas evolved.

$$C_2H_5OH + PCl_5 = C_2H_5Cl + POCl_3 + HCl$$

$$3 CH_3OH + PCl_3 = 3 CH_3Cl + H_3PO_3$$

4. The concentrated sulphuric acid catalyses the reaction, probably by protonating the acid, making the carbon atom of the carboxyl group more susceptible to nucleophilic attack by the oxygen atom of the alcohol, and also helps to increase the yield.

5. The mixture is warmed to increase the rate of the reaction.

6. Ethyl acetate has a slightly stronger smell than methyl acetate, but the difference is not sufficiently striking to form the basis of a test.

7. Methyl salicylate smells of oil of wintergreen and has a much stronger smell than ethyl salicylate; thus this reaction could be used to distinguish between methanol and ethanol but there are more conclusive tests.

8. The contents of the tube containing methanol do not change in appearance but iodoform is produced in the tube containing ethanol. This is characterized by the 'clinical' smell and the solution becoming cloudy and eventually producing a yellow precipitate.

9. The iodoform test identifies the functional groups

$$CH_3-\overset{\overset{\displaystyle O}{\|}}{C}-X \quad \text{and} \quad CH_3-\underset{\underset{\displaystyle OH}{|}}{\overset{\overset{\displaystyle H}{|}}{C}}-X \quad \text{where } X = H \text{ or } C$$

10. Propan-2-ol, $CH_3CH(OH)CH_3$, does give a positive result to the iodoform test.

11. The reduction of potassium permanganate in alkaline solution by these alcohols gives green potassium manganate and finally brown manganese (IV) oxide.

12. In this test, methanol is oxidized successively to formaldehyde, formate and carbonate, which on acidification produces carbon dioxide. By contrast, ethanol is oxidized to acetaldehyde and ultimately the acetate ion, which on acidification produces acetic acid but *no* carbon dioxide. The reaction sequence may be summarized as follows:

methanol, $CH_3OH \rightarrow HCHO \rightarrow HCOO^- \rightarrow CO_3^{2-} \overset{acid}{\rightarrow} CO_2$

ethanol, $C_2H_5OH \rightarrow CH_3CHO \rightarrow CH_3COO^- \overset{acid}{\rightarrow} CH_3COOH$

13. All three alcohols turn the dichromate solution a blue/green colour and produce distinctive smells. Methanol is oxidized to the pungent-smelling formaldehyde; Ethanol is oxidized to acetaldehyde, which has a smell of rotting apples; Propan-2-ol is oxidized to the sweet-smelling acetone.

14. (a) If acetaldehyde is to be prepared it must be removed from the vicinity of the oxidizing agent before it is oxidized further to acetic acid. This can be done by adding ethanol to the oxidizing agent at a temperature above the boiling point of acetaldehyde so that acetaldehyde evaporates as soon as it is formed.
(b) To prepare acetic acid from ethanol the acetaldehyde must be kept in contact with the oxidizing agent. This can be done by heating the mixture under reflux.

15. The copper spiral becomes coated with a layer of oxide when it is heated in air, and the removal of this when the spiral is introduced into the alcohol vapour is readily observed. This would suggest that it may be the copper oxide which oxidizes the alcohol. The copper will thus act as a catalyst by alternately being oxidized by the air and reduced by the methanol. Attractive colours may be seen as a result of differing thicknesses of the oxide film giving different interference phenomena.

Assignment 39

Reactions of Aldehydes and Ketones

INTRODUCTION

These compounds contain the carbonyl group $>$C=O which has polar character because of the difference in electronegativity of carbon and oxygen. The aldehydes have a hydrogen atom attached to the carbon of the carbonyl group; the ketones have two alkyl groups (and hence no hydrogen atom) attached to the carbon of the carbonyl group. As a result of having the hydrogen directly linked to the carbonyl group the aldehydes are more susceptible to oxidation than the ketones.

The unsaturated carbonyl group undergoes addition reactions with nucleophilic reagents, such as the negative ions CN^-, HSO_3^-, or neutral molecules like NH_3, NH_2OH etc., which possess an unshared pair of electrons. In some cases the initial step of the addition reaction is attack of the nucleophile on the carbon of the carbonyl group; in others a proton may first be added to the oxygen of the carbonyl group thus enhancing the electrophilic nature of the carbon atom (acid catalysis). After addition of a nucleophile and a proton a simple substance such as water may be eliminated. Such a reaction involving addition followed by elimination is sometimes called a condensation reaction.

1. Bearing in mind the mechanism of addition to the unsaturated carbonyl group, predict the relative reactivity of formaldehyde, acetaldehyde and acetone. Recall the electron donating property of the methyl group encountered in methanol.

2. Consider the influence of molecular weight on the solubility of compounds in a given solvent and thus predict the relative solubility of addition compounds of formaldehyde, acetaldehyde and acetone.

3. Predict the relative ease of oxidation of formaldehyde, acetaldehyde and acetone.

EXPERIMENTAL WORK

(I) Reducing properties of carbonyl compounds
Use aqueous solutions of the carbonyl compounds unless otherwise instructed

(a) *With acidified potassium dichromate solution*
Compare the ease of oxidation and hence reducing power of formaldehyde, acetaldehyde and acetone by adding 5 drops of each substance *in turn* to 2 drops of potassium dichromate solution and 10 drops of dilute sulphuric acid in a test tube. Note the relative rates of reaction, if any.

4. Do your results agree with your predictions?

(b) *With ammoniacal siver oxide (Tollen's reagent)*
To 10 drops of silver nitrate solution in a *clean test tube*, add 1 drop of sodium hydroxide followed by drops of dilute ammonia solution until the precipitate just redissolves. Add 5 drops of each carbonyl compound to separate samples and warm the resulting solutions in a beaker of hot water. Record your observations.

5. What is the precipitate formed by adding sodium hydroxide to silver nitrate solution?

6. Why does it dissolve in ammonia solution?

(c) *With copper (II) hydroxide dissolved in potassium sodium tartrate (Fehling's solution)*
Mix 10 drops of Fehling's solution A with an equal volume of Fehling's solution B and add 5 drops of each carbonyl compound in turn. Warm the mixtures gently and record your observations. Attempt to explain your observations.

7. Fehling's test is used to detect sugar in the urine of people suffering from diabetes. Why do you think sugars can be detected in this way?

(II) Addition reactions
(a) *Addition of sodium bisulphite*
To about $1cm^3$ of saturated sodium bisulphite solution add about $\frac{1}{2}cm^3$ of each carbonyl compound in turn (use pure acetaldehyde and acetone rather than aqueous solutions). Cool each tube under the tap and record your observations.

8. How would you establish that any crystalline product is a bisulphite addition compound?

9. What evidence is there of reaction other than the formation of a crystalline product?

10. Write the structural formula of the bisulphite ion.

(b) *Reaction with Schiff's reagent*
Schiff's reagent is a magenta dye decolourized by sulphur dioxide.

11. Predict the effect of boiling a few drops of Schiff's reagent.
Try this and explain what happens. Try other ways of removing the sulphur dioxide. What does this suggest about the mechanism of the reaction of Schiff's reagent with carbonyl compounds?
Now add a few drops of Schiff's reagent to each carbonyl compound in turn and note the relative rates of reaction.

12. Attempt to explain your observations in terms of the relative reactivity of the three carbonyl compounds, the mechanism of their reaction with bisulphite ions, and the reversible reactions involved.

(III) Polymerization reactions
(a) *Action of heat*
Place about $1cm^3$ of formaldehyde solution on a watch-glass and heat it over a beaker of boiling water for above five minutes.
Examine the product (paraformaldehyde) and investigate the action of heat on it, using a hard-glass test tube.

13. Would you expect paraformaldehyde to show reducing properties? Carry out experiments to test your predictions.

14. Do similar conditions bring about polymerization of the other carbonyl compounds? Does this agree with your order of reactivity?

(b) *Action of alkali*
Boil $5cm^3$ of sodium hydroxide solution with 5 drops of each of the carbonyl compounds in turn. Which compound appears to polymerise?

15. For polymerization to occur it is reasonable to suggest that a nucleophile must be produced from the carbonyl compound. Suggest how this might be formed. What role does the sodium hydroxide play?

16. Suggest a mechanism for this polymerization reaction and use it to explain the relative ease of polymerization of these carbonyl compounds in alkaline solution.

17. How would you establish whether a reaction has occurred in the cases where no *visible* change takes place?

232

18. Predict the reaction which propionaldehyde would undergo in similar alkaline conditions. Why does benzaldehyde not undergo a similar reaction?

(IV) Condensation reactions

Carbonyl compounds undergo condensation reactions with hydroxylamine, hydrazine and phenylhydrazine, but these are of little use in identifying the first few members of the aldehyde and ketone series.

19. What feature have these reagents in common? Use this to explain the mechanism of these condensation reactions.

20. The most useful reagent for the identification of early members of the aldehyde and ketone series is 2:4-dinitrophenylhydrazine. What advantage has it over the simpler reagents mentioned above?

Condensation with 2:4-dinitrophenylhydrazine

Add 2 or 3 drops of each of the carbonyl compounds, in turn, to about $3cm^3$ of the solution of 2:4 dinitrophenylhydrazine in hydrochloric acid. Record your observations.

21. How could your products be used to identify the original carbonyl compounds?

22. Could this reaction be used as a general test for carbonyl compounds? Explain.

(V) The iodoform reaction

Action of an alkaline solution of iodine

To 5 drops of each carbonyl compound, in turn, add about $1cm^3$ of a solution of iodine in aqueous potassium iodide, followed by sodium hydroxide solution added dropwise until the colour of the iodine is removed. Warm, if necessary, and note the smell and appearance of the mixtures.

23. Which of the carbonyl compounds have produced iodoform?

24. Which functional group must be present for this test to be positive?

25. Why is sodium carbonate solution to be preferred to sodium hydroxide in this test?

26. Make a list of reactions you could use to distinguish between formaldehyde, acetaldehyde and acetone.

Notes 39

Standard: **

Time required: ½ hour preparation; 1½ hours practical time

Reagents required:

Pure samples of acetaldehyde and acetone	(10cm^3)
40% aq. solutions of formaldehyde, acetaldehyde and acetone	(10cm^3)
potassium dichromate solution	(1cm^3)
Fehling's Solutions A and B	(3cm^3)
saturated sodium bisulphite solution	(5cm^3)
Schiff's reagent	(1cm^3)
chlorine water	(1cm^3)
2:4 dinitrophenylhydrazine reagent	(10cm^3)
iodine in aq. potassium iodide solution	(5cm^3)
common laboratory reagents	

Apparatus required:

test tubes	hard glass test tube
teat pipettes	bunsen burner
watch glass	

Notes on introduction

1. The relative reactivity of formaldehyde, acetaldehyde and acetone in addition reactions is likely to depend on the polarity of the carbonyl group. Release of electrons on to the carbon atom will decrease its susceptibility to nucleophilic attack and hence the predicted order is:

$$\underset{H}{\overset{H}{>}}C=O \text{ more reactive than } \underset{H}{\overset{CH_3}{>}}C=O \text{ more reactive than } \underset{CH_3}{\overset{CH_3}{>}}C=O$$

2. All other things being equal the greater the molecular weight of a compound the lower its solubility. Thus, assuming similar polarity of the addition compounds of formaldehyde, acetaldehyde and acetone, one would expect the formaldehyde compounds to be the most soluble and the acetone compound the least soluble.

3. Since a hydrogen atom directly attached to the carbon atom of a carbonyl group is readily converted to a hydroxyl group by oxidation one would predict that formaldehyde is most readily oxidized, acetaldehyde less readily oxidized and that acetone is only oxidized with difficulty.

Notes on experimental work and questions

(I) (a) Formaldehyde turns the dichromate solution blue/green after about one minute. Acetaldehyde turns the dichromate solution blue/green after five to ten minutes. Acetone has no effect on the colour of the dichromate solution.

4. This is as predicted and is presumably related to the number of hydrogen atoms attached to the carbon atom of the carbonyl group.

234

(b) Formaldehyde and acetaldehyde give a silver mirror with a clean test tube (or a precipitate of silver if the surface of the tube is greasy). Acetone shows no change.

5. and 6. Silver oxide is formed on addition of sodium hydroxide to silver nitrate solution and this dissolves in ammonia solution as the diammino silver (I) complex ion $[Ag(NH_3)_2]^+$ is formed.

(c) Formaldehyde gives a reddish precipitate of copper (I) oxide (Cu_2O) and the solution remains blue because of the excess copper (II) ions.
Acetaldehyde gives a greenish solution with oily droplets and possibly some copper (I) oxide, but it is difficult to prevent the aldehyde resin formed in the alkaline conditions from masking the formation of the copper (I) oxide.
Acetone does not alter the blue solution; no precipitate is formed.
The formation of the red copper (I) oxide requires reduction of the complexed copper (II) ions in the Fehling's solution, consequently it is a test for reducing agents, and thus formaldehyde and acetaldehyde would be expected to give a positive result; acetone a negative one.

7. In the test for sugar in urine, the sugars can be detected because they possess a group with reducing properties—usually the aldehyde group.

(II) (a) 40% solutions give no precipitates. With pure acetaldehyde a precipitate may be obtained on cooling; with acetone a precipitate is usually formed.

8. To establish that the precipitate is a bisulphite addition compound, one could separate it and hydrolyse with acid or alkali and test for the original carbonyl compound and sulphur dioxide or sulphite.

9. Heat is evolved when the substances are mixed, but this may be heat of mixing, not involving the formation of an addition compound. The addition of alcohol to the saturated sodium bisulphite solution liberates heat—and forms a precipitate (presumably sodium bisulphite).

10. Structural formula of bisulphite ion
$$H-O\diagdown \atop {}^-O\diagup S \to O$$

The mechanism of the bisulphite addition is uncertain but it has been shown that the sulphur atom of the bisulphite ion becomes directly attached to the carbon atom of the carbonyl group. It may well be that it is the sulphite ion that is involved in the reaction.

(II) (b) On boiling Schiff's reagent the magenta colour returns, presumably because of displacement of the equilibrium as sulphur dioxide leaves the solution.

11. The sulphur dioxide may be removed by oxidation, e.g. with chlorine water, in which case the magenta colour may be restored provided an excess of chlorine is not used. This suggests that the mechanism of this reaction is that the free sulphur dioxide adds in a similar way to the bisulphite (above) and as the equilibrium is adjusted the magenta colour appears.
Formaldehyde and acetaldehyde restore the colour almost immediately; acetone very slowly.

12. The more reactive the carbonyl compound, the more quickly free sulphur dioxide will be removed and the equilibrium concentrations adjusted, resulting in re-formation of the magenta dye in its coloured form.

(III) (a) After heating the formaldehyde solution for five minutes the residue solidifies on cooling—suggesting that polymerization has occurred. The product melts on heating and will burn if exposed to a naked flame. (Similar compounds are used as solid fuels).

13. If paraformaldehyde is a cyclic polymer the carbonyl groups will probably be involved in the polymerization and the polymer would then not show reducing properties

unless depolymerization occurred. On the other hand, if the polymer is a linear molecule some carbonyl groups are likely to be free and reducing properties would be expected, but to a lesser degree than in the monomer.

The polymer does give positive results with Fehling's solution and ammoniacal silver nitrate.

14. Other carbonyl compounds need stronger conditions for polymerization e.g. acetaldehyde requires the presence of alkali, and acetone needs to be heated for some time with strong alkali.

Thus these reactions follow the order of activity outlined above.

(III) (b) The acetaldehyde solution forms yellow oily droplets, suggesting that polymerization has occurred.

15. A nucleophile may be produced from a carbonyl compound by the removal of a proton which is adjacent to the polarized carbonyl group.

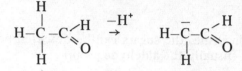

Sodium hydroxide being a base (proton acceptor) will assist the formation of the nucleophile in this way.

16. A likely mechanism for the polymerization of acetaldehyde is

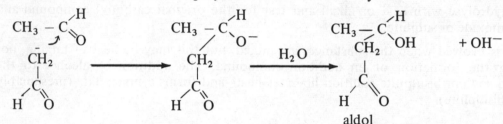

The carbon atom of the carbonyl group in acetaldehyde is more electrophilic than that in acetone and hence the carbanion will be formed more readily from acetaldehyde than from acetone.

17. Evidence of a reaction could be obtained by determination of molecular weight of the species present in solution, or possibly viscosity of the solution, or possibly a change in volume.

18. It is reasonable to predict that the proton of the carbon atom nearest to the carbonyl group of propionaldehyde (the α-carbon atom) would be most readily removed by the alkali, resulting in the following reaction

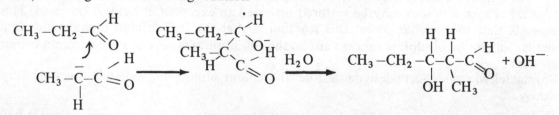

Benzaldehyde does not undergo a similar polymerization because it does not have a hydrogen atom on the carbon atom α to (adjacent to) the carbonyl group and cannot therefore form a nucleophilic species equivalent to $^-CH_2CHO$ or $CH_3\bar{C}HCHO$.

(IV) 19. Condensation reactions: Hydroxylamine, hydrazine and phenylhydrazine all contain a nitrogen atom bearing a lone pair of electrons and two hydrogen atoms.

In the reaction of all these reagents with carbonyl compounds the initial step is an addition reaction in which the lone pair of electrons on the nitrogen atom attacks the electrophilic carbon atom of the carbonyl group. Subsequently water is eliminated—a

236

condensation reaction involves an addition reaction followed by an elimination reaction.

e.g.

$$CH_3-\overset{\underset{\uparrow}{\underset{HO-N-H}{}}}{\overset{H}{\underset{}{C}}}{=}O \longrightarrow CH_3-\overset{H}{\underset{HO-N-H}{\overset{|}{C}}}-OH \longrightarrow CH_3-\overset{H}{\underset{N-OH}{C}} \quad +H_2O$$

20. The condensation products formed from the first few members of the aldehyde and ketone series on reaction with hydroxylamine, hydrazine or phenylhydrazine do not readily crystallize. On the other hand 2:4-dinitrophenylhydrazine forms crystalline products with these simple carbonyl compounds.

All three carbonyl compounds give an immediate yellow crystalline condensation product on treatment with the 2:4-dinitrophenylhydrazine reagent.

21. Purification of these products by recrystallization and determination of the melting point may be used to identify the original carbonyl compound. When the melting points of two compounds are similar the addition of a known sample of the 2:4-dinitrophenyl-hydrazone may be used to distinguish. A mixture of identical samples should have the usual melting point; a mixture of two different samples will have a lower and less sharp melting point.

22. This condensation reaction proceeds if 2:4-dinitrophenylhydrazine is mixed with a compound containing the carbonyl group. It could thus be used as a general test for carbonyl compounds.

(V) 23. Iodoform is produced by acetaldehyde and acetone but not by formaldehyde.

24. To produce iodoform a compound must contain the group:

$$CH_3-\overset{}{\underset{\overset{||}{O}}{C}}-X \qquad X = H \text{ or } C \qquad \text{or} \qquad CH_3-\overset{}{\underset{\overset{/\backslash}{H\ \ OH}}{C}}-X$$

which would be oxidized to the former under the conditions of the iodoform test.

25. Sodium carbonate is preferred to sodium hydroxide in these test because the stronger alkali might cause polymerization, obscuring the result.

26. Formaldehyde and acetaldehyde can be distinguished by the following reactions:

Action of alkali
Iodoform reaction

Acetaldehyde and acetone may be distinguished by the following reactions:

Action of acidified potassium dichromate
Action of Tollen's reagent
Action of Fehling's reagent
Action of alkali

The following reactions may be used to distinguish between aldehydes and ketones generally:

Action of acidified potassium dichromate
Action of Tollen's reagent
Action of Fehling's reagent

FURTHER PROJECT

A thorough investigation of the reaction of carbonyl compounds with sodium bisulphite solution and Schiff's reagent.

REFERENCES

James, *A Mechanistic Introduction to Organic Chemistry* Mills and Boon (1968).
Karrer, *Organic Chemistry,* Elsevier (1950). (Discussion of Schiff's Reagent)

Assignment 40
Reactions of Carboxylic Acids

INTRODUCTION

1. What are the structures of anhydrous nitric acid and sulphuric acid? (i.e. un-ionized)

2. Phosphorous acid, H_3PO_3, is a *di*basic acid. Suggest a structure for the undissociated acid.

3. What functional grouping is frequently associated with acidity?

4. What class of organic compounds contains this functional grouping alone?

5. The molecular formulae of formic, acetic and oxalic acids are H_2CO_2, $H_4C_2O_2$ and $H_2C_2O_4$ respectively. Given that the first two are monobasic acids while the latter is dibasic, suggest structural formulae for the three acids. (carboxylic acids)

6. How do you account for the high acidity of formic acid ($K_a = 1\cdot8 \times 10^{-4}$ mol dm^{-3} at 25°C) relative to water ($K_a = 1\cdot8 \times 10^{-16}$ mol dm^{-3})?

7. The boiling points of methanol and ethanol are 65°C and 78°C, respectively, while those of formic acid and acetic acid are 101°C and 118°C. How do these data support your reasoning?

8. Predict, giving your reasons, the relative values of the dissociation constants, K_a, for formic, acetic and oxalic acids.

9. Formic and acetic acids are far more acidic than the corresponding alcohols. Can you name one reaction that is common to both classes of compounds?

10. Carboxylic acids do *not* undergo condensation reactions with phenylhydrazine and acetic acid does *not* give a positive iodoform test. From this information and a consideration of your answer to question 9, what can you say about the nature of the carboxyl group, $-CO_2H$?

EXPERIMENTAL WORK

Section 1: acetic acid
N.B. In each of the experiments you must make careful observations and record these in your notes.

Experiment (a)
Dissolve about 1g of sodium acetate in 2–3cm³ of distilled water. Add a similar volume of dilute sulphuric acid and warm. Smell the vapour evolved and examine its effect on damp litmus paper.

11. What can you say about: (i) the solubility of acetic acid in water? (ii) its volatility?

Experiment (b)
Make 2–3cm³ of an aqueous solution of sodium acetate as described above. To this add a few drops of neutral iron (III) chloride solution. (The latter can be made by adding dilute

ammonia solution dropwise to about 2cm³ of bench aqueous iron (III) chloride solution until the first *trace* of permanent precipitate appears) Perform a blank experiment by adding the same number of drops of neutral iron (III) chloride solution to 2—3cm³ of distilled water.

12. What explanation can you offer for the effect of sodium acetate on neutral iron (III) chloride solution?

Experiment (c)
Mix 1—2cm³ of dilute sulphuric acid with a like volume of glacial acetic acid. Add 3 drops of bench potassium permanganate solution and warm the mixture for about a minute.

13. Is acetic acid easily oxidized?

14. What effect would you expect acetic acid to have on an aqueous solution of silver nitrate? (Consider your answer to question 13)

Experiment (d)
Test your prediction by adding about 5 drops of glacial acid to a mixture of about 1cm³ of silver nitrate solution with a like volume of dilute ammonia solution. Try warm-the mixture.

15. What can you deduce about the solubility of silver acetate in water?

Experiment (e)
Run 1—2cm³ of concentrated sulphuric acid into a pyrex test-tube and *warm* it gently. (*Take care; do not boil*). Using a dropper, add 3 drops of *glacial* acetic acid. Observe closely for signs of gas evolution. If you detect a gas, try to identify it. *Remember to pour the contents of the tube into a sink of cold water. Never* add water to the tube.

16. Bearing in mind the result of this experiment and that of Experiment (c), would you say that acetic acid shows any reducing properties?

17. Is there any evidence to suggest that acetic acid is susceptible to dehydration?

Experiment (f)
To 1—2cm³ of ethanol add a like volume of concentrated sulphuric acid. Pour a *few drops* of glacial acetic acid onto the mixture and warm it gently. Note the smell of the vapour evolved.

18. Assuming that the function of the concentrated acid is to facilitate a condensation reaction between the acetic acid and the ethanol by removing water, suggest a structural formula for the principle product of the reaction.

Experiment (g)
To 1—2cm³ of glacial acetic acid add a like volume of bench calcium chloride solution.

19. What can you say about the solubility of calcium acetate in water?

Section 2: Formic Acid and Oxalic Acid

The reactions of acetic acid are typical of those of most monocarboxylic acids. However, a characteristic of many homologous series is that the first members frequently show somewhat anomalous behaviour. Accordingly, it is worth comparing the reactions of acetic acid with those of formic acid, the simplest monocarboxylic acid, and oxalic acid, the simplest dicarboxylic acid.
Repeat Experiments (a)—(g) on both formic and oxalic acids. Record your observations and answer the following questions:

20. What can you say about the volatility of oxalic acid compared with that of formic acid and acetic acid?

21. Could you use the iron (III) chloride test to distinguish between (a) formic and acetic acids? (b) acetic and oxalic acids?

22. What evidence is there to show that formic acid and oxalic acid are both reducing agents? Which of the two would seem to be the stronger reducing agent?

23. What are the products of the dehydration of (a) formic acid? (b) oxalic acid?

24. Give three ways in which you could distinguish between formic acid and oxalic acid.

25. Can you suggest a way in which you could separate a mixture of formic acid and oxalic acid?

Notes 40

Standard: *

Time required: 1½ hours for practical work. The introductory section should be covered before the laboratory session.

Reagents required:

sodium acetate	(2g)	glacial acetic acid	(5cm^3)
sodium formate	(2g)	anhydrous formic acid	(5cm^3)
sodium oxalate	(2g)	oxalic acid crystals	(5g)
dilute sulphuric acid	(15cm^3)		
concentrated sulphuric acid	(12cm^3)		
ethanol	(6cm^3)		
litmus papers			
iron (III) chloride solution	(5cm^3)		
dilute ammonia solution	(10cm^3)		
potassium permanganate solution	(1cm^3)		
silver nitrate solution	(3cm^3)		
calcium chloride solution	(6cm^3)		

Apparatus required:

Test-tubes, including at least one pyrex tube

2 droppers or teat pipettes

Notes on introduction and experimental work

1. The structures of undissociated nitric acid and sulphuric acid can be represented as

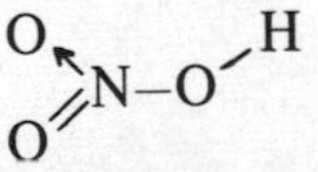

and

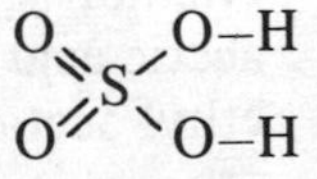

2. Since phosphorous acid is dibasic rather than tribasic, only two of the three hydrogen atoms in each molecule are acidic. By analogy with the structures for HNO_3 and H_2SO_4 given above, this suggests that only two of the three hydrogen atoms are attached to oxygen atoms.

The structure of phosphorous acid can thus be assumed to be:

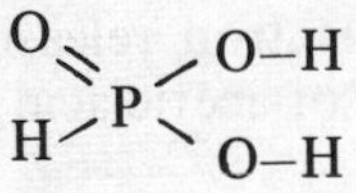

N.B. The presence of a P–H bond confers reducing properties on this molecule.

3. The great majority of compounds which behave as acids in aqueous solution owe their acidity to the presence of the –O–H functional group.

4. Alcohols are the simplest class of organic compounds which contain the –O–H functional group.

5. Valency considerations and the reasoning put forward in the answer to question 2 suggest the following structural formulae

241

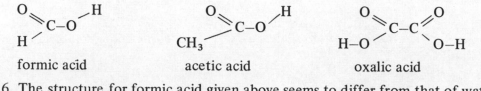

formic acid   acetic acid   oxalic acid

6. The structure for formic acid given above seems to differ from that of water merely by the insertion of a carbonyl group,

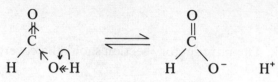

Since oxygen is much more electronegative than carbon, this can be expected to cause a further inductive displacement of electrons from hydrogen to oxygen in the neighbouring O–H bond, increasing the tendency of that bond to ionize:

A second point favouring ionization of the formic acid is that the resultant anion is stabilized by resonance to a greater degree than the undissociated acid:

7. The fact that the boiling points of the acids are higher than those of the comparable alcohols implies that greater intermolecular forces exist in the acids than in the alcohols. This is consistent with stronger hydrogen bonding in the former than in the latter and suggests that the carboxylic –O–H group is more polar than that of alcohols.

If it is protested that the higher boiling points of the acids are due primarily to the fact that they have higher molecular weights than the comparable alcohols, it can be pointed out that the esters have even higher molecular weights and yet have lower boiling points than the parent acids.

e.g.	boiling point/°C		boiling point/°C
methanol	65	ethanol	78
formic acid	101	acetic acid	118
ethyl formate	54	ethyl acetate	77

8. We have seen that the introduction of a carboxyl group confers marked acidity on a molecule. It seems reasonable, therefore, that a molecule with two *adjacent* carboxyl groups can be expected to be even more acidic, i.e. We can expect K_a for oxalic acid to be greater than that for formic acid.

Earlier experiments (e.g. comparison of the ease with which sodium reacts with water and with ethanol) should have suggested that alkyl groups have a weak electron releasing inductive effect. Assuming this to be so, we can expect the –O–H bond of acetic acid to be less acidic than that of formic acid.

i.e. We can predict K_{a1} oxalic acid $> K_a$ formic acid $> K_a$ acetic acid

       or   pK_{a1} oxalic acid $<$ pK_a formic acid $<$ pK_a acetic acid

Actual pK_a values are: oxalic acid 1·2; formic acid 3·8; acetic acid 4·8

9. Both carboxylic acids and alcohols react with sodium to form salts and hydrogen. However, the former react with considerably more violence than the latter.

242

10. If acetic acid gave a positive iodoform test it would indicate that it contains an acetyl group, as is suggested by its structural formula. However, it does not do so, and neither do carboxylic acids undergo condensation reactions with phenyl hydrazine, a reaction which typifies a carbonyl group,

$$-\overset{\overset{\displaystyle O}{\|}}{C}-$$

We are forced to conclude that the presence of an $-O-H$ group on the carbonyl carbon atom virtually destroys (or at least grossly modifies) the properties of both groups.
e.g. carboxylic acids show virtually none of the properties of aldehydes or ketones and they are much more acidic than alcohols.

It is, in fact, better to consider the carboxyl group, $-\overset{\overset{\displaystyle O}{\|}}{C}-OH$, as a new functional group possessing unique properties.

Section 1.

Experiment (a)
When a concentrated solution of sodium acetate is acidified no precipitate forms. On warming, vinegar-like fumes can be smelled which turn damp blue litmus red.

11. It follows that acetic acid is: (i) reasonably soluble in water and (ii) fairly volatile.

Experiment (b)
Neutral iron (III) chloride solution produces a red-orange colouration (no precipitate) when it is added to an aqueous solution of sodium acetate. The blank solution appears only a very pale yellow.

12. Clearly, a reaction takes place between the two solutions. Since no precipitate is observed it is probable that a complex ion is formed between hydrated iron (III) ions and acetate ions.

$$\text{e.g.} \quad Fe^{3+}_{(aq)} + CH_3CO_2^-{}_{(aq)} \rightleftharpoons [FeCH_3CO_2^{2+}{}_{(aq)}]$$

(D.D. Perrin *J. Phys. Chem*, **62**, 767 (1958) cites a value of $10^{3 \cdot 2}$ mol^{-1} dm^3 for the equilibrium constant of the above reaction at 25°C)

Experiment (c)
No apparent reaction takes place when acetic acid is mixed with a few drops of potassium permanganate solution, even if the mixture is warmed for some time.

13. Since acetic acid does not reduce potassium permanganate, it cannot itself be easily oxidized.

14. The silver ion is a weaker oxidizing agent than the permanganate ion (see table of redox potentials) and so it is unlikely that silver nitrate can succeed in oxidizing acetic acid since potassium permanganate cannot do so.

Experiment (d)
No apparent reaction takes place between ammoniacal silver nitrate and acetic acid.

15. Strictly speaking one cannot infer anything about the solubility of silver acetate as a result of adding a few drops of acetic acid to some ammoniacal silver nitrate. Could one comment about the solubility of silver chloride as a result of adding a few drops of hydrochloric acid to some ammoniacal silver nitrate? In fact, silver acetate has a modest solubility in pure water (about 1g per 100g of water at room temperature).

Experiment (e)
A lot of acetic acid vapour is evolved, but otherwise there is no apparent reaction when acetic acid is *warmed* with concentrated sulphuric acid.

16. Hot, concentrated sulphuric acid is a potent oxidizing agent. Since neither it nor potassium permanganate can easily oxidize acetic acid, it can be assumed that the latter is not a reducing agent.

243

17. Hot, concentrated sulphuric acid is also a powerful dehydrating agent. Its apparent failure to react easily with glacial acetic acid also shows that the latter is not highly susceptible to dehydration.

Experiment (f)

On warming a mixture of ethanol and glacial acetic acid with some concentrated sulphuric acid, the highly characteristic 'pear-drop' smell of ethyl acetate can be detected.

18. If the sulphuric acid removes a water molecule from one molecule of acetic acid and one of ethanol, the reaction can be visualized as:

$$CH_3.CH_2-O-H \ + \ H-O.\overset{\overset{O}{\|}}{C}.CH_3 \ \rightleftharpoons \ CH_3.CH_2-O-\overset{\overset{O}{\|}}{C}-CH_3 \ + \ H_2O$$
$$\text{ethyl acetate}$$

N.B. Isotope tracer studies have shown that it is the ethanol oxygen atom that is retained.

Experiment (g)

No apparent reaction takes place between calcium chloride solution and glacial acetic acid.

19. Since no precipitate is formed we can assume that calcium acetate is at least moderately soluble in water. (Actual solubility is about 35g per 100g of water at 20°C)

Section 2

Summary of observations for Experiments (a)–(g) using formic acid or oxalic acid instead of acetic acid:

Experiment	Formic Acid	Oxalic Acid
(a) sodium salt + dilute H_2SO_4	Sharp smell on warming; vapour turned moist blue litmus red	No apparent effect. No smell on warming. Vapour has no effect on blue litmus.
(b) sodium salt + $FeCl_3$	Red-orange colouration as for acetic acid	Very pale yellow solution; almost identical with the water blank.
(c) Acid + dilute H_2SO_4 + $KMnO_4$	Purple colour slowly discharged on warming	On warming, the purple colour is discharged rapidly and gas is evolved
(d) Acid + ammoniacal $AgNO_3$	On warming, a grey-black deposit of metallic silver is obtained. There may be a silver mirror on the tube.	No sign of metallic silver, but a white precipitate of silver oxalate may form if insufficient ammonia is present.
(e) Acid + hot, conc. H_2SO_4 (*care* is needed when doing these experiments)	Carbon monoxide evolved readily. (Burns with blue flame giving CO_2)	CO_2 and CO are both evolved. (Test for CO_2 with lime water; then collect some of the gas over aqueous NaOH and show that the residual gas burns)
(f) Acid + ethanol + conc. H_2SO_4	Fruity smells can be detected in both cases, but students should not be encouraged to smell the vapours since they will almost certainly contain some carbon monoxide. Some students might like to consider how ethyl formate could be prepared	
(g) Acid + $CaCl_2$ solution	No apparent effect	A white precipitate of calcium oxalate forms at once

244

20. Experiment (a) suggests that oxalic acid is not very volatile, whereas both formic acid and acetic acid are. This can be confirmed by comparing the states of the three acids; oxalic acid is the only one of the three which is a solid at room temperature.

21. It would be very difficult to distinguish between formic acid and acetic acid by means of a qualitative iron (III) chloride test. However, since oxalic acid appears to be little affected by iron (III) chloride, it is easy to distinguish between oxalic and acetic acids by this method.

22. Since formic acid will reduce both acid permanganate and ammoniacal silver nitrate whereas oxalic acid only reduces the former, it seems reasonable to assume that formic acid is a stronger reducing agent than oxalic acid.

23. Formic acid yields carbon monoxide on dehydration whereas oxalic acid produces a mixture of carbon monoxide and carbon dioxide.

24. Of the tests studied, Experiments (a), (b), (d), (e) and (g) could be used to distinguish between oxalic acid and formic acid.

25. Formic acid could be freed from oxalic acid by precipitating the latter as the calcium salt. However, if both acids are to be obtained from the mixture, distillation would offer a convenient method since formic acid is volatile but oxalic acid is not.

FURTHER PROJECTS

1. Prepare copper (II) acetate (and/or lead formate) and investigate how the free acid can be regenerated from its salt.
2. Carry out an investigation to establish whether the iron (III) chloride test can be used for the quantitative estimation of the acetate and formate ions by means of colorimetry.
3. The preparation of *cis*- and *trans*-potassium dioxalato-diaquo chromate (III). (See Reference 3)

REFERENCES

1. *A Mechanistic Introduction to Organic Chemistry*, G.H. James, Mills and boon (1968) p46.
2. *Basic Organic Chemistry: A Mechanistic Approach* (Part I), J.M. Tedder and A. Nechvatel, Wiley and Sons (1966).
3. *Practical Inorganic Chemistry*, G. Pass and H. Sutcliffe, Chapman and Hall (1968).
N.B. The first two references contain very helpful discussions of the carboxyl group and its reactions.

Assignment 41

Acetyl Chloride and Acetic Anhydride

INTRODUCTION

Both of these compounds contain the acetyl group, $CH_3 - \overset{O}{\underset{\|}{C}} -$, and may thus be regarded as of the same general formula, $CH_3 - \overset{O}{\underset{\|}{C}} - X$

where X = Cl in the case of acetyl chloride and X = $-O - \overset{O}{\underset{\|}{C}} - CH_3$ in the case of acetic anhydride.

1. The similarity of these compounds to ethyl acetate and ethanamide (acetamide) is seen if the general formula, $CH_3 - \overset{O}{\underset{\|}{C}} - X$, is considered. What would X represent in the case of (i) ethyl acetate. (ii) ethanamide (acetamide)?

The most important reactions of these compounds are nucleophilic substitutions, in which a nucleophile attacks the carbon atom of the carbonyl group and the group X (sometimes together with a proton) is displaced.

2. What are the characteristic features of a nucleophile?

3. What factors will determine the facility of these nucleophilic reactions?

4. Which of the two substances, acetyl chloride and acetic anhydride, would you expect to undergo reaction with nucleophiles more readily?

5. How would ethyl acetate and ethanamide (acetamide) fit into this order of reactivity?

EXPERIMENT WORK

Some of these reactions are violent and it is advisable to do them in a fume cupboard, with the eyes protected by the safety glass. In each case record your observations and write an equation where possible.

(a) *Reaction with water*
(i) Add 1cm³ of acetyl chloride to 1cm³ of water. Identify the gas evolved, explaining the test used.
Neutralize the solution in the test tube and add a few drops of neutral iron (III) chloride solution. (This can be made by adding dilute ammonia solution to iron (III) chloride solution until a precipitate is formed, using the supernatant liquid.)

6. What are the products of this reaction?

7. Write an equation for the reaction, suggesting a mechanism if you can.
(ii) Repeat the experiment, substituting acetic anhydride for acetyl chloride.

8. Is any gas evolved in this reaction?

9. Which of the two substances reacts more vigorously with water? Is this in agreement with your prediction in question 4? If not, try another explanation of the reaction.

246

(b) *Reaction with ethanol*

10. Would you expect ethanol to react more or less vigorously than water with acetyl chloride? Explain

(i) Add 1cm³ of acetyl chloride dropwise to an equal volume of ethanol, then pour the mixture into about 50cm³ of water in a beaker.

11. What product can you smell?

12. Does the reaction of acetyl chloride with ethanol appear to be more vigorous than its reaction with water? Are the conditions comparable?

(ii) Add ½cm³ of acetic anhydride to 1cm³ of ethanol and warm. Allow the mixture to cool, add sodium carbonate solution to react with unchanged acetic anhydride and pour the mixture into about 50cm³ of water in a beaker.

13. Cautiously smell the mixture. Can you detect the same smell as in b(i)?

(c) *Reaction with 0·88 ammonia solution*

14. Would you expect ammonia solution to react more or less vigorously with these substances than water does? Explain.

(i) Add 1cm³ of acetyl chloride dropwise to an equal volume of 0·88 ammonia solution (*care!*)

15. What do you think the solid organic product is?

16. How could you confirm your predictions?

(ii) Repeat c(i), but substituting acetic anhydride for acetyl chloride.

17. Do you think ammonia reacts more or less vigorously with these substances than water? Does this confirm your prediction in question 12. If not, think again.

(d) *Reaction with aniline*

18. Would you expect aniline to react more or less readily with acetyl chloride than ammonia does? Explain.

(i) Add 1 cm³ of acetyl chloride dropwise to an equal volume of aniline in a boiling tube, shaking after the addition of each drop.

(ii) Repeat d(i) but substituting acetic anhydride for acetyl chloride.

19. What do you think the solid organic product is, in each case?

20. Do your experiments suggest that aniline reacts more or less readily with these substances than does ammonia? Does this confirm your prediction in question 18? If not, try a new explanation.

21. List the order of reactivity of water, ethanol, ammonia and aniline with acetyl chloride.

22. Does this list compare with the order of basic strength of these four reagents?

23. Comment on the relationship between basic strength and the nucleophile reactivity of substances.

Notes 41

Standard: *
Time required: 1½ hours
Reagents required:

acetyl chloride	$(10 cm^3)$
acetic anhydride	$(10 cm^3)$
ethanol	$(10 cm^3)$
0·88 ammonia solution	$(5 cm^3)$
aniline	$(3 cm^3)$
aq. sodium hydroxide	$(10 cm^3)$
distilled water	$(10 cm^3)$
aq. iron (III) chloride	$(2 cm^3)$
aq. silver nitrate	$(10 cm^3)$

Apparatus required:
  test tubes (dry)
  2 dropping pipettes
  2 beakers (100 or 150cm³)
  2 boiling tubes
  bunsen burner

Notes on experimental work and questions

1. In the case of ethyl acetate, X would represent $-OC_2H_5$
In the case of ethanamide (acetamide), X would represent $-NH_2$

2. A nucleophile is a negatively charged ion or a neutral molecule with an unshared pair of electrons.

3. The facility of these reactions will depend on
(i) the electron-pair-donating properties of the nucleophile
(ii) the strength of the C−X bond
(iii) the stability of the X⁻ ion, which is expelled.

4. Acetyl chloride might be expected to undergo reaction with nucleophiles more readily since (i) one might expect the chlorine atom to hold its electrons more strongly than the oxygen atom of the acetic anhydride, in which case the C−X bond of acetyl chloride would not be strengthened by conjugation as much as the C−X bond of acetic anhydride. (H−Cl is a stronger acid than $H-O-\overset{..}{\underset{..}{O}}-CH_3$, which suggests that the chlorine has a

stronger hold of its electrons than the oxygen atom of the acetate group.) (ii) the chloride ion is more stable than the acetate ion; in this context this probably means the chloride ion is a weaker base than the acetate ion.

5. Ethyl acetate would be expected to be less reactive than both acetyl chloride and acetic anhydride and acetamide even less reactive.
The nitrogen atom of acetamide would donate an electron pair, by conjugation, to strengthen the C−X bond more readily than the oxygen of the ethyl acetate, and this

248

effect would be more pronounced in both these compounds than in acetyl chloride and acetic anhydride.

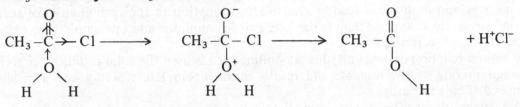

The NH_2^- ion is less stable than the ethoxide ion, both being less stable than the chloride and acetate ions.

(a) (i) Initially two layers form, but after a few seconds a violent reaction occurs and steamy fumes of hydrogen chloride are evolved. The fumes can be shown to be hydrogen chloride by passing into aq. silver nitrate acidified with dilute nitric acid. A white precipitate, soluble in ammonia solution is formed.
On neutralization and addition of neutral iron (III) chloride, a red colouration is seen indicating that acetic acid is left in the tube.

6. Acetic acid and hydrogen chloride.

7. $CH_3COCl + H_2O = CH_3COOH + HCl$

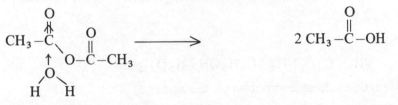

(ii) Two layers separate on standing and little reaction occurs unless the mixture is warmed, whereupon the two layers coalesce.

8. No gas is evolved.

$$CH_3-C \longrightarrow 2 CH_3-C-OH$$

9. Acetyl chloride reacts more vigorously with water than does acetic anhydride. The possible explanation is as in question 4.

(b) 10. Assuming that the reactivity of the nucleophile depends on the tendency to donate a lone pair of electrons one might expect ethanol to be the more reactive because of the electron-releasing property of the ethyl group, but it is possible that other factors should be considered e.g. the degree of ionization which is greater in the case of water.

$$C_2H_5 \diagup O \diagdown H \qquad H \diagup O \diagdown H$$

(i) A violent reaction occurs as acetyl chloride is added to ethanol and steamy fumes are evolved.

11. On pouring the mixture into water the smell of ethyl acetate is very strong.

12. The reaction with ethanol appears to be more vigorous than with water, but one should be careful about drawing conclusions as the conditions are not quite the same. The acetyl chloride and ethanol are miscible, but acetyl chloride and water do not mix and reaction can then only occur at the interface.

(ii) 13. There is no obvious sign of a reaction until the mixture is warmed. The unpleasant fumes of unchanged acetic anhydride and acetic acid may mask the smell of the ethyl acetate but it can usually be detected. Care should be taken when smelling this mixture and pupils should be warned to do it cautiously.

(c) 14. The lone pair of electrons on the nitrogen atom of ammonia is more readily donated than the lone pair on the oxygen of water, and thus one would expect ammonia to be more reactive.

(i) A very violent reaction occurs on adding acetyl chloride to ammonia and dense white fumes of ammonium chloride are produced.

15. The solid organic product is acetamide.

$$CH_3COCl + NH_3 = CH_3CONH_2 + HCl$$

16. The identity could be confirmed by recrystallizing from ethanol and determining the melting point.

c(ii) On adding acetic anhydride to ammonia solution an immediate and vigorous reaction occurs, producing fumes of ammonium acetate and a white solid.

17. Ammonia obviously reacts more readily with these reagents than water, as is predicted in question 12.

(d) 18. The lone pair of electrons on the nitrogen atom of aniline conjugates with the benzene ring and is thus less readily available for donation to the carbon atom of acetyl chloride or acetic anhydride than is the lone pair in ammonia, and one would thus expect aniline to react less readily.

(i) A violent reaction occurs, and unless a boiling tube is used the solid produced prevents thorough mixing of the reagents and results in an incomplete reaction and a product which is difficult to purify.

(ii) No apparent reaction occurs immediately and the reagents need to be refluxed for about half an hour to complete the reaction.

19. The solid organic product is acetanilide.

20. Aniline reacts less readily than ammonia with these reagents. This confirms the prediction in question 18.

21. The order of reactivity is

$$NH_3 \rangle C_6H_5NH_2 \rangle C_2H_5OH \rangle H_2O$$

22. The order of basic strength of these compounds is the same.

23. The same order is obtained in both cases because the basic strength is an indication of the tendency to accept a proton, by donation of a lone pair of electrons to the proton. This is thus a type of nucleophilic reaction and one would thus expect the order of basic strength and the order of reactivity as a nucleophile to be the same.

FURTHER PROJECT

Isolate and purify the products of reactions c(i) and d(i) and determine the melting point of the pure compounds.

REFERENCE

James, *A Mechanistic Introduction to Organic Chemistry* Mills and Boon (1968).

Assignment 42

Aminoethane (ethylamine), Ethanamide (acetamide) and Urea

1. A Comparison of aminoethane and ethanamide:

1. What are the structural formulae of these two compounds?

Aminoethane, like ammonia, is a gas at room temperature (but only just so: boiling point 16°C) and is soluble in water. In this study you will be using a solution of aminoethane in water.

2. Knowing the structure of ethanamide, and bearing in mind the relative electronegativities of carbon, nitrogen and oxygen:
(a) is it reasonable that ethanamide is a solid at room temperature?
(b) is it likely to be more soluble in water than it is in hexane? Check your prediction experimentally.

Experiment (i)

Dissolve about 0·5g of ethanamide in about 3cm^3 of distilled water. Divide this about equally between three test tubes (a), (b) and (c).
Test (a) with litmus. To (b) add 1 drop of iron (III) chloride solution. To (c) add 1 drop of copper (II) sulphate solution. Record your observations. Repeat these three tests on 1cm^3 portions of the aminoethane solution.

3. What evidence is there that aminoethane is a base?

4. Give an equation to illustrate why an aqueous solution of aminoethane is alkaline.

5. Why can aminoethane react with water?

6. What is meant by (a) the term 'dissociation constant of a base in water', K_b?
    (b) the expression pK_b?

7. From your experimental results decide whether you think that ethanamide is distinctly basic, neutral or distinctly acidic.

8. The pK_b values for aminoethane and ethanamide are either 3·3 and 12·6, respectively or *vice-versa*. Which value applies to which compound? Give your reasons.

9. If the pK_b of ammonia is 4·75, what can you say about the affinity of the ethyl group for electrons relative to that of hydrogen?

10. Can you provide an electronic explanation for the great difference in pK_b values between aminoethane and ethanamide?

11. Would you expect ammonia to be a more powerful nucleophilic reagent than aminoethane?
Explain your reasoning.

12. Would you expect the carbonyl group of ethanamide to be more sensitive to nucleophilic attack than the carbonyl group of typical aldehydes and ketones? Why?

Experiment (ii)

Treat about 0·2g of ethanamide with 2—3cm³ of bench sodium hydroxide solution and warm. Smell the gas evolved and test it with red litmus paper. Repeat the experiment using 1cm³ of the aqueous aminoethane solution and another 2—3cm³ of sodium hydroxide solution. Record your observations noting carefully any slight difference in smell between the two gases.

13. Can you identify the two gases?

14. What is the equation for the reaction of ethanamide with sodium hydroxide solution?

Experiment (iii)

Repeat the previous experiment using dilute sulphuric acid instead of the sodium hydroxide and damp blue litmus paper instead of red.

15. Suggest equations for the reactions of the two compounds with dilute sulphuric acid. Comment on the evidence for your suggestions.

16. You should have found that ethanamide can be hydrolysed in the presence of either acid or alkali. Water is a nucleophilic reagent. Suggest why acid catalyses the hydrolysis of ethanamide more effectively than alkali does.

Experiment (iv)

Make a solution of about 2g of sodium nitrite in about 5cm³ of water and cool it in an ice bath. In another tube place about 0·2g of ethanamide and dissolve it in about 3cm³ of dilute sulphuric acid. Cool this tube for a minute or so and then gently add about 1—2cm³ of the cool sodium nitrite solution. You will see some brown nitrogen dioxide; try to decide whether it is formed in the solution or in the air. Are any other gases (e.g. CO_2 or N_2) being evolved?

When the reaction has subsided, conduct an iodoform test on the residual solution.

Repeat the above experiment (including the final iodoform test) using about 1cm³ of aqueous aminoethane solution with about 3cm³ of dilute sulphuric acid instead of the acidified ethanamide.

17. What sort of compounds give a positive iodoform test?

18. Bearing in mind the results of your iodoform tests and assuming that nitrogen is the chief gas evolved when nitrous acid reacts with either ethanamide or aminoethane, write equations for the overall reaction of nitrous acid with (a) ethanamide and (b) aminoethane.

19. What is the structure of nitrous acid? Would you expect the nitrogen atom in nitrous acid to be electrophilic or nucleophilic?

2. Urea in relation to aminoethane and ethanamide

20. What is the structural formula of urea?

Look up (or measure) the melting point of urea. Roughly check its solubility in water and in hexane.

21. As far as physical properties are concerned which of the compounds aminoethane and ethanamide most closely resembles urea?

Experiment (v)

Carry out Experiment (i) on a solution of about 0·5g of urea in about 3cm³ of distilled water. Record your observations.

22. What evidence is there to suggest that solid urea does *not* have the structure shown below?

252

23. What evidence is there to suggest that urea does *not* behave as follows to any significant extent in water:

$$H_2N.CO.NH_2 + H_2O \rightleftharpoons H_2N.CO.NH_3{}^+OH^-$$

Experiment (vi)

The previous experiment shows that urea is not a strong base. To investigate whether a substance is a weak base the logical procedure is to treat it with a strong acid in concentrated solution. Test concentrated aqueous solutions of ethanamide and urea with (a) concentrated nitric acid and (b) concentrated oxalic acid solution. Record your observations.

24. Analysis shows that the products of the reactions of urea with nitric acid and with oxalic acid have the molecular formulae $CH_5O_4N_3$ and $C_3H_6O_5N_2$ respectively. Suggest structural formulae for these compounds.

Experiment (vii)

Carry out tests to establish whether urea can be hydrolysed by boiling with (a) dilute sodium hydroxide solution and (b) dilute sulphuric acid. Record your observations, being careful to identify any gases evolved. Write equations for any reactions which you think may have taken place.

25. Assuming that the reactions of urea generally resemble those of ethanamide, predict the products of the reaction of urea with nitrous acid.

Experiment (viii)

Repeat Experiment (iv) using urea instead of ethanamide. (There is no need to conduct an iodoform test in this case). Record your observations and carry out tests to check your answer to question 25.

Write a short paragraph comparing the chemistry of urea with those of ethanamide and aminoethane. Comment on the fact that urea is known to have the following molecular dimensions: Both $C-N$ bonds are 0.137nm long (c.f. 0.147nm for most amines) and the $C-O$ distance is 0.125nm long (c.f. 0.122nm for most ketones).

3. Other reactions of importance:

Experiment (ix)

Put about 0.2g of urea in a test-tube and warm it gently. Identify the gas evolved. When no further change appears to be taking place, allow the tube to cool. The substance remaining in the tube has the trivial name of biuret.

26. Assuming that the reaction which has taken place involves the condensation of two molecules of urea with the elimination of a simple gas, suggest a structure for biuret.
Dissolve the biuret in $2-3$cm³ of bench sodium hydroxide solution and add 1 drop of dilute copper (II) sulphate solution. Record the colour of the resultant solution. This is a useful test for biuret and compounds containing similar groups e.g. proteins.

Experiment (x)

Take about 0.2g of ethanamide and add 5 drops of bromine (*care*) followed by about 2cm³ of distilled water and 5 pellets of sodium hydroxide. Warm gently and try to identify the gas evolved. After a few minutes, allow the tube to cool and acidify carefully with dilute sulphuric acid. Again try to identify the gas.
Repeat the experiment using urea instead of ethanamide.

27. Write overall equations for the reactions of urea and ethanamide with bromine in the presence of alkali.

28. Why is the reaction of acid amides with bromine in the presence of alkali of general importance?

Notes 42

Standard: **

Time required: About 2 hours of practical work (best split into 2 sessions) and a similar length of time needed to answer all the questions.

Reagents required:

aminoethane solution in water [70% w/w in water] ($10cm^3$)
ethanamide (5g)
urea (5g)
iron (III) chloride solution ⎫
copper (II) sulphate   ⎪ all these
dilute sodium hydroxide   ⎬ are
dilute sulphuric acid   ⎪ bench
sodium hypochlorite   ⎪ solutions
potassium iodide   ⎭
lime water
concentrated nitric acid ($5cm^3$)
bromine ($1cm^3$)
solid sodium hydroxide (1g)
solid oxalic acid (5g)
solid sodium nitrite (5g)
hexane or petroleum ether ($5cm^3$)

Apparatus required:

test-tubes, an ice-bath

1. A Comparison of aminoethane and ethanamide

1. The structural formulae are: $CH_3.CH_2.NH_2$ aminothane

and $CH_3.CO.NH_2$ ethanamide

2. (a) Since oxygen and nitrogen are both more electronegative than carbon and hydrogen, it is reasonable to expect ethanamide to have a more polar molecule than that of aminoethane. In addition, the former has a higher molecular weight than the latter. For both these reasons it is to be expected that ethanamide will have a higher melting point than aminoethane. Ethanamide melts at 82°C while pure aminoethane does so at −81°C.

(b) In view of its polar nature ethanamide should be more soluble in water than it is in hexane.

Experiment (i)

	aminoethane	ethanamide
(a) effect on litmus	aqueous solution turns red litmus blue.	aqueous solution has no effect on litmus

(b) FeCl$_3$ solution   red-brown precipitate   no apparent effect

(c) CuSO$_4$ solution   deep blue solution resembling the colour of the copper (II) tetrammine ion.   no apparent effect

3. The fact that an aqueous solution of aminoethane is alkaline shows that the compound can act as a base. This is confirmed by tests (b) and (c).

4. The following equation illustrates why an aqueous solution of aminoethane is alkaline:

$$CH_3.CH_2.NH_2 + H_2O \rightleftharpoons CH_3.CH_2.NH_3^+ + OH^-$$

5. Aminoethane can react with water because its nitrogen atom has a lone pair of electrons which it can donate to protons from water:

$$-\ddot{N}H_2 \longrightarrow -\overset{\overset{\textstyle H}{\uparrow}}{N}H_2^+$$

6. (a) The dissociation constant of a base in water refers to the equilibrium constant for the hydrolysis reaction quoted in the answer to question 4.

i.e. $$K_b = \frac{[CH_3.CH_2.NH_3^+]\ [OH^-]}{[CH_3.CH_2.NH_2]}$$

The concentration of water usually being effectively constant, the [H$_2$O] term is incorporated in the constant, K_b.

(b) Just as pH = $-$lg[H$^+$], so pK_b = $-$lg K_b. It is more convenient to quote pK_b values than K_b values.

7. Experiment (i) shows that aqueous solutions of ethanamide are effectively neutral. If it is a base it must be a very weak one.

8. The weaker the base (i.e. the smaller the K_b) the bigger its pK_b value is. Thus, aminoethane being more basic than ethanamide, the former will have a smaller pK_b value than the latter. It follows that the pK_b of aminoethane is 3·3 while that of ethanamide is 12·6.

9. Since ammonia has a larger pK_b than aminoethane, the latter must be the stronger base of the two. This means that the lone pair of electrons on the nitrogen atom is more readily available to an electrophile attacking aminoethane than to one attacking ammonia. Thus, we can deduce that the ethyl group has less affinity for electrons than a hydrogen atom has:

H $-$ NH$_2$ C$_2$H$_5$ $\twoheadrightarrow$NH$_2$

10. The fact that the lone pair of electrons on the nitrogen atom of ethanamide is less readily donated than that in aminoethane is probably due to the inductive effect of the oxygen in ethanamide and to partial conjugation of the nitrogen lone pair of electrons with the carbonyl group:

CH$_3$ $-$ C $-$ NH$_2$ CH$_3$ $-$ C $=$ NH$_2^+$

Presumably, withdrawal of electrons by the electronegative oxygen atom more than offsets the inductive release of electrons by the methyl group.

11. Since the nitrogen lone pair is more readily donated by aminoethane than by ammonia, we would expect the former to be the more powerful nucleophilic reagent. e.g. Contrast the relative reactivities of the two compounds with alkyl halides.

12. The carbonyl group of ethanamide is to be expected to be less sensitive to nucleophilic attack than that of most aldehydes and ketones. In ethanamide the positive charge on the carbon atom of the carbonyl group is reduced by partial donation of the neighbouring nitrogen lone pair. (See answer to question 10.)

Experimental data for Experiments (ii)–(iv)

	aminoethane	*ethanamide*
Experiment (ii) Effect of bench NaOH	On warming both compounds release colourless gases which turn red litmus blue. The gas from ethanamide smells like ammonia, while that from aminoethane is similar but with a fishy tang	
Experiment (iii) Effect of dilute H_2SO_4	No apparent reaction* No smell on warming *N.B. If the aminoethane solution is old, it may have absorbed CO_2 from the air. This will be released on acidification.	No apparent reaction, but a vinegar like smell is noticed on warming. The vapour turns blue litmus red.
Experiment (iv) Effect of $NaNO_2/HCl$	Brown gas forms near the mouth of the test-tube in both cases. This suggests the evolution of NO. In view of the volume of gas evolved it is reasonable to assume that another gas is evolved besides NO or NO_2. Negative tests can be done (e.g. glowing splint, lime water) to narrow the field of suspects, but nitrogen cannot be positively identified.	
Subsequent iodoform test: (KI solution followed by NaOCl solution is suitable)	Pale yellow solid with an antiseptic smell forms on cooling. This dissolves on warming and recrystallizes on cooling again.	No precipitate or characteristic smell. i.e. Test is negative.

13. The gases are ammonia from the ethanamide and aminoethane itself. Identification of the latter will probably have to be left to inspired guess work.

14. The equation for the reaction of ethanamide with sodium hydroxide solution is

$$CH_3.CO.NH_2 + OH^- \rightarrow CH_3CO_2^- + NH_3$$

15. Aminoethane is volatile, but when it is warmed with dilute sulphuric acid no gas is evolved. This is consistent with the amine being converted into an ionic (non-volatile) form:

$$CH_3.CH_2.NH_2 + H^+ \rightleftharpoons CH_3.CH_2.NH_3^+$$

The vinegar smell formed when ethanamide is warmed with dilute sulphuric acid (a non-volatile acid) suggests that acetic acid is formed. It seems likely that the ethanamide is hydrolysed:

$$CH_3.CO.NH_2 + H_2O + H^+ \rightarrow CH_3CO_2H + NH_4^+$$

16. Although ethanamide is only a very weak base hydrogen ions can attack the lone pair of electrons on its nitrogen atom to some extent:

$$CH_3.CO.NH_2 + H^+ \rightleftharpoons CH_3.CO.NH_3^+$$

The positive charge on the nitrogen atom of the resulting ion will, in turn, lead to a greater positive charge on the carbon atom of the carbonyl group. This will make it easier for it to be attacked by water, a nucleophilic molecule.

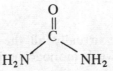

17. The iodoform test is only exhibited by compounds containing an acetyl group, CH_3CO-, or some group easily oxidized to it. e.g.

$$CH_3.CH(OH)-$$

18. Knowing the structures of ethanamide and aminoethane and that aminoethane reacts with nitrous acid to form a substance which exhibits the iodoform test, whereas ethanamide does not, it seems reasonable to assume that nitrous acid converts aminoethane to ethanol and ethanamide to acetic acid. Thus the appropriate equations are:

$$CH_3.CO.NH_2 + HO.NO \rightarrow CH_3CO.OH + N_2 + H_2O$$

and $$CH_3.CH_2.NH_2 + HO.NO \rightarrow CH_3.CH_2.OH + N_2 + H_2O$$

19. Nitrous acid has the structure $H-O-N=O$. Since oxygen is more electronegative than nitrogen it is probable that the lone pair of electrons on the nitrogen atom of nitrous acid will not be strongly nucleophilic and may even be electrophilic. (It is useful to establish this point if one wants to attempt a discussion of the mechanism of the reaction of nitrous acid with amines and with acid amides)

2. Urea in relation to aminoethane and ethanamide

20. The structural formula of urea is

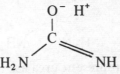

Its melting point is 132°C. It is quite soluble in water but effectively insoluble in non-polar solvents.

21. Both solubilities and melting points suggest that urea resembles ethanamide more closely than it does aminoethane.

Experiment (v)
Urea exerts no apparent effect on litmus, iron (II) chloride or copper (II) sulphate solution.

22. If solid urea did exist as

it ought to have a higher melting point than 132°C. It is quite soluble in water but effectively insoluble in non-polar solvents.

23. Urea cannot be hydrolysed to any extent in water or its aqueous solution would turn red litmus blue and have effects on $FeCl_3$ and $CuSO_4$ solutions similar to those exerted by aminoethane.

Experiment (vi)
Concentrated nitric acid reacts immediately with a concentrated aqueous solution of urea to form a fine, white precipitate. Considerable heat is evolved. Oxalic acid reacts in a similar way but rather less heat is evolved.

24. The molecular formulae are consistent with the urea behaving as a monoacidic base in its reactions with both nitric and oxalic acids. The precipitates have the structural formulae:

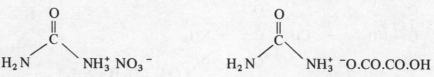

Experiment (vii)

(a) There is rather reluctant release of ammonia when urea is warmed with dilute sodium hydroxide solution.

(b) At first sight, warming with dilute sulphuric acid seems to have no effect on urea. Nothing can be smelled and there is no sign of effervescence. Great care is needed to establish that carbon dioxide is evolved slowly.

$$H_2N.CO.NH_2 + H_2O + 2\,H^+ \rightarrow CO_2 + 2\,NH_4^+$$

25. In the reaction of ethanamide with nitrous acid the $-NH_2$ group is replaced by $-OH$ and an acid is formed. If urea follows the same pattern, we can expect the substitution of both $-NH_2$ groups by $-OH$ groups. This will result in the formation of carbonic acid which, of course, will readily decompose to give carbon dioxide. Thus, the products of the reaction of nitrous acid with urea should be carbon dioxide, water and nitrogen.

Experiment (viii)

When urea is treated with cool nitrous acid there is a ready release of gas, which seems to be less brown than the gas from ethanamide under comparable conditions. The presence of carbon dioxide can be readily established by means of lime water.

Assuming that, as before, nitrogen is also evolved, the overall reaction is presumably

$$H_2N.CO.NH_2 + 2\,HO.N{:}O \rightarrow 3\,H_2O + 2\,N_2 + CO_2$$

Summary

Urea shows virtually all the properties of an acid amide such as ethanamide. It is, however, a weak monoacidic base, and so to a slight degree it shows some resemblance to aminoethane.

Since both C–N bonds in urea are of the same length, they must be identical in nature. Furthermore, as they are shorter than the usual C–N single bonds (as in aminoethane), they must have some double bond character. In addition, the C–O bond in urea is longer than the usual carbonyl bond. All this is powerful evidence for partial conjugation of the lone pairs of electrons on the nitrogen atoms of urea with its carbonyl bond, i.e. urea can be considered to be a resonance hybrid of the following canonical forms:

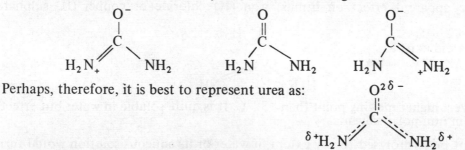

Perhaps, therefore, it is best to represent urea as:

Using this structure as a model it is easy to see why urea is not a strong base and one can also understand why it will not accept two protons when treated with concentrated nitric acid.

3. Other reactions of importance

Experiment (ix)

On warming, urea melts easily and forms a colourless liquid. Further heating causes a little sublimation, but the most obvious effect is a brisk effferversence as a stream of

258

ammonia is evolved. After about two minutes heating evolution of ammonia ceases and one is left with an amorphous white deposit at the bottom of the tube. This is biuret.

26. If two molecules of urea react and ammonia is eliminated, the likely reaction is

$$2\,H_2N.CO.NH_2 \rightarrow H_2N.CO.NH.CO.NH_2 + NH_3$$
biuret

When biuret is dissolved in aqueous alkali and treated with a drop of copper (II) sulphate solution, a complex ion is formed which imparts a characteristic purple colour to the solution.

Experiment (x)
This procedure is usually known as the Hofmann Degradation. On warming the mixture of ethanamide, bromine and sodium hydroxide solution, a colourless gas is evolved with a very ammonia-like smell (probably some NH_3 and some $CH_3.NH_2$). The gas turns damp red litmus blue. After warming for about a minute the contents of the tube solidify to a white powder. When this residue is treated with acid, carbon dioxide is evolved copiously, suggesting that the primary reaction produces sodium carbonate.
Urea behaves very similarly with bromine and sodium hydroxide, although in this case a mixture of hydrazine and nitrogen is evolved.

27. A little inspired guessing, guided by the teacher, can lead to the equations

$$CH_3.CO.NH_2 + Br_2 + 4\,OH^- \rightarrow CH_3NH_2 + CO_3^{2-} + 2\,Br^- + 2\,H_2O$$

and
$$H_2N.CO.NH_2 + Br_2 + 4\,OH^- \rightarrow H_2N.NH_2 + CO_3^{2-} + 2\,Br^- + 2\,H_2O$$

but much of the hydrazine is destroyed by excess bromine

$$H_2N.NH_2 + 2\,Br_2 + 4\,OH^- \rightarrow N_2 + 4\,H_2O + 4\,Br^-$$

28. The Hofmann Degradation is important as it affords a general way of descending an homologous series via one carbon steps

$$\text{i.e. } R.CO.NH_2 \rightarrow R.NH_2$$

FURTHER WORK

1. An investigation of the acetylation of amines. What are the relative merits of acetyl chloride and acetic anhydride as acetylating agents?
2. What effects do solutions of sodium hypochlorite and/or sodium hypobromite have on urea? Can hydrazine be identified as a product?
3. A study of the inclusion compounds of urea.

REFERENCES

1. Good general discussion of acid derivatives from mechanistic viewpoint: James, *A Mechanistic Introduction to Organic Chemistry,* Mills and Boon (1968).
2. Urea inclusion compounds: Vogel, *Elementary Practical Organic Chemistry,* Part I (2nd Edition) Longmans. p.395.

Assignment 43
Esterification and Ester Hydrolysis

INTRODUCTION

The reaction between acetic acid and ethanol, producing ethyl acetate and water, is reversible.

$$CH_3COOH + C_2H_5OH \rightleftharpoons CH_3COOC_2H_5 + H_2O$$

The two experiments described below illustrate methods which can be used to obtain the products of a reversible reaction in reasonable yield and to do it as quickly as possible. Some data relating to the reactants is given in the chart, which follows:

Reactant	b.p./°C	density/g cm^{-3}	solubility in water	mol. wt.
acetic acid	118	1·05	soluble	60
ethanol	78	0·79	soluble	46
ethyl acetate	77	0·90	slightly soluble	88

1. Relate the boiling-points and solubilities, in water, of these compounds to their molecular weights and structures.

EXPERIMENTAL WORK

Preparation of ethyl acetate

Pour 12cm³ of glacial acetic acid and 8cm³ of ethanol into a 50cm³ round-bottomed flask. Add carefully, with shaking, 8cm³ of concentrated sulphuric acid. Attach a fractionating column and arrange for distillation from the top of the column.

Heat the mixture, carefully at first, and continue distilling until the thermometer reads about 90°C. Shake the distillate so obtained with about 10cm³ of sodium carbonate solution. Separate the two layers and stand the organic layer over anhydrous calcium chloride overnight.

Finally redistil, collecting the fraction coming over when the thermometer indicates a temperature between 74 and 78°C.

2. Why is one of the reactants present in excess?

3. Which one of the reactants is in excess?

4. Why is *this reactant* chosen to be in excess?

5. What functions does the concentrated sulphuric acid perform in this preparation?

6. What is the function of the fractionating column in this experiment?

7. Explain the origin of any impurities which might be present in the original distillate.

8. Explain the methods used to remove these impurities.

Hydrolysis of ethyl acetate

Heat 2cm³ of the ester with 20cm³ of approximately 2M sodium hydroxide solution in a 50cm³ round-bottomed flask fitted with a reflux condenser until the mixture becomes homogeneous. (About 15 or 20 minutes should be sufficient.) Allow the apparatus to cool and arrange it for distillation. Distil over about 2cm³ of liquid.

Take about 1cm³ of this liquid and test it for the presence of ethanol by carrying out the iodoform reaction. (To the distillate add about 2cm³ of iodine in potassium iodide solution and a few drops of 2M sodium hydroxide solution until the iodine colour just disappears, and warm.) Compare the behaviour of this distillate in the iodoform reaction with that of ethyl acetate, using 1cm³ of an aqueous solution of ethyl acetate instead of the distillate.

Render the residue in the distillation flask acidic, by adding a slight excess of dilute sulphuric acid, and again distil, collecting about 2cm³ of the distillate. Note the smell of the distillate. Test for the presence of a carboxylic acid (presumably acetic acid) using neutral iron (III) chloride solution. For this test the acetic acid must be neutralised so take about 1cm³ of the distillate and add a slight excess of dilute ammonia solution, removing the excess ammonia by boiling. To this solution, after cooling, add five drops of neutral ferric chloride solution. Compare the result with that obtained by adding five drops of the neutral ferric chloride solution to 1cm³ of distilled water and 1cm³ of aqueous ethyl acetate solution respectively. (The neutral iron (III) chloride solution may be prepared by adding dropwise dilute sodium hydroxide solution until a slight permanent precipitate is formed. The supernatant liquid may then be used.)

9. If Quickfit apparatus is used for reactions involving sodium hydroxide it is particularly important to wash the apparatus thoroughly, immediately after use. Why is this?

10. Why does homogeneity imply completion of the hydrolysis of ethyl acetate? How accurate is this indication?

11. Since a catalyst is effective for both forward and backward reactions of a reversible change dilute sulphuric acid could have been used for the hydrolysis reaction. Why then is sodium hydroxide solution used in this case?

12. Is the iodoform test specific for ethanol? Or do other simple aliphatic alcohols perform this reaction? Explain.

13. Why is it necessary to acidify the residue in the distillation flask before making the second distillation?

14. Why is sulphuric acid chosen, rather than one of the other mineral acids?

15. Why is iron (III) chloride solution not neutral in the first place?

16. Explain why the iron (III) chloride test for carboxylic acids will not work if the solution is (a) alkaline (b) acidic.
Perform the test in the presence of (a) sodium hydroxide solution (b) dilute hydrochloric acid. Record your observations.
Compare the effect of neutral iron (III) chloride solution on an aqueous solution of (a) phenol (b) benzoic acid, with the effect obtained with aliphatic carboxylic acids. Make a list of the observations you have made of the reactions of neutral iron (III) chloride solution with these substances, for which it can be used as a test.

17. If the ester used in the hydrolysis experiment had been phenyl acetate ($CH_3COOC_6H_5$), phenol (C_6H_5OH) would not have distilled until the solution had been acidified. Does this suggest that the phenyl group is electron-repelling or electron-attracting? Explain your reasoning.
Obtain further information on this subject by examining the solubility of phenol in (a) water (b) dilute sodium hydroxide solution. Does this concur with your explanation?
Caution: Phenol is poisonous and harmful by skin absorption.

Notes 43

Standard: *

Time required: Preparation of ethyl acetate-45 minutes plus 10 minutes for redistillation.
Hydrolysis of ethyl acetate-1 hour.

Reagents required:

glacial acetic acid	(12cm³)	iron (III) chloride	
ethanol	(8cm³)	solution	(2cm³)
ethyl acetate	(5cm³)	iodine in potassium	
concentrated sulphuric acid	(8cm³)	iodide solution	(5cm³)
dilute sodium carbonate solution	(10cm³)	dilute sulphuric acid	(10cm³)
anhydrous calcium chloride	(1g)	dilute ammonia	
dilute sodium hydroxide solution	(30cm³)	solution	(5cm³)
		phenol	(0·5g)
		benzoic acid	(0·5g)

Apparatus required:

50cm³ round-bottomed flask
measuring cylinder (20cm³ to read to 1cm³)
thermometer (110°C to read to 1°C)
fractionating column
distillation apparatus (flask, adaptor, condenser, collecting vessel)
separating funnel
small conical flask and bung (50 or 100cm³)
test tubes
dropping pipette

Notes on experimental work and questions:

1. Acetic acid is the most polar of the three substances and is probably associated to some extent by hydrogen bonding as shown:

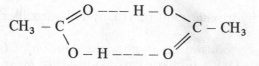

It is not therefore surprising that it has the highest boiling-point of the three, and as water is a polar solvent, dissolving polar substances, it is also not surprising that it is soluble in water.

Ethanol contains the highly-polar hydroxyl group and the relatively strong intermolecular forces resulting from this polarity may explain why ethanol has a similar boiling-point to that of ethyl acetate, yet a much smaller molecular weight. The interaction between the polar hydroxyl groups of the ethanol and the polar water molecules is a likely explanation of the solubility of ethanol in water.

Ethyl acetate is much less polar than the other two substances, but the presence of the oxygen atoms presumably introduces sufficient polarity to the molecule to give it an appreciable solubility in water (8·6g per 100cm³ of water at 20°C).

262

The fractionating column, for use in the preparation of ethyl acetate, can easily be built up from an air condenser. Small pieces of glass tubing (about ½inch in length) make an effective packing material and can be held in the condenser by fitting a copper spiral at the bottom to prevent them falling through.

2. If one of the reactants is in excess, it increases the yield of products which can be obtained from the other reagent. The reason for requiring as much ethanol as possible to be converted is given in the notes on question 4. (In many cases, however, excess of the cheaper reagent is used, though this is not the case here.)
The equilibrium constant for the reaction may be written as:

$$K = \frac{[CH_3COOC_2H_5]\ [H_2O]}{[CH_3COOH]\ [C_2H_5OH]}$$

To illustrate this point teachers may like to set the following problem:
Calculate the number of moles of ethanol in the equilibrium mixture if the initial number of moles of reactants used were (a) 2 moles of each (b) 2 moles of ethanol and 3 of acetic acid. Take the value of the equilibrium constant to be 4.
Answers (a) 0·67 moles (b) 0·43 moles of ethanol.

In the preparation of ethyl acetate the number of moles of ethanol in the equilibrium mixture will also be reduced by the reaction between the water produced and the concentrated sulphuric acid.

3. The glacial acetic acid is in excess.

$$\text{Number of moles of acetic acid} = \frac{12 \times 1\cdot05}{60} = 0\cdot21 \text{ moles}$$

$$\text{Number of moles of ethanol} \quad = \frac{8 \times 0\cdot79}{46} = 0\cdot14 \text{ moles}$$

4. The acetic acid is chosen, in spite of the fact that it is more expensive than ethanol, because it has a higher boiling-point than ethanol. The b.p. of ethanol is similar to that of ethyl acetate and it would not be possible to distil the ethyl acetate without the excess ethanol coming over as well.

5. The concentrated sulphuric acid performed two functions; firstly hydrogen ions catalyse the reaction, probably by the mechanism:

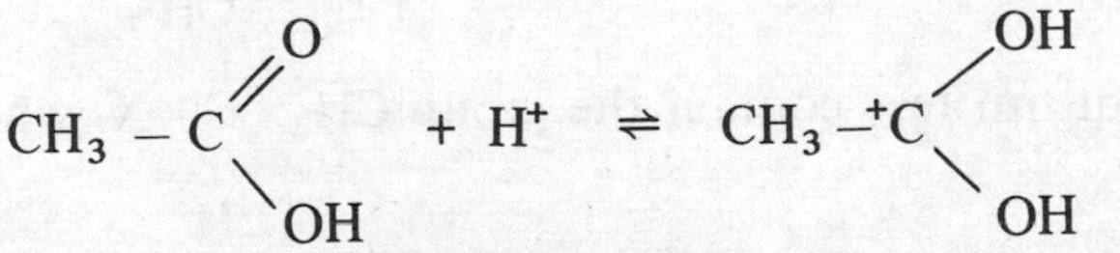

which renders the acetic acid more susceptible to attack by the nucleophilic ethanol:

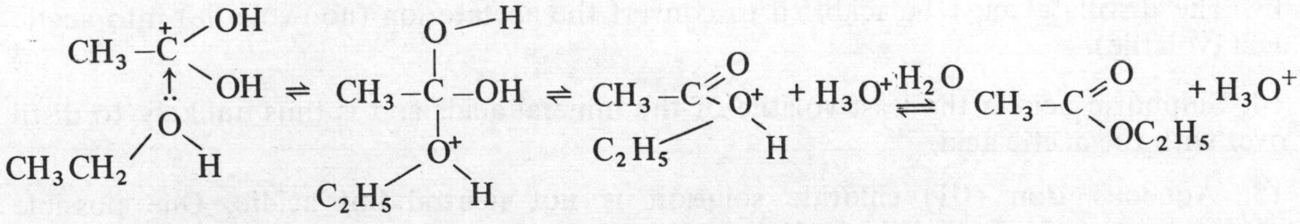

and the sulphuric acid will provide these hydrogen ions; secondly the concentrated sulphuric acid will react with water molecules as they are produced and thus reduce their effective concentration (activity), thus increasing the number of moles of ethyl acetate in the equilibrium mixture.

6. The function of the fractionating column is to prevent the escape of substances of higher boiling point than 90°C from the reaction vessel whilst it is being heated. Thus, with excess acetic acid being used (b.p. 118°C) and with the effect of the concentrated

263

sulphuric acid (mentioned earlier), most of the ethanol should have reacted and the acetic acid should be condensed in the fractionating column so that the distillate should be largely ethyl acetate.

7. Some ethanol may distil before it has reacted; some ether (and ethylene) may be produced from reaction between the ethanol and the concentrated sulphuric acid. Also, reduction of the concentrated sulphuric acid by ethanol, and possibly carbon from charring, may produce carbon dioxide and sulphur dioxide. Some water (and possibly a little acetic acid) may also distil over.

8. The acidic impurities are removed as salts by shaking with sodium carbonate solution. Ethanol will be absorbed, as will water, by the anhydrous calcium chloride. Any ether and ethylene should escape before the fraction containing the ethyl acetate is collected.

Hydrolysis of ethyl acetate.
The first distillate gives a distinctive smell and precipitate of iodoform under the conditions of the test. If the test is repeated with ethyl acetate there is no reaction at first but, of course, after a long period the alkali will bring about hydrolysis and the result will be similar to that with the first distillate. However, the distinction is sufficient to establish that the boiling with alkali has changed the ethyl acetate.
After acidification of the residue a vinegar smell is noticeable suggesting the presence of acetic acid. The result of testing this second distillate with neutral iron (III) chloride is a red colouration, quite easily distinguished from the yellowish colour obtained with both distilled water and ethyl acetate.

9. Sodium hydroxide solution reacts with the silica in the glass and if it is not washed immediately the ground glass joints may become fused.

10. Ethyl acetate is only slightly soluble in water but the products of hydrolysis in alkaline solution, ethanol and the acetate ion, are readily soluble. Thus homogeneity really indicates that there is less ethyl acetate left than is needed to saturate the water, i.e. the reaction is almost complete—a further five minutes boiling should finish it completely.

11. Sodium hydroxide is used since the products are then ethanol and the *acetate ion* (not acetic acid) and under these circumstances the reaction is not reversible. With dilute sulphuric acid the products would be ethanol and acetic acid and an equilibrium mixture would result.

12. The alcohols which perform the iodoform test contain the group $CH_3-\underset{\underset{H}{|}}{\overset{\overset{OH}{|}}{C}}-X$, where X=C or H.

Thus the simple alcohols (up to four carbon atoms) which do it are ethanol, propan-2-ol and butan-2-ol. Those *not* doing it are methanol, propan-1-ol and butan-1-ol.

13. The distillate must be acidified to convert the acetate ion (non-volatile) into acetic acid (volatile).

14. Sulphuric acid is the least volatile of the mineral acids and is thus unlikely to distil over with the acetic acid.

15. Aqueous iron (III) chloride solution is not neutral but acidic. One possible explanation of this is that the hydrated iron (III) ion releases protons to give an excess of hydrogen ions over hydroxide ions in the solution. It is suggested that the small, highly charged iron (III) ion attracts electrons in the water molecules, surrounding it in an octahedral arrangement, and thus makes it easier for protons to leave the hydrated ion, producing an acidic solution.

16. If the iron (III) chloride test is carried out in alkaline conditions the iron (III) ions are precipitated as iron (III) hydroxide and do not form a complex with the carboxylic acid. In acid solution the coloured complex is broken down.

264

The observations made when acetic acid, phenol and benzoic acid are treated with neutral iron (III) chloride solution are given in the following chart:

Substance	Observation
acetic acid	red colouration
phenol	violet colouration
benzoic acid	buff precipitate

17. Phenol, in the alkaline conditions of the experiment, would exist in the form of the phenate ion ($C_6H_5O^-$). The release of a proton suggests that electrons tend to be drawn away from the hydroxyl group; in other words the phenyl group (C_6H_5-) is presumably electron-attracting.

The fact that phenol is only partially soluble in water but quite soluble in dilute sodium hydroxide solution suggests that phenol forms an ionic compound in the presence of alkali whereas it is largely in the molecular form in water. This points to the acidic character of phenol which could be explained if the phenyl group were electron-attracting.

Assignment 44

Preparation and Properties of Aniline

(I) PREPARATION

(a) Reduction of nitrobenzene

Place 4cm³ of nitrobenzene and 10g of tin in a 250cm³ round-bottomed flask fitted with a reflux condenser. Add excess concentrated hydrochloric acid, by adding it to the flask a few cm³ at a time, until a total of 24cm³ has been added. It is most convenient to pour the acid down the condenser, and it is advisable to shake the flask between each addition. When all the acid has been added heat the reaction mixture on a water-bath for 15 minutes.

(b) Steam distillation

Cool the flask and add sodium hydroxide solution until the solution is strongly alkaline. The hydroxide of tin, which is precipitated first, should be dissolved—about 50cm³ of 30% sodium hydroxide solution should be sufficient.
Set up the apparatus for steam distillation and proceed until oily droplets of aniline are no longer visible in the distillate coming over.

(c) Ether extraction

Add concentrated hydrochloric acid to the distillate, until the solution is acidic—about 3 or 4cm³ of acid should be needed—and, when cool, transfer the solution to the separating funnel. Extract with two separate 5cm³ portions of ether. After shaking the separating funnel invert it and open the tap to release the ether vapour. Discard the ether layer in each case (run it into the ether residues bottle).
Transfer the aqueous layer to a beaker and add sodium hydroxide pellets, one at a time, until the solution is alkaline.
Shake this alkaline solution, in a separating funnel, with three 5cm³ portions of ether. *Retain the ether layer* from this separation.
Dry the ethereal extract, by standing it over potassium hydroxide pellets, in a stoppered flask until the next practical session.

(d) Ether distillation

Heat a water bath to about 70°C and, after extinguishing all flames, decant the ethereal solution into a 50cm³ round-bottomed flask fitted with a stillhead adaptor and water condenser. Heat the flask in the water bath until no more ether distils.
Replace the water condenser by an air condenser, fit a thermometer pocket and 250°C thermometer to the stillhead adaptor and heat the flask over a gauze using a Bunsen burner. Collect the fraction which distils between 180 and 185°C and record the yield.

1. In an alternative procedure the reflux condenser is removed and the reaction mixture is heated on a water bath prior to making the solution alkaline for the steam distillation. The later, ether extraction of the acid solution is then omitted. Explain this procedure.

2. Why must the solution be made alkaline before steam distillation?

266

3. The aniline formed by reduction exists as anilinium chloride and also as anilinium hexachlorostannate (IV). Write formulae for these two compounds.

4. Why is the reaction mixture cooled before the addition of sodium hydroxide in part (b)?

5. Would you expect a mixture of aniline and water to boil at a temperature above, or below, the boiling point of water? Explain your answer.

6. Why is hydrochloric acid added to the distillate before the first ether extraction, and why is this ethereal solution discarded?

7. Why is sodium hydroxide added before the second ether extraction and why is this ethereal solution retained?

8. Why are two separate $5cm^3$ portions of ether used in part (c), rather than one $10cm^3$ portion?

9. Why is potassium hydroxide used for drying aniline, rather than the cheaper calcium chloride?

(II) PROPERTIES

(a) Shake a few drops of aniline with water in a test tube, and add a piece of red litmus paper to the solution.
Add a few drops of aniline to $2cm^3$ of dilute hydrochloric acid in a test tube.
Describe your observations and explain the difference in solubility of aniline in the two solutions.

10. Would you expect aniline to be more, or less, basic than methylamine?

(b) In a fume-cupboard warm *one drop only* of aniline with a pellet of potassium hydroxide, a few drops of chloroform and a few drops of ethanol. Destroy the product of the reaction, by adding excess concentrated hydrochloric acid, before discarding.

11. What is the odorous product of this reaction?

12. What is the equation for the reaction?

13. Which functional group can this reaction be used as a test for?

(c) To five drops of aniline add concentrated hydrochloric acid until the aniline dissolves. Add bromine water and note the rapid reaction producing 2:4:6-tribromoaniline.

14. Why does bromine substitute so readily?

(d) To three drops of aniline add $5cm^3$ of 10% sodium hydroxide solution followed by five drops of benzoyl chloride. Stopper the test tube and shake until a solid product is formed. Isolate the product and, if time permits, recrystallize from hot ethanol and determine the melting point of the benzanilide.

(e) Carefully add two or three drops of acetyl chloride to two drops of aniline in a dry test tube. (Since this reaction may be violent it is best done in the fume cupboard.)

15. What are the relative merits of benzoyl chloride and acetyl chloride for the production of crystalline derivatives of aniline?

(f) Add sodium hypochlorite solution to one drop of aniline in a test tube.

16. What type of reaction do you think the aniline has undergone? What did you observe?

(g) To three drops of aniline in a test tube add concentrated hydrochloric acid and a little water until the solid formed dissolves. Cool the tube in ice and then add a few crystals of sodium nitrite. Keep half of the solution in ice and heat the other portion gently over a Bunsen.

17. What do you observe in each of the two samples? What can you smell in the tube that has been heated?

18. Compare the reaction of aniline in experiment (g), with the behaviour of aliphatic amines on treatment with sodium nitrite and hydrochloric acid.

19. Why is a mixture of hydrochloric acid and sodium nitrite used in these reactions, rather than nitrous acid?

Notes 44

Standard: *

Time required: 2 x 1½ hours sessions

Reagents required:

nitrobenzene (4cm³)

granulated tin (10g)

conc. hydrochloric acid (35cm³)

approx. 30% aqueous sodium hydroxide solution (50cm³)

ether (30cm³)

sodium hydroxide pellets (5g)

potassium hydroxide pellets (5g)

aniline (5cm³)

dilute hydrochloric acid (10cm³)

chloroform (1cm³)

ethanol (20cm³)

bromine water (5cm³)

10% aqueous sodium hydroxide solution (5cm³)

benzoyl chloride (5 drops)

acetyl chloride (5 drops)

sodium hypochlorite solution (5cm³)

ice (50g)

sodium nitrite (0·5g)

Apparatus required:

10cm³ measuring cylinder

25cm³ measuring cylinder

250cm³ round-bottomed flask (Quickfit B14/23 Cat. No. FR 250/1S)

water-bath

liebig water condenser (Quickfit B14/23 Cat. No. C1/11)

stillhead adaptor (Quickfit B14/23 Cat. No. SH 4/11)

cone/rubber tubing adaptor (Quickfit B14/23 Cat. No. MF 15/1)

separating funnel

2 x 150cm³ beakers

100cm³ conical flask and bung

50cm³ round-bottomed flask (Quickfit B14/23 Cat. No. FR 50/1S)

air condenser (Quickfit B14/23 Cat. No. C2/11)

thermometer pocket (Quickfit B14/23 Cat. No. SH 4A)

250°C thermometer

Bunsen burner, tripod and gauze

test-tubes (2 fitted with corks)

melting point tubes and apparatus for determining melting point

Buchner funnel and filter papers

Notes on questions

(I) PREPARATION

1. In acid solution the aniline is in the form of anilinium ions, which exert a very low vapour pressure, whereas the nitrobenzene is in the molecular form and exerts a higher vapour pressure. Heating the mixture, which contains water, on a water-bath will cause steam distillation of the nitrobenzene to occur, thus removing this impurity from the product.

2. The solution must be made alkaline before the steam distillation to convert the anilinium ions into aniline molecules, which exert a much higher vapour pressure than the ion and thus allow steam distillation of the aniline.

3. Anilinium chloride has the formula $[C_6H_5NH_3]^+Cl^-$; anilinium hexachlorostannate (IV) has the formula $[C_6H_5NH_3^+]_2 SnCl_6^{2-}$.

4. If the reaction mixture were not cooled steam distillation of the aniline could occur as soon as the alkali is added and thus some of the product could be lost, thereby reducing the yield.

5. Boiling occurs when the vapour pressure above a liquid reaches the external pressure. For a mixture of immiscible liquids, each exerting a significant vapour pressure, boiling will occur when the sum of the vapour pressures equals the external pressure, and this will therefore always occur below the normal boiling point of any of the liquids present in the mixture.

6. The distillate consists of water, aniline and nitrobenzene. In order to separate the nitrobenzene the aniline is treated with acid which converts it into the water-soluble anilinium ion ($C_6H_5NH_3^+$), whereas the nitrobenzene, which is not basic, remains in the molecular condition and is thus dissolved in the ether. Thus the ether layer, which contains only the nitrobenzene, is discarded.

7. The addition of the sodium hydroxide converts the anilinium ion into the molecular aniline, by removal of a proton. The aniline will now be much more soluble in ether than in water, and thus the ethereal solution is retained.

8. In solvent extraction more of the solute can be extracted by using the solvent in several small portions than can be extracted by using the same total volume of solvent in one extraction. To illustrate this the following example may be of use:
Calculate the weight of solute extracted from $10cm^3$ of water, containing 1g of solute, by using $10cm^3$ of ether (a) in one portion, (b) in two separate $5cm^3$ portions.
The solute has a partition coefficient of 3 between ether and water.
(a) $\dfrac{\text{Concentration in ether}}{\text{Concentration in water}} = 3$, hence 3 parts of the solute dissolve in the ether and one part in the water if equal volumes of the two solvents are used; thus the weight of solute extracted by one $10cm^3$ portion of ether is $\frac{3}{4}$ x 1g which equals 0·75g.
(b) If two $5cm^3$ portions of ether are used, the ratio of the weight of solute extracted by the first portion to the weight of solute remaining in the water is

$$\frac{3 \times 5}{1 \times 10}$$

Hence 15 parts by weight dissolve in the ether and 10 parts in the water; thus the weight of solute extracted is $\frac{15}{25}$ or 0·6 x 1g = 0·6g.

In the second extraction $\frac{15}{25}$ of the weight of solute remaining in the water will be extracted i.e. 0·6 x 0·4g = 0·24g.
Thus by using two portions of $5cm^3$ of ether 0·84g of solute are extracted as opposed to 0·75g extracted using one portion of $10cm^3$.

9. Calcium chloride reacts with aniline so is unsuitable as a drying agent in this case; potassium hydroxide is more efficient than sodium hydroxide.

(II) PROPERTIES

(a) Aniline forms an emulsion with water but sufficient aniline mixes with the water to give an alkaline reaction to litmus paper. On addition of acid the anilinium salt is formed, which is ionic and thus water-soluble, so the emulsion becomes a clear solution. When water is added to aniline in neutral or alkaline conditions the aniline is molecular and being not very polar it is only slightly soluble in water.

10. The methyl group of methylamine releases electrons towards the nitrogen atom of the amine and makes it accept protons more readily than the nitrogen atom of ammonia, so it is a stronger base; the benzene ring in aniline accepts electrons from the nitrogen atom which accepts protons less readily than the nitrogen atom of ammonia. Thus one would expect aniline to be less basic than methylamine.

(b) Students should be warned of the extremely poisonous and offensive-smelling vapour which will be produced, and should therefore not exceed the quantities stated.

11. The odorous product of the reaction is phenyl isocyanide, otherwise known as carbylamine.

12. The equation for the reaction is:

$$C_6H_5NH_2 + CHCl_3 + 3KOH = C_6H_5NC + 3KCl + 3H_2O$$

13. This reaction can be used as a test for the $-NH_2$ group of primary amines.

(c) 14. Bromine substitutes readily in aniline because the lone pair of electrons on the nitrogen atom of the $-NH_2$ group can be fed into the benzene ring. Since bromination, like other aromatic substitutions, operates by an electrophilic mechanism, extra electrons fed into the ring will aid substitution.

(d) The melting point of benzanilide is 162°C.

15. (e) Acetyl chloride is a very reactive compound and its reaction with aniline is difficult to control; benzoyl chloride reacts much more slowly and the reaction can be performed without difficulty. The greater molecular weight of benzoyl derivatives relative to acetyl derivatives means that the product is more likely to be crystalline.

(f) 16. Aniline gives a purple colour on treatment with hypochlorite, resulting from oxidation of the aniline.

(g) 17. In the mixture, cooled in ice, a small quantity of gas may be evolved by decomposition of the nitrous acid, but no other change can be observed in the solution. The mixture which is heated liberates a colourless gas, oily droplets form in the solution and a strong smell of phenol can be detected.

18. The reaction of nitrous acid on aliphatic amines is to substitute a hydroxyl group for the amino group e.g.

$$C_2H_5NH_2 + HONO = C_2H_5OH + N_2 + H_2O$$

The reaction of aniline with nitrous acid at temperatures above room temperature is analogous:

$$C_6H_5NH_2 + HONO = C_6H_5OH + N_2 + H_2O$$

At 0°C aniline undergoes a reaction with nitrous acid, in the presence of excess dilute hydrochloric acid, for which there is no counterpart in the chemistry of aliphatic amines:

$$C_6H_5NH_2 + HONO + HCl = C_6H_5N_2^+Cl^- + 2H_2O$$

19. Nitrous acid is not very stable at room temperature and the reagent cannot be conveniently stored. Sodium nitrite is stable at room temperature and can thus be kept in stock and the free acid obtained from the salt by acidification with dilute hydrochloric acid.

FURTHER PROJECT

Preparation of a selection of azo dyes and investigation of the effect of sunlight on solutions of the dyes.

Assignment 45

An Investigation of the Relative Reactivity of Chlorine in Organic Compounds

INTRODUCTION

Organic chlorine compounds may undergo either a substitution or an elimination reaction if treated with a base. In aqueous solutions the reaction is usually a substitution e.g.

$$-CH_2CH_2Cl + OH^- \rightarrow -CH_2CH_2OH + Cl^- \text{ (substitution)}$$

whereas in alcoholic solutions of alkalis, an elimination reaction is more likely e.g.

$$-CH_2CH_2Cl + OH^- \rightarrow -CH=CH_2 + Cl^- + H_2O \text{ (elimination)}$$

The more reactive compounds may react with water, in which case the reaction will be a substitution.

In all these cases chloride *ions* are produced and in this series of experiments we are concerned with the ease with which chloride *ions* are produced, rather than establishing by which type of reaction they are produced.

EXPERIMENTAL WORK

1. In the table on the next page, write the structural formula of each compound in the appropriate space.

Test each compound as follows:
(a) Place 3 drops of the compound in a test tube and add 3cm³ of ethanol, followed by 5 drops of dilute nitric acid and 5 drops of aqueous silver nitrate solution. Record your observations in the appropriate place in the table, keeping the solutions for about five minutes if there is no immediate reaction.

If a precipitate does not occur immediately the silver nitrate solution is added then:
(b) Place 3 drops of the compound in a test tube and add 3cm³ of ethanol and 3 drops of aqueous sodium hydroxide solution. Heat the tube over a Bunsen flame until the liquid starts to boil and then add 5 drops of dilute nitric acid, followed by 5 drops of aqueous silver nitrate solution. Observe the mixtures for about five minutes and record your observations in the table.

After you have carried out the experiments and filled in the table, answer the following questions:

2. List these compounds in order of ease of formation of chloride ions in these experiments.

3. Why was ethanol added in these experiments?

4. Do the reactions you have studied involve homolytic or heterolytic fission of C—Cl bonds?

5. Is the ease of rupture of the C—Cl bond affected by other atoms or groups attached to the carbon atom of the C—Cl bond?

6. What explanation can you give for the relative ease of rupture of the C—Cl bond in the case of 1-chlorobutane, 2-chlorobutane and 2-chloro-2-methyl-propane?

7. What structural difference could explain the difference in ease of rupture of the C—Cl bond in chlorobenzene and benzyl chloride?

8. How can you explain the relative ease of rupture of the C—Cl bond in acetyl chloride?

Name	Structural formula	Test (a)	Test (b)
trichloromethane (chloroform)			
1-chlorobutane (n-butyl chloride)			
2-chlorobutane (sec-butyl chloride)			
2-chloro-2-methyl-propane (tert. butyl chloride)			
acetyl chloride			
chlorobenzene			
benzyl chloride			
anilinium chloride (aniline hydrochloride)			

Notes 45

Standard: **

Time required: 1½ hours to complete

Reagents required:

ethanol	$(50cm^3)$
dilute nitric acid	$(10cm^3)$
aqueous silver nitrate solution	$(10cm^3)$
aqueous sodium hydroxide solution	$(10cm^3)$
chloroform	$(0\cdot5cm^3)$
1-chlorobutane	$(0\cdot5cm^3)$
2-chlorobutane	$(0\cdot5cm^3)$
2-chloro-2-methyl-propane	$(0\cdot5cm^3)$
acetyl chloride	$(0\cdot5cm^3)$
chlorobenzene	$(0\cdot5cm^3)$
benzyl chloride	$(0\cdot5cm^3)$
anilinium chloride (a few crystals)	
chlorocyclohexane $(0\cdot5cm^3)$ optional extra	

Apparatus required:

test tubes

teat pipettes

Bunsen burner

Notes on questions and results

It may be noted that anilinium chloride differs from the other compounds in many ways. Firstly it contains an ionic chloride, so rather than undergo a reaction with water or alkali it simply dissociates forming chloride ions which will react immediately with silver ions; secondly it is a solid, not a liquid as are all the other compounds to be studied; thirdly it does not contain a C—Cl bond. Nevertheless, it is worthy of comparison with the other chloro-compounds as an illustration of the behaviour of an ionically bonded chlorine in an organic compound.

Confusion may arise in students' minds if they do not adhere to the recommended quantities of reagents, since if a higher proportion of water is present some of the reagents may form a white emulsion which might be confused with a precipitate of silver chloride. Should an emulsion be formed it can be detected as such by the addition of more ethanol, which will clear the emulsion but not a precipitate.

1 and Results		Test (a)	Test (b)
trichloromethane (chloroform)	$H-C\begin{smallmatrix}\diagup Cl\\ \diagdown Cl\\ \diagdown Cl\end{smallmatrix}$	Forms a cloudiness rapidly as a fine precipitate forms	Forms a cloudiness immediately the $AgNO_3$ is added

273

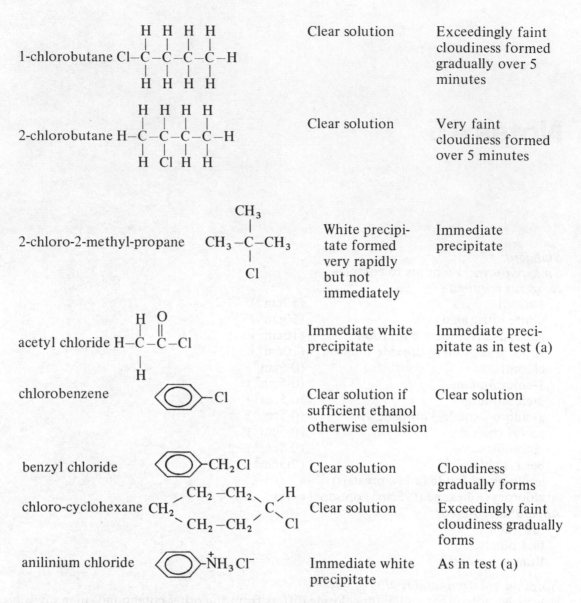

1-chlorobutane	Cl–C–C–C–H (with H atoms)	Clear solution	Exceedingly faint cloudiness formed gradually over 5 minutes
2-chlorobutane	H–C–C–C–C–H (with Cl)	Clear solution	Very faint cloudiness formed over 5 minutes
2-chloro-2-methyl-propane	CH₃–C–CH₃ (with CH₃ and Cl)	White precipitate formed very rapidly but not immediately	Immediate precipitate
acetyl chloride	H–C–C–Cl (with O)	Immediate white precipitate	Immediate precipitate as in test (a)
chlorobenzene	⬡–Cl	Clear solution if sufficient ethanol otherwise emulsion	Clear solution
benzyl chloride	⬡–CH₂Cl	Clear solution	Cloudiness gradually forms
chloro-cyclohexane	cyclohexane–Cl	Clear solution	Exceedingly faint cloudiness gradually forms
anilinium chloride	⬡–N⁺H₃Cl⁻	Immediate white precipitate	As in test (a)

2. The order of ease of formation of chloride ions in these experiments is

anilinium chloride > acetyl chloride > 2-chloro-2-methyl propane > trichloromethane > 2-chlorobutane, benzyl chloride > 1-chlorobutane, chloro-cyclohexane > chlorobenzene.

3. Ethanol was added in these experiments to prevent some of the chlorocompounds forming an emulsion with the water present, since this can be confused with the formation of a precipitate of silver chloride.

4. The C–Cl bonds, which exist in all the compounds under investigation, break to form chloride ions (Cl⁻) as shown by the formation of the silver chloride precipitate. The chlorine atom must take both of the electrons constituting the covalent bond; i.e. heterolytic fission occurs if the bond breaks at all.

5. The ease of rupture is very much affected by the other groups attached to the carbon atom of the C–Cl bond. Hence the varied results shown above.

6. Alkyl groups, particularly the methyl group, release electrons to the atom they are attached to more readily than does a hydrogen atom. The carbon atom of the C–Cl bond in 2-chloro-2-methyl-propane has three electron-releasing methyl groups attached to it, the carbon atom of the C–Cl bond in 2-chlorobutane has one methyl and one ethyl group attached to it, and the carbon atom of the C–Cl bond in 1-chlorobutane has *no* methyl

274

groups, just one n-propyl group attached to it. Thus the chlorine atom is most readily detached as a chloride ion (Cl⁻) in 2-chloro-2-methyl-propane and least readily detached in 1-chlorobutane.

7. In chlorobenzene the chlorine atom is bonded to one of the carbon atoms of the benzene ring and one of the lone pairs of electrons of the chlorine atom may be fed into the benzene ring as the whole represents a conjugated system; in the case of benzyl chloride there is a saturated carbon atom between the benzene ring and the chlorine atom and the reactivity of the chlorine atom is comparable to that in a chloroalkane.

8. The relative ease of rupture of the carbon-chlorine bond in acetyl chloride is due to the $\delta+$ nature of the carbon atom of the C—Cl bond caused by its attachment to two electronegative atoms (O and Cl). This renders this carbon atom liable to nucleophilic attack by such reagents as water or the hydroxide ion. When these nucleophiles are linked to the carbon atom of the C—Cl bond, the chlorine can split off as a negative ion by heterolytic fission of the C—Cl bond.

Assignment 46

The Effect of Sustituents in the Benzene Ring on Further Substitution in the Ring

INTRODUCTION

In this experiment the relative rates of substitution of chlorine atoms for hydrogen atoms of the benzene ring are determined.

Since chlorine produces a yellow solution when dissolved in either dichloromethane (methylene chloride) or acetic acid the time taken for the disappearance of the yellow colour, after addition of the aromatic compound, can be taken as an indication of the relative rates of substitution.

EXPERIMENTAL WORK

If possible place a loosely-stoppered bottle containing about $10cm^3$ of chlorine in dichloromethane solution, in direct sunlight.

1. What do you observe?

2. By what mechanism does the reaction take place?

3. Why does sunlight have this effect?

Carry out the following experiments out of direct sunlight and place about $2cm^3$ of the chlorine in dichloromethane solution in a test-tube as a control experiment. Place $2cm^3$ of the chlorine in dichloromethane solution in a dry test-tube and add 10 drops of one of the compounds listed below (or 10 drops of a concentrated solution in dichloromethane if the substance is a solid). Note the time taken for the yellow colour to disappear from the solution. Repeat the experiment with the other substances—it is not necessary to wait for one experiment to finish befpre starting the next provided the times of starting are recorded.

Some substances may not decolourize the solution in half an hour. For these substances repeat the experiment but use a solution of chlorine in acetic acid rather than in dichlorobenzene.

4. What is the mechanism for substitution of chlorine in an aromatic ring?

5. Why is chlorine in acetic acid likely to react more rapidly than chlorine in dichloromethane?

6. What would be the rate of substitution of chlorine dissolved in carbon tetrachloride relative to its solution in dichloromethane and in acetic acid?

Name of compound	Structure	Cl$_2$ in CH$_2$Cl$_2$		Cl$_2$ in CH$_3$COOH	
		Time at mixing	Time at decolour-ation	Time at mixing	Time at decolour-ation
benzene					
phenol					
toluene					
chlorobenzene					
methylphenyl ether (anisole)					
1:2 dimethylbenzene (o-xylene)					
1:3 dimethylbenzene (m-xylene)					
1:4 dimthylbenzene (p-xylene)					
1:3:5: trimethyl-benzene (mesitylene)					
1-chloro-4-methoxybenzene (p-chloroanisole)					
NN-dimethylaniline					
benzoic acid					

7. Which three substituents most actively facilitate substitution?

8. What common feature have these three substituents?

9. Where substituents consist of more than one element, suggest a relationship between the position of the more electronegative element and the effect of the substituent on the rate of further substitution.

10. What is the effect of methyl groups on further substitution? Do the positions of the methyl groups in the ring modify their effect?

Notes 46

Standard: ***
Time required: 1½ hours
Reagents required:
saturated solution of chlorine in dichloromethane	(40cm^3)
saturated solution of chlorine in glacial acetic acid	(20cm^3)
benzene	(20 drops)
phenol dissolved in dichloromethane	(10 drops)
toluene	(20 drops)
chlorobenzene	(20 drops)
methyl phenyl ether	(10 drops)
1:2 dimethylbenzene	(20 drops)
1:3 dimethylbenzene	(20 drops)
1:4 dimethylbenzene	(20 drops)
1:3:5 trimethylbenzene	(10 drops)
1-chloro-4-methoxylbenzene	(20 drops)
N,N-dimethylaniline	(5 drops)
benzoic acid solution in dichloromethane	(20 drops)

Apparatus required:
   test-tubes
   teat pipettes
   small stoppered bottle (not essential for all students)
   ultra-violet lamp (if available, and as a substitute for sunlight)
   colorimeter (not essential, but may be useful in some cases)

Notes on questions and results
1. If the solution of chlorine in dichloromethane is exposed to direct sunlight, or failing that an ultra-violet lamp, the yellow colour disappears in a few minutes (less than 2 minutes in bright sunlight; about 5 minutes using the lamp) and fumes of hydrogen chloride are produced which may force out the stopper.

2. This is strong evidence that the chlorine has substituted the remaining hydrogen atoms in dichloromethane. This type of substitution of the hydrogen atoms of a saturated compound takes place by a mechanism involving radicals produced by homolytic fission of the Cl–Cl bond. This experiment illustrates the acceleration of such a radical reaction caused by ultra-violet radiation.

3. Energy is required to break the Cl–Cl bond (bond energy = 243 kJ mol^{-1}) and this is provided by ultra-violet radiation, and can be provided by heating. Teachers may point out the conditions used for side-chain substitution of aromatic compounds.
N.B. The experiment should be conducted away from direct sunlight or the chlorine will readily react with the dichloromethane.
In the experimental work a procedure for timing should be adopted at the start of the experiment and this should be adhered to throughout. To obtain a comparative order for

some substances a colorimeter may prove useful, the time could then be taken for the samples to reach a certain degree of colour intensity as shown on the colorimeter.

N.B. Only 2 drops of NN-dimethylaniline should be used; more produces a brown colour.

4. Substitution in the aromatic ring takes place by an electrophilic mechanism. This requires heterolytic fission of the Cl—Cl bond.

5. Since heterolytic fission brings about the substitution, the more polar the solvent, the more readily heterolytic fission will occur, and the more rapidly the chlorine will substitute. Thus acetic acid, being more polar than dichloromethane, will aid substitution.

6. Carbon tetrachloride is less polar than dichloromethane and thus a solution of chlorine in carbon tetrachloride would react less rapidly than the two solutions used.

Results
The actual times for decolouration of the chlorine solution depend on several variable factors, such as the amount of light in the room, the freshness of the chlorine solution etc., but the relative values are significant.

Name of compound	Structure	Time to decolourize Cl_2 in CH_2Cl_2	Time to decolourize Cl_2 in CH_3COOH
benzene		No visible change	Longer than 1 hour but paler than control
phenol		Instantaneous	–
toluene		30 minutes	15 minutes
chlorobenzene		No visible change	No change in 1 hour
methyl phenyl ether		Instantaneous	–
1:2 dimethylbenzene		20 minutes	12 minutes
1:3 dimethylbenzene		15 seconds	–
1:4 dimethylbenzene		12 minutes	7 minutes
1:3:5 trimethylbenzene		Instantaneous	–
1-chlor-4-methoxy-benzene		7 minutes	4 minutes
NN-dimethylaniline		Instantaneous (using only 2 drops)	–
benzoic acid		No visible change	No change in 1 hour

279

7. The three substituents which most actively facilitate substitution are

$$-OH, -OCH_3, -N(CH_3)_2$$

8. In each case the most electronegative atom is joined to the benzene ring and it bears one, or more, lone pair of electrons.

9. If the most electronegative atom of the substituent is closest to the benzene ring and bears one, or more, lone pair of electrons, as is usually the case, electrons are fed into the ring and it is activated. If the most electronegative atom of the group is further from the benzene ring than a less electronegative atom, and is joined to it by a multiple bond, electrons are drawn towards the more electronegative element and thus out of the ring, which is thereby de-activated.

10. Methyl groups release electrons into the ring more readily, than hydrogen atoms do and thus activate the ring. The *ortho* and *para* positions are activated by each methyl group and thus if they are placed so that each is activating the same position the effect is most marked e.g. in 1:3 dimethylbenzene each methyl group activates the carbon atom between the two methyl groups and reaction is quite rapid.

FURTHER PROJECT

Investigation of substitution of bromine in organic compounds using a solution of bromine in carbon tetrachloride.

REFERENCE

F.L. Lambert, *J. Chem. Ed.,* **35**, 7 (1958).

Assignment 47

An Investigation of the Kinetics of Hydrolysis of 2-chloro-2-methyl-propane (tertiary butyl chloride)

INTRODUCTION

The equation for the reaction is

$$(CH_3)_3CCl + OH^- \rightarrow (CH_3)_3COH + Cl^-$$

In this series of experiments the order of this reaction is to be determined and also the dependence of the rate of reaction on (a) the polarity of the solvent and (b) the temperature.

The order of the reaction is determined by finding the time taken for one-tenth of the initial quantity of 2-chloro-2-methyl-propane to be converted into 2-hydroxy-2-methyl -propane, with different initial concentrations. A 0·10M solution of 2-chloro-2-methyl -propane in acetone and a 0·010M aqueous solution of sodium hydroxide are used, with bromophenol blue added to indicate when virtually all the hydroxide ions have reacted. The indicator is blue in the presence of high concentrations of hydroxide ions but changes to yellow as the hydroxide concentration drops below a certain value (approximately 10^{-10} mol dm^{-3}).

1. Does the concentration of hydroxide ions remaining, when the indicator has turned yellow, represent a significant proportion of the initial hydroxide ion concentration?

2. Is it reasonable to assume that the number of moles of hydroxide ion that have reacted is approximately equal to the number of moles of sodium hydroxide added (i.e. the fraction of a cubic decimeter of the solution added, multiplied by its molarity)?

The number of moles of hydroxide ion taken is one-tenth of the number of moles of 2-chloro-2-methyl-propane taken, and thus the time for the indicator to change colour is the time for one-tenth-change ($t_{\frac{1}{10}}$ for the reaction).

3. What reason is there for using a *small* number of moles of hydroxide ion relative to 2-chloro-2-methyl-propane (i.e. taking the time for a *small* fractional change)?

EXPERIMENTAL WORK

(I) Determination of order

Run 9·0cm³ of the 2-chloro-2-methyl-propane solution from a burette into a dry conical flask. Into a second flask run 9·0cm³ of 0·010M NaOH followed by 12·0cm³ of distilled water and three drops of bromophenol blue. Note the time as the 2-chloro-2-methyl-propane solution is poured into the second flask, swirl the mixture immediately and pour it back into the other flask. It is important to adopt a standard procedure for mixing the solutions to start the reaction. Note the time when the solution turns yellow. Repeat this experiment twice more and calculate the average time for one-tenth change under these conditions. Note also the variation you have in your three results.

Use the same experimental procedure as above for two further determinations *but* add 30cm³ of a 70% water-30% acetone solution to the flask containing the aqueous sodium hydroxide, in each case, before mixing.

4. What conditions are altered by the addition of the $30cm^3$ of 70% water-30% acetone solution?

5. How is the time for a given fractional change (e.g. $t_{\frac{1}{2}}$ or $t_{\frac{1}{10}}$) related to the initial concentration of the reactants when the reaction is (a) first order, (b) second order?

6. What conclusions do you draw about the order of this reaction? Give your reasoning?

7. Bearing in mind the order of the reaction, what suggestions can you make for the mechanism of the reaction?

8. Consider the mechanism of the reaction and predict the effect you would expect the polarity of the solvent to have on the rate of the reaction.

(II) Dependence of rate of reaction on solvent polarity

Run $6·0cm^3$ of 0·10M 2-chloro-2-methyl-propane in acetone solution into a dry conical flask. Into a second flask run $6·0cm^3$ of 0·010M NaOH, followed by $18·0cm^3$ of distilled water and three drops of bromophenol blue. Perform the experiment as in Section I.

9. What is the percentage composition of the solvent in the reaction mixture?
Design and carry out an experiment to determine the time for one-tenth change of 2-chloro-2-methyl-propane in a 60% water-40% acetone solvent. Repeat for other percentage compositions of solvent according to the time available.

10. Is it important to determine the time for the same fractional change as in Section I? Why?

11. Is the initial concentration of the 2-chloro-2-methyl-propane the same in all these experiments, and the same as in Section I?

12. If the initial concentration differs in some of your experiments, how do you justify comparison of the times for one-tenth change?

13. What conclusions can you draw regarding the dependence of the rate of this reaction on the solvent polarity?

14. What explanation can you offer for this?
If you have sufficient results, plot a graph of the rate of the reaction (expressed as the reciprocal of the time for one-tenth change) against the percentage of water in the solvent.

15. What approximations are being made in expressing the rate as the reciprocal of the time for one-tenth change?

(III) Dependence of rate of reaction on the temperature

Prepare a water-bath at about 10°C below room temperature, allow the reactants to reach this temperature and proceed as in Section I.
Repeat this experiment at other temperatures within about 10°C of room temperature.
Derive an expression for the rate constant in terms of the time for one-tenth change for a reaction of the order which you have established in Section I.
The integrated form of the Arrhenius equation relates the rate constant to temperature as follows:

$$\ln k = \frac{-E}{RT} + \text{constant}$$

16. What would you plot to obtain a linear graph from which the value of E could be obtained?

17. What is the value of E, the energy of activation of the reaction, as calculated from your graph?

Notes 47

Standard: ***

Time required:
    Part One–½ hour
    Part Two–½ hour
    Part Three–½ hour (minimum)
    Preparation (reading instructions, answering introductory questions etc.)–¾ hour

Reagents required:
    0·10M 2-chloro-2-methyl-propane in acetone solution [11·0cm³ of 2-chloro-2-methyl-propane per litre] (100cm³)
    0·010M aqueous sodium hydroxide solution (200cm³)
    70% water-30% acetone solution [by volume] (100cm³)
    bromophenol blue indicator (2cm³)
    distilled water (200cm³)
    acetone [optional]
    ice

Apparatus required:
    2 100cm³ conical flasks (minimum)
    3 burettes
    pipette filler
    stopclock
    thermometer
    thermostatically controlled water-bath or large beaker (800cm³), bunsen burner, tripod and gauze

Notes on questions and typical results

1. The initial hydroxide concentration $\simeq \dfrac{9 \cdot 0}{30} \times 0 \cdot 010$ mol dm^{-3} = $3 \cdot 0 \times 10^{-3}$ mol dm^{-3} so it is reasonable to say that 10^{-10} is a negligible proportion of this.

2. It therefore follows that it is a fair approximation to say that the number of moles of hydroxide ion that have reacted is equal to the number of moles of sodium hydroxide added i.e. $\dfrac{9 \cdot 0}{1000} \times 0 \cdot 010 = 9 \cdot 0 \times 10^{-5}$ mol.

3. As the reagents are used up the reaction will become slower and if a larger fraction than one-tenth change is followed the rate of change of pH becomes slower and errors are incurred in taking the time at which the indicator changes colour. If only one-tenth of the 2-chloro-2-methyl-propane is used up the rate of the reaction will not vary very much; this is important in Section III where the rate is expressed as the reciprocal of the time; for one-tenth change.

Specimen results for part (I)
Using 9·0cm³ of 2-chloro-2-methyl-propane, 9·0cm³ of 0·010M NaOH and 12·0cm³ of water, four results were obtained within the range of 64-69 seconds at a temperature of 22·5°C.

When the experiment was repeated with 30cm³ of 70% water-30% acetone solution added, four readings were obtained in the range of 71-78 seconds at a temperature of 21°C.

4. The addition of the solvent maintains the same solvent composition but halves the concentration of the hydroxide ion and of the 2-chloro-2-methyl-propane.

5. First order

$$t_{\frac{1}{2}} = \frac{0 \cdot 69}{k}$$ i.e. is independent of the initial concentration

$$t_{\frac{1}{10}} = \frac{\ln\frac{10}{9}}{k}$$ i.e. is independent of the initial concentration

Second order

$$t_{\frac{1}{2}} = \frac{1}{ka} \qquad t_{\frac{1}{10}} = \frac{1}{9ka}$$ i.e. inversely proportional to the initial concentration

6. The results for the reaction in diluted solution show that the time for one-tenth change is very close to that in the first series of experiments. (The slightly lower temperature may be partly responsible for the higher values of $t_{\frac{1}{10}}$ in diluted solution, as recorded in the notes on question 3.) If the reaction were second order the times should be doubled. It is thus fair to assume that the major part of the change is effected by a first order mechanism, though it is possible that a small amount may be effected by second order mechanism.

7. If the order of the reaction is one, the rate-determining step must involve just one species and so the reaction must involve more than one step. A likely rate-determining step is therefore

$$(CH_3)_3CCl \rightarrow (CH_3)_3C^+ + Cl^-$$

followed by the relatively rapid reaction

$$(CH_3)_3C^+ + OH^- \rightarrow (CH_3)_3COH$$

8. If this mechanism is correct it is reasonable to predict that the greater the polarity of the solvent (i.e. the greater the percentage of water), the more readily the ionization of 2-chloro-2-methyl-propane will take place. Thus one would expect the reaction to be faster, the greater the polarity of the solvent.

(II) Specimen results

% water	83·3	80	75	70	60	50
% acetone	16·7	20	25	30	40	50
temp./°C	23·5	24·0	23·5	22·5	23·0	22·5
$t_{\frac{1}{10}}$/s	21	26	41	67	197	840 (approx.)

9. The solvent composition is 80% water—20% acetone

The experiment may be carried out in different solvent compositions as follows:

	1st flask	2nd flask
60% water—40% acetone	9·0cm³ of 2-chloro-2-methyl-propane in acetone	9·0cm³ of 0·010M NaOH
	3·0cm³ of acetone	9·0cm³ of dist. water.
50% water—50% acetone	9·0cm³ of 2-chloro-2-methyl-propane in acetone	9·0cm³ of 0·010M NaOH
	6·0cm³ of acetone	6·0cm³ of dist. water

75% water—25% acetone $6{\cdot}0\,cm^3$ of 2-chloro-2-methyl- $6{\cdot}0\,cm^3$ of $0{\cdot}010M$ NaOH
propane in acetone
$1{\cdot}5\,cm^3$ of acetone $16{\cdot}5\,cm^3$ of dist. water

Many other combinations are possible, of course.

10. The time for a *given* fractional change is independent of the initial concentration for a first order reaction, but the times for different fractional changes differ. (See question 5 above.) If the results of Sections (I) and (II) are to be compared all conditions must be identical except the solvent polarity (the effect of which is being investigated) and the initial concentration.

11. The initial concentrations are different in these experiments.

12. If the reaction can be shown to approximate to first order kinetics then the different initial concentrations will not, in themselves, affect the time for one-tenth change.

13. It is reasonable to conclude that the greater the solvent polarity (the higher the proportion of water in the solvent), the faster the reaction proceeds.

14. The greater the polarity of the solvent, the more readily the 2-chloro-2-methyl-propane will ionise. If this is the rate-determining step in the reaction then the greater the polarity of the solvent, the faster this reaction will proceed.

15. The rate, expressed as the reciprocal of the time for one-tenth change, represents the average rate over this period of time. As the concentration of the 2-chloro-2-methyl-propane only changes by 10% the rates will not vary greatly from the average value during this period of time.

(III) This part of the experiment may be conveniently done as a co-operative class experiment with each pupil being allocated a different temperature at which to work.
The reaction having been shown to be first order the relationship between time for one-tenth change and the rate constant for the reaction can be derived from the integrated form of the first order rate law.

$$kt = \ln\left(\frac{a}{a\text{-}x}\right) \quad \text{where } a = \text{initial molar concentration}$$
$$x = \text{molar conc. at time } t$$

Hence when $t = t_{\frac{1}{10}}$, $kt_{\frac{1}{10}} = \ln\dfrac{10}{9} = 2{\cdot}303\ \lg 1{\cdot}11$

Thus $k = \dfrac{0{\cdot}105}{t_{\frac{1}{10}}}$

16. To obtain a linear graph from which the value of E could be obtained one could plot
ln k against $\dfrac{1}{T}$ in which case the gradient of the graph would equal $\dfrac{-E}{R}$ or, preferably, plot

lg k against $\dfrac{1}{T}$ in which case the gradient would equal $\dfrac{-E}{2{\cdot}303R}$

Typical class results

t/°C	T/K	(T/K)$^{-1}$	$t_{\frac{1}{10}}$/s	k/s^{-1}	lg(k/s^{-1})
34	307	0·00326	10	$1{\cdot}05 \times 10^{-2}$	$\bar{2}{\cdot}021$
33	306	0·00327	14	$7{\cdot}50 \times 10^{-3}$	$\bar{3}{\cdot}875$
30	303	0·00330	20	$5{\cdot}25 \times 10^{-3}$	$\bar{3}{\cdot}720$
29	302	0·00331	20	$5{\cdot}25 \times 10^{-3}$	$\bar{3}{\cdot}720$
24	297	0·00337	34	$3{\cdot}09 \times 10^{-3}$	$\bar{3}{\cdot}490$

19	292	0·00342	75	$1\cdot40 \times 10^{-3}$	$\bar{3}\cdot146$
18	291	0·00344	80	$1\cdot32 \times 10^{-3}$	$\bar{3}\cdot121$
15	288	0·00348	135	$7\cdot78 \times 10^{-4}$	$\bar{4}\cdot891$
6	279	0·00358	360	$2\cdot92 \times 10^{-4}$	$\bar{4}\cdot465$
3	276	0·00363	1560	$6\cdot74 \times 10^{-5}$	$\bar{5}\cdot829$

From the graph of lg k against $1/T$,

$$\text{Gradient} = -\frac{2\cdot00}{3\cdot9 \times 10^{-4}} = -5\cdot13 \times 10^3 = \frac{-E}{2\cdot303R}$$

Hence $E = 5\cdot13 \times 10^3 \times 2\cdot303 \times 8\cdot31\text{J mol}^{-1}$
$E = 98\text{kJ mol}^{-1}$

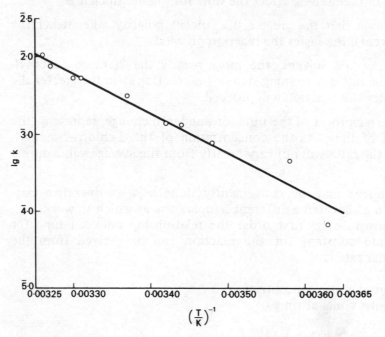

Fig 47.1
Graph of the logarithm of the rate constant for the hydrolysis of 2-chloro-2-methyl propane against the reciprocal of the Kelvin temperature

FURTHER PROJECT

Investigate the kinetics of hydrolysis of other halogeno-alkanes, e.g. 2-bromobutane, 1-bromobutane, iodomethane.

REFERENCE

J.A. Landgrebe, *J. Chem. Ed.*, **41**, 10 (1964).

Assignment 48

Determination of the Solubility of Ammonium Chloride by Back Titration

INTRODUCTION

This experiment illustrates the use of the technique of back-titration which may be used to determine the number of moles of a substance present in a sample when a direct titration is not possible. The procedure is to add to the substance a known excess of a reagent which reacts with it (albeit slowly) and can be titrated against a third substance to determine how much remains in excess and thus, by difference, how much reacted.

EXPERIMENTAL WORK

You are provided with a solution of ammonium chloride, saturated at room temperature, which has been filtered or decanted.

Pipette $5.0cm^3$ of this solution into a $250cm^3$ graduated flask and make up to $250cm^3$ with distilled water. Shake the flask until the solution is homogeneous and pipette $20.0cm^3$ portions of this solution into each of three $250cm^3$ titration flasks. Add $20.0cm^3$ of 0.2M sodium hydroxide solution to each of the titration flasks and heat until the solutions start to boil. Adjust the flame so that the solutions boil gently and continue heating until ammonia is no longer evolved. Cool each flask and titrate the contents against 0.1M hydrochloric acid using methyl orange (or screened methyl orange as indicator).

Record the results as follows:

	Flask 1	Flask 2	Flask 3
Final reading/cm^3			
Initial reading/cm^3			
Result/cm^3			

Mean titre = cm^3

1. Why can the solubility of ammonium chloride not be determined by evaporating a saturated solution to dryness and weighing?

2. What are the equations for (a) the reaction of the sodium hydroxide with the ammonium chloride (b) the reaction of the excess sodium hydroxide with the hydrochloric acid?

3. Why can the ammonium chloride not be titrated directly against the sodium hydroxide?

4. Why must all the ammonia be expelled?

5. How do you know when no more ammonia is being evolved?

6. Does it matter if some of the water evaporates from the titration flask?

7. Does it matter if some of the solution splashes out of the flask when it is being heated?

CALCULATION

8. How many moles of sodium hydroxide are present in $20.0cm^3$ of $0.20M$ sodium hydroxide solution?

9. How many moles of hydrochloric acid were added in your titration?

10. How many moles of sodium hydroxide were left after boiling with the ammonium chloride solution?

11. How many moles of sodium hydroxide reacted with $20.0cm^3$ of ammonium chloride solution?

12. How many moles of ammonium chloride were present in $20.0cm^3$ of the diluted solution?

13. How many moles of ammonium chloride were present in $5.0cm^3$ of the saturated solution?

14. What is the solubility of ammonium chloride in water at room temperature in grams per cubic decimetre of solution?

15. What other information would you need to enable you to express the solubility of ammonium chloride at room temperature in grams per 100g of water?

Obtain this information and calculate the solubility of ammonium chloride in g per 100g of water.

Notes 48

Standard: *

Time required: 1½ hours (with saturated solution provided). If a saturated solution is to be made up, about 15 minutes will be required on the previous day.

Reagents required:

saturated NH_4Cl solution, previously filtered	$(15cm^3)$
0·20M NaOH solution	$(100cm^3)$
0·10M HCl solution	$(100cm^3)$
methyl orange or screened methyl orange	(20 drops)
distilled water	$(300cm^3)$
red litmus paper	

Apparatus required:

$5·0cm^3$ pipette
$250cm^3$ graduated flask
$20·0cm^3$ pipette (minimum—2 if possible)
3 x $250cm^3$ titration flasks
burette
bunsen burner, tripod and gauze

Notes on questions and typical results

1. Ammonium chloride undergoes thermal dissociation so evaporating the solution to dryness is likely to drive off some of the ammonium chloride as well.

2. Equations (a) $NH_4Cl + NaOH = NaCl + NH_3 + H_2O$

or ionically $\quad NH_4^+ + OH^- = NH_3 + H_2O$

(b) $NaOH + HCl = NaCl + H_2O$

or ionically $\quad OH^- + H^+ = H_2O$

3. The ammonium chloride cannot be titrated directly against the sodium hydroxide because the ammonia formed is released from the solution only slowly on boiling, and while the ammonia is present in the solution it will affect the indicator.

4. All the ammonia must be evolved because the required end-point of the titration is when as many moles of hydrochloric acid have been added as moles of sodium hydroxide were present in excess. If ammonia remains in solution at this point it will make the solution alkaline with respect to the indicator.

5. When no more ammonia is being evolved the smell of the gas will no longer be detectable and a piece of moist red litmus paper, held just above the neck of the flask, will remain red.

6. Water is bound to evaporate from the flask but provided the solution is not evaporated to dryness this does not matter. It is the number of moles of solute present in the flask that is critical, not the absolute molarity. If the quantity of water evaporating is considerable, distilled water should be added to make up to the original volume.

7. If some of the solution splashes out of the flask during the heating, some of the solutes will escape and an error will be introduced. This must be avoided by using a small bunsen flame.

Specimen results and calculation (Temperature of saturated solution = 16°C)

19·0cm^3 of 0·10M HCl neutralizes the excess sodium hydroxide from 20·0cm^3 of dilute solution

8. 20·0cm^3 of 0·20M NaOH contain $\frac{20\cdot0}{1000}$ x 0·20 mol

9. 19·0cm^3 of 0·10M HCl were added, containing $\frac{19\cdot0}{1000}$ x 0·10 mol

10. The number of moles of sodium hydroxide left after boiling with the ammonium chloride solution is equal to the number of moles of hydrochloric acid added in the titration i.e. 1·90 x 10^{-3} mol.

11. The number of moles of sodium hydroxide which reacted with 20·0cm^3 of the ammonium chloride solution is the difference between the number of moles added and the number of moles left after the reaction i.e. 4·00 x 10^{-3} − 1·90 x 10^{-3} mol which is 2·10 x 10^{-3} mol.

12. The number of moles of ammonium chloride in 20·0cm^3 of the diluted solution is equal to the number of moles of sodium hydroxide which reacted i.e. 2·10 x 10^{-3} mol.

13. Since 5·0cm^3 of saturated ammonium chloride solution was diluted to 250cm^3 the number of moles of ammonium chloride in this volume of the saturated solution is

2·10 x 10^{-3} x $\frac{250}{20}$ = 2·62 x 10^{-2} mol.

14. The solubility of ammonium chloride in water at room temperature thus determined is 2·62 x 10^{-2} x $\frac{1000}{5}$ x 53·5g dm^{-3}.

$$\text{Solubility} = 281\text{g dm}^{-3}$$
(The formula weight of ammonium chloride = 53·5)

15. In order to convert the solubility in g dm^{-3} of solution to the value expressed in g per 100g of solvent, the density of the saturated solution must be known.

The density can be determined by pipetting 20·0cm^3 of the saturated solution into a weighed beaker and reweighing.

The density of saturated ammonium chloride solution at 16^{c}C = 1·07g cm^{-3}

Thus 1dm^3 of solution weighs 1070g and of this 281g is ammonium chloride.

Thus 281g of ammonium chloride saturates 790g of water at 16°C

Solubility of ammonium chloride in water at 16°C = $\frac{281}{7\cdot9}$ = 35·6g per 100g of water.

This compares well with literature values of 34g at 10°C and 37g at 20°C.

FURTHER PROJECT

Determine the concentration of a solution of ammonium chloride by adding excess formaldehyde which produces hexamethylene tetramine and hydrochloric acid.

Assignment 49

Determination of the Empirical Formula of an Acid-Oxalate [KxHy(C₂O₄)z] by Titration with Standard Potassium Permanganate Solution

INTRODUCTION

In this experiment the number of moles of hydrogen ions obtained from one mole of the acid-oxalate is determined by titration against standard sodium hydroxide solution, using phenolphthalein as indicator.

Investigate the action of the indicator by adding a drop of phenolphthalein solution, in turn, to a few cm^3 of solutions of potassium hydrogen oxalate, potassium oxalate and sodium hydroxide. Record the results of these experiments in tabular form.

The number of moles of oxalate ion in one mole of the acid-oxalate is determined by titration against standard potassium permanganate in acid solution.

EXPERIMENTAL WORK

Solution A is an aqueous solution of an acid-oxalate $(KxHy(C_2O_4)z)$, the concentration (in $g\ dm^{-3}$) of which you will be told.

(a) Pipette $20\cdot0cm^3$ of solution A into a $250cm^3$ titration flask, add three drops of phenolphthalein solution as indicator and titrate against $0\cdot10M$ sodium hydroxide solution. Repeat the titration until two concordant readings are obtained.

1. Write the ionic equation for this neutralization reaction.

(b) Pipette $20\cdot0cm^3$ of solution A into a $250cm^3$ titration flask and add about $20cm^3$ of approximately 1M sulphuric acid. Warm the contents of the flask to about 60°C and titrate against $0\cdot020M$ potassium permanganate solution, maintaining the temperature of the solution at approximately 60°C throughout the titration.

Repeat the titration until two concordant readings are obtained.

Set out results of titrations (a) and (b) as shown:

	(a)		(b)	
Final burette reading/cm^3	....	....	....	....
Initial burette reading/cm^3	....	....	....	....
Result/cm^3	_____	_____	_____	_____

2. How is the end-point for a permanganate titration indicated?

3. Write the ionic half-equation (involving electrons) for the reduction of permanganate ions (MnO_4^-) in acid solution.

4. Write the ionic half-equation (involving electrons) for the oxidation of oxalate ions ($C_2O_4^{2-}$)

5. Multiply the half-equations by a factor which makes the number of electrons involved in each half-equation the same and combine the two half-equations. What is the overall equation?

CALCULATION

6. How many moles of hydrogen ions (H^+) were present in $20 \cdot 0 cm^3$ of solution A?

7. How many grams of hydrogen were present in the quantity of acid-oxalate present in one cubic decimetre of solution A?

8. How many moles of permanganate ions (MnO_4^-) were needed in the titration for $20 \cdot 0 cm^3$ of solution A?

9. How many moles of oxalate ions ($C_2O_4^{2-}$) were present in $20 \cdot 0 cm^3$ of solution A?

10. How many grams of oxalate ion ($C_2O_4^{2-}$) were present in the quantity of the acid-oxalate in one cubic decimetre of solution A?

11. How many grams of potassium were present in this same quantity of acid-oxalate?

12. Taking the formula weights $H = 1$; $C_2O_4 = 88$; $K = 39$, calculate the empirical formula of the acid-oxalate.

Notes 49

Standard: **
Time required: 1½ hours
Reagents required:

Solution A, which is a solution of potassium tetroxalate. Prepare it by weighing accurately between 7·6 and 7·8g of 'analar' potassium tetroxalate crystals (KHC_2O_4, $H_2C_2O_4.2H_2O$) per cubic decimetre of solution. Multiply the weight of crystals, per cubic decimetre, by 218/254 to obtain the number of grammes of the anhydrous salt, per cubic decimetre of solution, and announce this figure to the students. Since the number of molecules of water of crystallization may vary, it is advisable to standardise this solution before use.   ($100cm^3$)

0·10M NaOH solution   ($100cm^3$)

0·020M $KMnO_4$ solution   ($100cm^3$)

approx. 1 M H_2SO_4 ($100cm^3$)

potassium hydrogen oxalate solution   ($3cm^3$)

potassium oxalate solution   ($3cm^3$)

phenolphthalein solution   (a few drops)

Apparatus required:

3 beakers ($150cm^3$ or $250cm^3$)

1 x $250cm^3$ conical flask for titration

burette

20·0cm^3 pipette (preferably two)

20cm^3 measuring cylinder (or test tube of about 20cm^3 volume)

bunsen burner, tripod and gauze.

thermometer

test-tubes.

Specimen results and answers to questions

Phenolphthalein plus potassium hydrogen oxalate	— colourless
Phenolphthalein plus potassium oxalate	— colourless
Phenolphthalein plus sodium hydroxide	— cherry red

Hence in the titration of the acid-oxalate against sodium hydroxide, using phenolphthalein as indicator, all the hydrogen atoms of the acid-oxalate will be replaced before the phenolphthalein indicates the end-point.

1. The ionic equation for the neutralization reaction is

$$H^+ + OH^- = H_2O$$

2. The end-point for a permanganate titration is indicated by the permanent pink colour which the excess permanganate solution imparts to the mixture.

3. The ionic half-equation for the reduction of permanganate ions in acid solution is

$$5e^- + 8H^+ + MnO_4^- = Mn^{2+} + 4H_2O$$

293

4. The ionic half-equation for the oxidation of oxalate ions is

$$C_2O_4{}^{2-} = 2CO_2 + 2e^-$$

5. To balance the number of electrons transferred, the permanganate equation must be multiplied by two; and the oxalate equation by five

$$10e^- + 16H^+ + 2MnO_4{}^- = 2Mn^{2+} + 8H_2O$$

$$5C_2O_4{}^{2-} = 10CO_2 + 10e^-$$

Combining $\qquad 5C_2O_4{}^{2-} + 16H^+ + 2MnO_4{}^- = 10CO_2 + 2Mn^{2+} + 8H_2O$

Results

7·85g of potassium tetroxalate crystals ($KHC_2O_4.H_2C_2O_4.2H_2O$) per cubic decimetre. Thus weight of anhydrous acid-oxalate = 7·85 x 218/254 = 6·74g per cubic decimetre.

20·0cm^3 of solution A $\equiv$ 18·6cm^3 of 0·10M sodium hydroxide solution.

20·0cm^3 of solution A $\equiv$ 24·7cm^3 of 0·020M potassium permanganate solution.

6. No. of moles of hydrogen ions (H$^+$) in 20·0cm^3 of solution A = 18·6 x 10^{-3} x 10^{-1} mol. = 1·86 x 10^{-3} mol

7. Weight of hydrogen in 6·74g of acid-oxalate = 1·86 x 10^{-3} x 50 x 1g = 9·30 x 10^{-2}g

8. Number of moles of permanganate ions (MnO$_4{}^-$) needed in the titration for 20·0cm^3 of solution A = 24·7 x 10^{-3} x 0·020 mol = 4·94 x 10^{-4} mol.

9. Number of moles of oxalate ions (C$_2$O$_4{}^{2-}$) in 20·0cm^3 of solution A

$$= 4·94 \times 10^{-4} \times \frac{5}{2} = 1·235 \times 10^{-3} \text{ mol.}$$

10. Weight of oxalate in 6·74g of acid-oxalate = 1·235 x 10^{-3} x 50 x 88g = 5·44g

11. Weight of potassium in 6·74g of acid-oxalate = 6·74−(5·44 + 0·093)g = 1·21g

12. Numerical ratios:

$$H = \frac{0·0933}{1} : C_2O_4 = \frac{5·44}{88} : K = \frac{1·29}{39}$$

$$H = 0·0933 : C_2O_4 = 0·0618 : K = 0·0311$$

Hence $\qquad H = 3·00 \qquad : C_2O_4 = 1·99 \qquad : K = 1·00$

Thus the empirical formula of the acid-oxalate = $KH_3(C_2O_4)_2$

Assignment 50

The Oxidation of Hydrazine

EXPERIMENTAL WORK

Pipette 20cm^3 of 0·025M hydrazine sulphate solution into a conical flask and add about 5cm^3 of concentrated hydrochloric acid. Pour off enough solution to fill a colorimeter tube and use this to 'zero' the colorimeter before returning the solution to the conical flask. Using a burette add 2cm^3 of 0·025M potassium iodate solution. Swirl the mixture and look at it closely. Again run off enough of the mixture to fill a colorimeter tube and determine the colorimeter reading (directly proportional to the intensity of the colour of the solution). Return the contents of the tube to the conical flask and add a further 2cm^3 of the potassium iodate solution. Continue in this way until 20cm^3 of the potassium iodate solution has been added.

Plot a graph of the colorimeter reading against the volume of potassium iodate solution added.

EXPERIMENTAL INTERPRETATION

1. What is the likely identity of the coloured species formed in the first stage of the titration?

2. What is the oxidation number of the iodine in this species?

3. What is the oxidation number of the iodine in the iodate ion?

4. What is the oxidation number of the nitrogen in hydrazine sulphate?

5. Assuming that your answer to question 1 is correct, what volumes of 0·025M potassium iodate solution would be needed to oxidize 20cm^3 of 0·025M hydrazine sulphate if the function of the former is to increase the oxidation number of *each* of the nitrogen atoms in a molecule of hydrazine by (a) 1 unit? (b) 2 units? (c) 3 units?

6. What volume of potassium iodate solution produced the maximum concentration of coloured species during the titration?

7. From your answers to the previous two questions try to infer the identity of the species to which the hydrazine has been oxidized.

8. Did you observe anything during the experiment to support your answer to question 7?

9. Assuming that the hydrogen ion concentration during the titration is 1M and given that the equilibrium constants at 25°C for the reactions:

$$N_2H_4 + H_2O \rightleftharpoons N_2H_5^+ + OH^-$$

$$N_2H_5^+ + H_2O \rightleftharpoons N_2H_6^{2+} + OH^-$$

are, respectively, 1·5 x 10^{-8} and 1·6 x 10^{-17} calculate which is the predominant hydrazine species under the conditions of this experiment.

295

10. Suggest half-equations for (a) the reduction of the iodate ion in the first stage of the titration; (b) the oxidation of the hydrazine sulphate.

11. Construct an equation to represent the reaction taking place during the first stage of the titration.

12. Using your experimental data speculate concerning the reaction taking place during the second stage of the titration (i.e. the removal of the coloured species), explaining any assumptions you make.

13. Suggest an equation for the overall reaction taking place when 20cm³ of 0·025M hydrazine sulphate solution is added to 20cm³ of 0·025M potassium iodate solution.

14. Pure hydrazine has a dipole moment. What can you infer about its structure?

15. In what respect does hydrazine resemble hydrogen peroxide?

296

Notes 50

Standard: **

Time required: 1 hour of practical time

Reagents required:

    0·025M hydrazine sulphate [3·25g $N_2H_4.H_2SO_4$ per dm^3] ($50cm^3$)

    0·025M potassium iodate solution [5·36g KIO_3 per dm^3] ($50cm^3$)

    concentrated hydrochloric acid ($20cm^3$)

Apparatus required:

    burette

    $20cm^3$ pipette

    $10cm^3$ measuring cylinder

    2 conical flasks

    1 colorimeter tube

    access to a colorimeter

N.B. One colorimeter can serve up to 4 pairs of students. If colorimeters are not available, the experiment may be performed using about $2-3cm^3$ of chloroform in the titration flask providing that the flask is shaken thoroughly after each addition of iodate. In this case the student must try to judge by eye when the intensity of colour in the chloroform is at its greatest (end of first stage) and at its least (end of second stage).

Experimental data and interpretation

A graph showing typical experimental data is shown in Figure 50.1.

1. The iodate ions are probably being reduced. In acid solution iodate ions can oxidize iodide ions to iodine and so the coloured species formed in the first stage is probably free iodine.

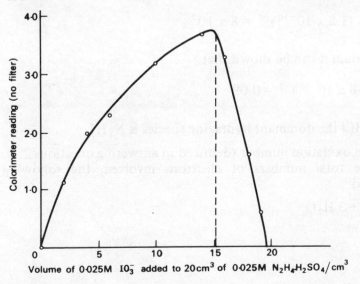

Fig 50.1

Figure 1: Colorimeter reading as a function of the volume of 0·025M KIO_3 added

2. The oxidation number of any free element is said to be zero and so the oxidation number of I_2 is zero.

3. The iodate ion has the formula IO_3^-. If oxygen has an oxidation number of $-II$, then that of iodine in IO_3^- must be $+V$ in order to account for the single negative overall charge of the ion.

4. Hydrazine has the formula N_2H_4. Taking the oxidation number of hydrogen as $+I$ gives an oxidation number for nitrogen of $-II$ in this compound. (The fact that hydrazine exists as $N_2H_5^+$ or $N_2H_6^{2+}$ in acid solution does not affect this conclusion)

5. $20cm^3$ of 0·025M hydrazine solution contains 0·0005 moles of hydrazine or 0·001 moles of N atoms. (a) If each N atom is oxidized by one unit, then 0·001 moles of electrons must be removed. Assuming the answers to questions 2 or 3, it can be deduced that one mole of IO_3^- ions can remove 5 moles of electrons. Thus, in this case, 0·001/5 moles of IO_3^- will be needed or 0·0002 moles.

If $y$cm^3 of 0·025M KIO_3 are needed, then: $\frac{y}{1000} \times 0\cdot025 = 0\cdot0002$

$$\text{and } y = \frac{1000 \times 0\cdot0002}{0\cdot025} = 8cm^3$$

Similarly, it could be shown that if the oxidation number of nitrogen in hydrazine is increased by (b) 2 units or (c) by 3 units then $16cm^3$ and $24cm^3$ of 0·025M KIO_3 respectively, would be needed.

6. The graph has a fairly well-defined maximum, which corresponds to $15-16cm^3$ of iodate solution being added.

7. This *suggests* that in the first stage of the titration the oxidation number of each nitrogen atom in hydrazine is increased by 2 units. This means that the nitrogen product probably has an oxidation number of zero (i.e. It probably exists as the free element, nitrogen gas)

8. Very close scrutiny is needed to observe the nitrogen being formed as the iodate solution is run into the acidified hydrazine, but it is usual to see bubbles of colourless gas collecting on the inside of the colorimeter tubes while measurements are being made.

9. $\dfrac{[N_2H_5^+][OH^-]}{[N_2H_4][H_2O]} = 1\cdot5 \times 10^{-8}$ $\dfrac{[OH^-]}{[H_2O]} = \dfrac{K_w}{[H_2O][H^+]} = \dfrac{K_w}{[H_2O]}$ in this case.

$$= \frac{10^{-14}}{55\cdot5} = 1\cdot8 \times 10^{-16}$$

Thus $\dfrac{[N_2H_5^+]}{[N_2H_4]} = 1\cdot5 \times 10^{-8} \times (1\cdot8 \times 10^{-16})^{-1} = 8 \times 10^7$

Similarly, for the second equilibrium it can be shown that

$$\frac{[N_2H_6^{2+}]}{[N_2H_5^+]} = 1\cdot6 \times 10^{-17} \times (1\cdot8 \times 10^{-16})^{-1} = 0\cdot09$$

Thus it can be seen that in 1 M HCl the dominant hydrazine species is $N_2H_5^+$

10. Assuming that the changes in oxidation number (deduced in answering questions 2, 3, 4, 5 and 7) are equal to the total numbers of electrons involved, the following half-equations can be constructed:

(a) $IO_3^- + 6H^+ + 5e^- \rightleftharpoons \frac{1}{2}I_2 + 3H_2O$

(b) $N_2H_5^+ \rightleftharpoons 5H^+ + N_2 + 4e^-$

11. Thus, multiplying (a) by 4 and (b) by 5 and adding we get

$$4 \, IO_3^- + 5 \, N_2H_5^+ \rightarrow 2 \, I_2 + 12 \, H_2O + 5 \, N_2 + H^+ \qquad \text{(Equation 1)}$$

as the equation for the first stage of the reaction.

12. If we assume that the hydrazine has been completely oxidized to N_2, and that the latter has either escaped into the air or remains in solution as inert molecules, the second stage of the titration must almost certainly be the oxidation of free iodine by the iodate ions.
This second stage of the reaction needs a further $4 \, cm^3$ of KIO_3 solution. (i.e. a quarter of the number of moles of iodate ion used in the first stage.) Applying this information to the equation suggested for the first stage (see answer to question 11.) we can infer that in the second stage a single iodate ion can oxidize two iodine molecules.

$$\text{i.e. } IO_3^- + 2 \, I_2 + x \, H^+ \rightarrow ?$$

If we assume that each of the iodine atoms in the free iodine has its oxidation number increased by one (to a species of oxidation number +I) it follows that the iodine of the iodate ion must be reduced 4 oxidation number units. (i.e. to a species of oxidation number +I)

$$\text{i.e. } I(+V) + 4 \, I(0) \rightarrow 5 \, I(+I)$$

and a *possible* equation is

$$IO_3^- + 2 \, I_2 + 2 \, H_2O \rightarrow 5 \, IO^- + 4 \, H^+ \qquad \text{(Equation 2)}$$

(N.B. It seems safe to conclude that the free iodine is not oxidized above an oxidation number of +I since this would involve the reduction of the iodate ion to a species of oxidation number *less* than that of the species to which the iodine molecules are oxidized)

13. Adding Equations 1 and 2 and simplifying we get for the overall equation:

$$IO_3^- + N_2H_5^+ \rightarrow IO^- + N_2 + 2 \, H_2O + H^+$$

14. Since pure hydrazine has a dipole moment we know that it *cannot* have a structure in which the hydrogen atoms on the two nitrogen atoms are trans to each other. (See figure 50.2)

15. Hydrogen peroxide also has an asymmetric structure which is often said to be most easily visualized in terms of an open book (See Figure 50.3). In addition H_2O_2 is more acidic than H_2O (i.e. less basic than H_2O) and N_2H_4 is less basic than NH_3.

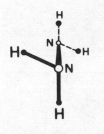

Fig 50.2 Figure 2: Hydrazine cannot exist in the
trans form

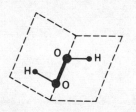

Fig 50.3 Figure 3: The structure of hydrogen
peroxide, in relation to an open book

FURTHER PROJECTS

1. Determine the pH-titration curve for the addition of hydrochloric acid to a standard solution of hydrazine. Are two steps detectable?

2. Compare the reactions of hydrazine with those of 1,2-diaminothane (i.e. ethylene diamine)

3. Investigate the effect of pH on the reaction of hydrazine with iodine (See Reference)

REFERENCE

Practical Inorganic Chemistry B.E. Dawson, Methuen (1963).

Assignment 51

Determination of Number of Molecules of Water of Crystallization in Barium Chloride Crystals [BaCl$_2$.xH$_2$O] by Titration Using Standard Silver Nitrate Solution

INTRODUCTION

A standard solution of silver ions may be used to determine the concentration of a solution of halide ions by titration. Potassium chromate may be used as the indicator subject to certain conditions. In the first part of this exercise you are to determine these conditions and explain the mode of action of the indicator.

Principles of silver ion/halide ion titrations using potassium chromate as indicator

Carry out the following experiments and record your observations:

(a) Add a few cm^3 of silver nitrate solution, in turn, to an equal volume of solutions of chloride, bromide and iodide ions.

(b) Add a few cm^3 of silver nitrate solution to an equal volume of sodium hydroxide solution.

(c) Add a few cm^3 of silver nitrate solution to three drops of potassium chromate solution, followed by dilute nitric acid until no further change is seen.

(d) Add a few cm^3 of barium chloride solution to three drops of potassium chromate solution.

Look up the solubility (or solubility product) of silver chloride, bromide, iodide and chromate, and barium chromate and sulphate.

1. Explain the use of potassium chromate as an indicator in this type of titration.

2. Could sodium chromate be used instead of potassium chromate?

3. Could such a titration, using potassium chromate as indicator, be performed in (a) acidic solution (b) alkaline solution (c) in the presence of free barium ions?

Titration of barium chloride solution against silver nitrate solution

Weigh accurately between 2·3 and 2·5g of barium chloride crystals into a clean, dry 100cm^3 beaker, add distilled water to dissolve the crystals and pour the solution into a 200cm^3 graduated flask. Wash the beaker twice with small portions of distilled water and pour the washings into the graduated flask. Make up to 200cm^3 with distilled water, and shake the contents of the flask until the solution is homogeneous.

Pipette 20·0cm^3 of this solution into a titration flask, add approximately 10cm^3 of 0·2M sodium sulphate solution and five drops of potassium chromate solution as indicator and titrate against 0·10M silver nitrate solution until a permanent red colour is produced. Repeat the titration until at least two concordant readings are obtained.

4. Why is sodium sulphate solution added to the titration flask?

5. Is the order of addition of sodium sulphate and potassium chromate important?

6. How could this method of titration be adapted to determine the concentration of a solution of hydrochloric acid?

Set out results as shown:

Weight of beaker + barium chloride crystals   =   g

Weight of beaker alone   =   g

Weight of barium chloride crystals taken   =   g

Final burette reading/cm^3

Initial burette reading/cm^3

Result/cm^3

Mean titre =   cm^3

CALCULATION

7. What is the equation for the reaction between silver nitrate and barium chloride?

8. How many moles of silver ions were added in the titration?

9. How many moles of chloride ions were there in 20·0cm^3 of the barium chloride solution?

10. How many moles of barium chloride ($BaCl_2$) were there in 200cm^3 of the barium chloride solution?

11. What value does this give for the formula weight of $BaCl_2.xH_2O$?

12. What is the formula weight of $BaCl_2$?

13. What is the value of x?

Notes 51

Standard: *

Time required: 1½ hours

Reagents required:

    aq. solutions of chloride, bromide and iodide ions as either sodium or potassium salts

                                                                                                 ($5cm^3$)

aq. barium chloride or nitrate	($5cm^3$)
aq. silver nitrate	($20cm^3$)
aq. sodium hydroxide	($5cm^3$)
aq. potassium chromate	($5cm^3$)
dilute nitric acid	($5cm^3$)
'Analar' barium chloride crystals ($BaCl_2.2H_2O$)	(3g)
distilled water	($250cm^3$)
approx. 0·2M aq. sodium sulphate	($50cm^3$)
0·10M silver nitrate solution	($100cm^3$)

Apparatus required:

    test-tubes

    $100cm^3$ beaker

    $200cm^3$ graduated flask

    $20·0cm^3$ pipette

    burette

    $250cm^3$ titration flask

    2 beakers for solutions (150 or $250cm^3$)

    $10cm^3$ measuring cylinder or test-tube of known volume

Notes on questions and typical results

(a) Silver nitrate forms a white precipitate (darkening in sunlight) of silver chloride on treatment with chloride ions; it forms a very pale yellow precipitate of silver bromide with bromide ions; and a pale yellow precipitate of silver iodide with iodide ions.

(b) With sodium hydroxide solution silver nitrate forms a brown precipitate of silver oxide, the hydroxide being unstable.

(c) With potassium chromate, silver nitrate forms a red precipitate of silver chromate which dissolves on addition of dilute nitric acid.

(d) Barium chloride forms a yellow precipitate of barium chromate when treated with potassium chromate.

Name of substance	solubility (g per 100g)	solubility product
silver chloride	$8·9 \times 10^{-5}$	2×10^{-10} mol^2 dm^{-6}
silver bromide	$8·4 \times 10^{-6}$	5×10^{-13} mol^2 dm^{-6}
silver iodide	3×10^{-7}	8×10^{-17} mol^2 dm^{-6}
silver chromate	$1·4 \times 10^{-3}$	2×10^{-12} mol^3 dm^{-9}
barium chromate	$3·4 \times 10^{-4}$	1×10^{-10} mol^2 dm^{-6}
barium sulphate	$2·2 \times 10^{-4}$	1×10^{-10} mol^2 dm^{-6}

1. Potassium chromate may be used as an indicator in silver ion/halide ion titrations because silver chromate is more soluble than silver chloride, bromide or iodide. Thus when silver ions are run in to a solution of halide and chromate ions, silver halide is precipitated in preference to silver chromate and thus when all the halide ions have been precipitated the red colouration due to the formation of silver chromate is seen.

Using the solubility product data:

Since silver ions are being run into a solution of chloride ions, the silver ion concentration will rise as the titration proceeds until at the end-point it reaches the same value as the chloride concentration. Thus $[Ag^+]=[Cl^-]=\sqrt{K_{AgCl}}=\sqrt{2 \times 10^{-10}}=1.4 \times 10^{-5}$ mol dm^{-3}

Assuming that the potassium chromate solution is approximately molar, and taking five drops as approximately $0.3cm^3$, the concentration of chromate ions in the titration flask near the end-point will be approximately $\frac{0.3}{50} \times 1M$, which is just less than $10^{-2}M$.

Hence before the permanent red colouration of silver chromate is formed the $[Ag^+]$ must rise to a value just in excess of $\sqrt{\frac{K_{AgCl}}{[CrO_4^{2-}]}}=\sqrt{\frac{2 \times 10^{-12}}{10^{-2}}}=1.4 \times 10^{-5}$ mol dm^{-3}.

Thus when all the chloride ions have been precipitated, the silver chromate will form.

2. Since it is chromate ions which react at the end-point to give the red colouration, a sodium chromate solution could be used.

3. (a) No. In acidic solution the silver chromate would not precipitate.
(b) No. In alkaline solution silver oxide would precipitate, masking the silver chromate. However a crude end-point might be achieved using the formation of silver oxide to indicate the end-point!
(c) No. Barium ions would remove the chromate ions from the solution leaving no indicator.

4. Sodium sulphate solution is added to precipitate the barium ions, as barium sulphate, for reasons explained above.

5. Yes. If sodium sulphate is added before the chromate ions it will prevent the precipitation of barium chromate; if it is added after the chromate ions it will not be very effective in bringing the chromate ions back into solution.

6. To determine the concentration of a hydrochloric acid solution by this method the acid must be neutralized without risk of making it alkaline by use of excess of the neutralizing agent. An insoluble base such as calcium carbonate is thus added, in excess.

Specimen results and calculation

Weight of barium chloride crystals taken = 2.38g
$20.0cm^3$ of barium chloride solution $\equiv 19.5cm^3$ of $0.10M$ $AgNO_3$
7. Equation $2 AgNO_3 + BaCl_2 = 2 AgCl + Ba(NO_3)_2$

or ionically $\qquad Ag^+ + Cl^- = AgCl$

8. The number of moles of silver ions added in the titration = 19.5×10^{-4} mol.

9. The number of moles of chloride ions in $20.0cm^3$ of barium chloride solution = 19.5×10^{-4} mol.

10. The number of moles of barium chloride in $200cm^3$ of solution = 9.75×10^{-3} mol

11. Hence formula weight of $BaCl_2.xH_2O = \dfrac{2.38}{9.75 \times 10^{-3}} = 244g$

12. The formula weight of $BaCl_2$ = 208g

13. Hence $x = \dfrac{36}{18} = 2$; i.e. Formula of barium chloride crystals = $BaCl_2.2H_2O$

Assignment 52

Analysis of a mixture of Chlorides - An Exercise in the Use of an Adsorption Indicator

You are provided with a dry, powdered mixture of sodium and potassium chlorides. By preparing a solution of this mixture and then titrating the solution with standard silver nitrate solution it should be possible to determine the composition of the sodium-potassium chloride mixture.

EXPERIMENTAL WORK

Accurately weigh out about 1g of the mixture of chlorides and dissolve it in distilled water. Make the solution up to a total volume of $200cm^3$ in a standard flask and shake until the solution is homogeneous.

Procedure 'A':

Pipette $20cm^3$ of this chloride solution into a conical flask. To this add:

(i) approximately $80cm^3$ of distilled water.

(ii) a pinch of dextrin (about $0.1g$)

(iii) 5–10 drops of dichlorofluorescein solution.

Titrate the mixture with $0.10M$ $AgNO_3$, carefully swirling throughout and paying close attention to the appearance of the precipitate, in particular looking for any signs of coagulation.

The end-point of the titration is indicated by an abrupt change in the colour of the precipitate. The last few drops of silver nitrate solution should be added very slowly. Repeat the experiment until two concordant results have been obtained.

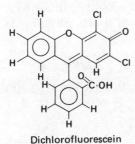

Dichlorofluorescein

Fig 52.1 The structure of dichlorfluorescein

Procedure 'B':

Repeat Procedure 'A' but this time *without* the dextrin and the extra distilled water. Give detailed descriptions of the appearance of the precipitate throughout titrations using both procedures.

Burette Readings

	Procedure 'A'		Procedure 'B'	
Final reading/cm^3				
Initial reading/cm^3	_____	_____	_____	_____
Result/cm^3	_____	_____	_____	_____

Mean volume of $0.10M$ $AgNO_3$ ≡ $20cm^3$ of chloride solution: _____

305

EXPERIMENTAL INTERPRETATION

1. What is the ionic equation for the major reaction occurring during titration?

2. Let HDf represent dichlorofluorescein which is a weak, monobasic acid:

$$HDf \rightleftharpoons H^+ + Df^-$$

Which of the ten hydrogen atoms in the molecule is acidic?

3. Why cannot silver nitrate titrations be performed in the presence of alkalies?

4. Most of the silver chloride precipitated initially (both titration procedures) remains in colloidal solution. Approximately what size are colloidal particles?

5. Why does silver chloride show little tendency to coagulate in the presence of excess chloride ions?

6. Why does this reluctance to coagulate diminish as the end-point is approached?

7. Why should the final stages of the titration be carried out slowly with thorough stirring?

8. In the presence of a slight excess of silver nitrate the particles of silver chloride become coated with the pink silver salt of dichlorofluorescein, AgDf. Why does the AgDf form on the surface of the silver chloride particles?

9. The purpose of adding both dextrin and extra distilled water in Procedure 'A' is to minimize the chance of silver chloride coagulating. Explain why they function in this fashion.

10. Why is it desirable to keep the silver chloride in colloidal solution and to use relatively small amounts of dichlorofluorescein?

11. Why cannot dichlorofluorescein titrations be carried out in solutions of low pH?

CALCULATION

12. How many moles of silver ion would be needed to react with the chloride ions in the 200cm³ of mixed chloride solution?

13. How many moles of chloride ion are there in the 200cm³ of mixed chloride solution?

14. If the approximately 1g of the mixed chlorides, which you weighed out, contained k gram of potassium chloride, what (in terms of k) were the numbers of moles of chloride ion which came from (a) the KCl, (b) the NaCl?

15. How can k be calculated?

16. What was the percentage by weight of potassium chloride in the KCl-NaCl solid mixture?

Notes 52

Standard: **
Time required: 1½ hours is usually ample
Reagents required:
   potassium chloride (6g)
   sodium chloride (14g) } sufficient for 15 experiments
   0·1M silver nitrate solution (80cm^3)
   dextrin (0·5g)
   dichlorofluorescein solution [approximately 1g of
   sodium dichlorofluoresceinate per litre of water] (2cm^3)
   distilled water (600cm^3)
Apparatus required:
   watch-glass
   200cm^3 standard flask
   burette and 20cm^3 pipette

Experiment

The results described here were obtained using an intimate mixture of 6·0g of KCl and 14·0g of NaCl. 1·00g of this mixture was dissolved in enough distilled water to prepare 200cm^3 of solution and this solution gave the following results:

Procedure 'A': 16·0cm^3 of 0·10M AgNO$_3$ per 20cm^3 of mixed chloride solution

Procedure 'B': 15·9cm^3 of 0·10M AgNO$_3$ per 20cm^3 of mixed chloride solution

The end-point is marked by a sharp change in the colour of the silver chloride from white to pink. Procedure 'A' should yield slightly more accurate results than Procedure 'B'. The purpose of carrying out both procedures is to emphasise the factors which oppose coagulation.

Notes on experimental interpretation and calculation

1. $Ag^+_{(aq)} + Cl^-_{(aq)} \rightarrow AgCl_{(s)}$

2. The hydrogen atom of the —CO.OH group is acidic. Even if the students have yet to study carboxylic acids they will be able to guess the correct answer to this question by noting that the other nine hydrogen atoms in the molecule occupy very similar sites.

3. In alkaline solution brown silver oxide, Ag$_2$O, would be precipitated.

4. Colloidal particles are customarily defined as particles with diameters in the range of 10^{-5} to 10^{-7} cms.

5. In the presence of excess chloride ions the colloidal silver chloride particles become negatively charged as a result of surface adsorption of some of the Cl$^-$ ions. Electrostatic repulsion between these negative particles tends to prevent coagulation.

6. As the end-point is reached and the Ag$^+$:Cl$^-$ ratio becomes 1:1, the colloidal particles cease to be negatively charged. (See next Question)

7. The final stages of the titration should be conducted slowly, with thorough stirring, in order to promote desorption of the adsorbed Cl^- ions. Unless care is taken in this respect the true end-point is likely to be passed before the fluorescein is adsorbed.

8. At the end-point of the titration virtually all the silver ions have been precipitated as AgCl. Thus, once the AgCl particles are no longer negatively charged, the negative dichlorofluoresceinate ions are able to approach sufficiently close to become adsorbed, thus giving the silver chloride particles a pink coat.

Since AgDf is more soluble than AgCl there is no possibility of Df^- ions reacting with the relatively small numbers of free Ag^+ ions in solution to precipitate AgDf (i.e. there is no possibility of the AgDf solubility product being exceeded).

9. The extra distilled water by diluting the solution decreases the frequency of collisions between the negatively charged silver chloride particles and positively charged ions in the solution. High concentrations of ions almost always promote coagulation of colloidal solutions and it is customary to use chloride concentrations in the range of 0·01M when carrying out this experiment.

The dextrin, a starch-like compound, is thought to provide the colloidal silver chloride particles with a protective, hydrophilic coating.

10. Dramatic end-points will be attained if a very high fraction of the dichlorofluorescein is suddenly adsorbed onto the AgCl. This condition is most likely to be achieved by using low concentrations of indicator and by keeping the AgCl in colloidal suspension, in which state it will have a very high specific surface area.

11. If the pH of the solution is too low (i.e. the solution is quite acidic) ionization of the dichlorofluorescein will be repressed and the concentration of free Df^- ions will be too low for significant amounts of the indicator to be adsorbed.

12. Volume of 0·1M $AgNO_3$ needed per 200cm³ of chloride solution $= \dfrac{200}{20} \times 16 = 160\text{cm}^3$

Thus, number of moles of silver ions needed $= \dfrac{160}{1000} \times 0 \cdot 1 = 16 \times 10^{-3}$ mol

13. Since 1 mole of Ag^+ reacts with 1 mole of Cl^-, the number of moles of Cl^- ion per 200cm³ of chloride solution must also be 16×10^{-3} mol

14. Molecular weights of KCl and NaCl are 74·6 and 58·5 respectively.

Thus moles of Cl^- per gramme of mixture are: (a) $\dfrac{k}{74 \cdot 6}$ from the KCl

and (b) $\dfrac{1-k}{58 \cdot 5}$ from the NaCl

15. Therefore: $\dfrac{k}{74 \cdot 6} + \dfrac{(1-k)}{58 \cdot 5} = 16 \times 10^{-3}$

whence $k = 0 \cdot 298$ g of KCl/g of mixture

16. It follows that the percentage by weight of KCl in the original mixture must be 29·8% (*cf.* 30·0% by weighing)

FURTHER PROJECT

Are adsorption indicators suitable for reactions which do *not* involve halide ions? Investigate whether dichlorofluorescein can be used:
1. To estimate the thiocyanate ion
2. To determine the end-point of the reaction of lead acetate with sodium hydroxide. (See Reference 2)

REFERENCES

1. *A Text-Book of Quantitative Inorganic Analysis* Arthur I. Vogel, (3rd Edition)' Longmans (1962).
2. *Practical Chemistry,* J. Lambert and T.A. Muir, Heinemann (1961).

Assignment 53

The Principles of Iodine/Thiosulphate Titrations and Determination of the Equation for the Reaction Between Iodide and Iodate Ions in Acid Solution

INTRODUCTION

Thiosulphate ions are oxidized by iodine according to the following half-equation:

$$2 S_2O_3^{2-} \rightleftharpoons S_4O_6^{2-} + 2 e^-$$

1. Write a half-equation for the reduction of the iodine.

2. How many moles of thiosulphate ions, $S_2O_3^{2-}$, react with one mole of iodine, I_2?

In iodine/thiosulphate titrations the usual procedure is to run a standard solution of thiosulphate ions from a burette into the iodine solution, with starch present to aid the detection of the end-point. In the presence of iodine starch forms a deep blue colour which disappears as the iodine is removed. It is advisable to add the starch solution when most of the iodine has been reduced as the reaction of the starch with iodine in high concentration is less readily reversed.

The major application of iodine/thiosulphate titrations is not the direct determination of the concentration of solutions of iodine but as a general method for the determination of the concentration of solutions of oxidizing agents. The technique is to add a known volume of the oxidizing agent to an excess of acidified potassium iodide solution and determine the quantity of iodine produced, using standard thiosulphate solution.

EXPERIMENTAL WORK

Pipette 20.0cm^3 of the potassium iodate solution (which contains 3.00g of KIO_3 per cubic decimetre (litre) of solution) into a 250cm^3 titration flask and add approximately 20cm^3 of the potassium iodide solution (which contains approximately 15g of KI per cubic decimetre (litre) of solution) and approximately 10cm^3 of molar sulphuric acid. Titrate the liberated iodine with the 0.10M sodium thiosulphate solution, adding about 1cm^3 of starch solution when the colour of the solution in the titration flask becomes pale yellow. The end-point is indicated by the sudden removal of the blue colour, leaving a colourless solution. Repeat until two concordant results are obtained.

Tabulate the results as follows:

Final reading/cm³			
Initial reading/cm³			
Titre/cm³			

Mean titre =   cm³

3. Balance the equation:

$$S_2O_3^{2-} + I_2 = S_4O_6^{2-} + I^-$$

4. How many moles of thiosulphate ions were used in the titration?

5. How many moles of iodine, I_2, were liberated by 20.0cm^3 of the potassium iodate solution?

6. How many moles of iodate ions, IO_3^-, are present in 20·0cm³ of the potassium iodate solution you used?

7. How many moles of iodine, I_2, are formed when one mole of iodate ions, IO_3^-, reacts with excess iodide ions?

8. Write a balanced equation for the reaction between iodate and iodide ions in acid solution.

Notes 53

Standard: *

Time required: 1½ hours

Reagents required:

    potassium iodate solution, containing 3·00g of KIO_3 per dm^3 ($100cm^3$)

    potassium iodide solution, containing approximately 15g of KI per dm^3 ($100cm^3$)

    approximately molar sulphuric acid ($50cm^3$)

    starch solution ($5cm^3$)

Apparatus required:

    burrete

    $20·0cm^3$ pipette

    $250cm^3$ conical flask

    $25cm^3$ measuring cylinder, or 5 x ⅝ inch test tube-volume: $20cm^3$

    3 beakers—100 or $150cm^3$

Notes on questions and specimen results

1. The half-equation for the reduction of iodine is:

$$I_2 + 2\,e^- = 2\,I^-$$

2. Hence two moles of thiosulphate ions react with one mole of iodine, I_2.

Teachers may wish to point out that it is possible to perform this titration without using starch as indicator. The yellow or brown colour of the iodine in the presence of excess potassium iodide solution, disappears at the end-point and this colour change is quite striking.

Results:

$16·7cm^3$ of 0·10M sodium thiosulphate solution is needed to react with the iodine liberated by $20·0cm^3$ of potassium iodate solution.

3. The balanced equation for the reaction between thiosulphate ions and iodine is:

$$2\,S_2O_3{}^{2-} + I_2 = S_4O_6{}^{2-} + 2\,I^-$$

4. The number of moles of thiosulphate ions used in each titration is:

$$\frac{16·7 \times 0·10}{1000}\text{ mol}$$

5. The number of moles of iodine, I_2, liberated by $20·0cm^3$ of potassium iodate solution is therefore:

$$\frac{16·7 \times 0·10}{2 \times 1000}\text{ mol} = 8·35 \times 10^{-4}\text{ mol}$$

6. The number of moles of iodate ions IO_3^-, present in $20·0cm^3$ of the potassium iodate solution used is:

$$\frac{20·0}{1000} \times \frac{3·00}{214} = 2·80 \times 10^{-4}\text{ mol}$$

7. The number of moles of iodine, I_2, formed when one mole of iodate ions, IO_3^-, react with excess iodide ions in acid solution is:

$$\frac{8\cdot35 \times 10^{-4}}{2\cdot80 \times 10^{-4}} = 3 \text{ mol}$$

8. The balanced equation for the reaction between iodate and iodide ions in acid solution is:

$$6\,H^+ + IO_3^- + 5\,I^- = 3\,I_2 + 3\,H_2O$$